FUTURE HUMANS TRILOGY

Book 1 - The Cosmic Keys of Our Future Becoming

The Quest of Rose

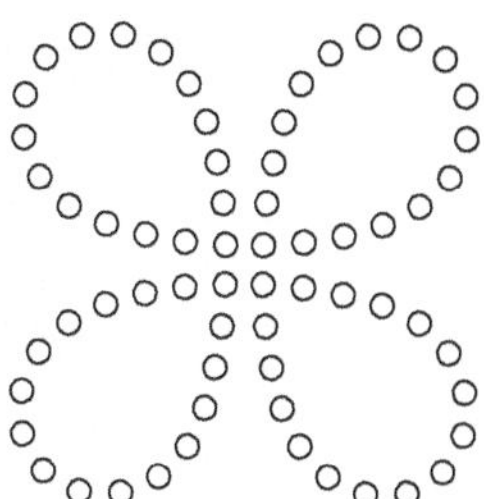

Anneloes Smitsman Ph.D. & Jean Houston Ph.D.

Foreword by Lynne McTaggart

The Quest of Rose

Anneloes Smitsman Ph.D. & Jean Houston Ph.D.

Future Humans Trilogy
Book 1: The Quest of Rose – The Cosmic Keys of Our Future Becoming

1st Edition. 1st printing 2021
Editor: Diane Nichols
Cover Artwork: Denise Kester
Cover Designer: Anneloes Smitsman, and Steve Walters, Oxygen Publishing
Interior Design: Steve Walters, Oxygen Publishing
Illustrators: Anneloes Smitsman, Patrice Offman, and Justine Page

Independently Published by
Oxygen Publishing Inc.
Montreal, QC, Canada
www.oxygenpublishing.com

ISBN: 978-1-990093-11-1
Imprint: Independently published

Dedication

To the children of the new time

PRAISE FOR THE FUTURE HUMANS TRILOGY

"Full of wisdom and insight, with a vision of the future everyone can benefit from in our age of change amid uncertainty. The *Future Humans Trilogy* is an act of true compassion, which exhibits empathy and understanding that leads to answers, and the answers are the essence of the world's wisdom traditions. The stories speak directly to the heart, where all inner journeys begin. When the heart awakens, the person is transformed. This trilogy is living proof that such a radical change is desirable, possible, and necessary in everyone's life."

~ **Deepak Chopra**, M.D. Author, *Total Meditation*

"The *Future Humans Trilogy* is pure inspiration—soul gold. As we spin in these winds of chaos, wondering where we are going and when the storms will end, the trilogy has emerged as a guidebook, instructing individuals on how to connect to the hidden power map governing this epic of transformation. Pure genius."

~ **Dr. Caroline Myss**, Ph.D. Author,
Intimate Conversations with the Divine

"In every generation there are breakthrough ideas that change the course of human evolution. These sparks originate in the generative depths of imagination. They ignite new ways of becoming fully human. Through the renaissance artistry of Jean Houston's life's work and the fresh brilliance of Anneloes Smitsman's attuned scholarship comes *The Quest of Rose*, a book as timeless as it is timely. The architectural tools, the creative means of unleashing your personal rebirth, wait to be discovered through engaging, heartfelt dialogues alive in these pages. The archetypal portals, the Cosmic Keys needed for the redesign of society, present themselves in masterful storytelling. This book is potent. It awakens latent purpose and inspires a joyful embrace of the new possible. The CALL goes out. The invitation is yours to receive. The time is now…"

~ **Dr. Stephen Aizenstat**, Ph.D. Founder of Pacifica Graduate Institute, The Academy of Imaginal Arts and Sciences, and Dream Tending

"A fabulous excursion into the true potentials—and if we are lucky, the future reality—of the human personality. We learn just about everything that is conceivable about the evolutionary possibilities of the human—a mind-boggling trip. To be read and lived with admiration and appreciation."

~ **Dr. Ervin Laszlo**, Ph.D. Nobel Peace Prize Nominee,
Award-Winning Author, Founder & President,
The Laszlo Institute of New Paradigm Research

"*The Quest of Rose* is so much more than a book! It is the start of a journey that can literally repattern your nervous system to better meet the trials of these challenging times. It confronts the greatest questions facing humanity, drawing at once on the power of story, glimpses into the cosmic order, the inspiration of a larger perspective, and simple practices that will expand the reach of your mind. This map into a more welcome future will speak to you personally as it also calls out to the culture that the path of greater possibilities for the human experiment is before us, our collective will must be rallied, and the time is now."

~ **Donna Eden** and **David Feinstein**, Ph.D. Co-Authors,
The Energies of Love

"Written with breathtaking beauty, warmth, and charm, Jean and Anneloes have done the Human Potential Movement a huge service by integrating the insights of the new paradigm sciences and the wisdom of ancient mystics in a magical storytelling way that catalyzes and ignites the reader with the turn of each page. Together they weave a very accessible and memorable roadmap for activating and developing the future potential of our species. Of enormous practical value are the nine Cosmic Keys of Consciousness and the twelve transformative practices, which are integrated into the rich story-line at the end of each chapter. The *Future Humans Trilogy* is a must read for everyone working to facilitate the evolution of consciousness."

~ **Dr. Claire Zammit**, Ph.D. Founder of FemininePower.com

"Like shamans on a magical journey of healing, in the *Future Humans Trilogy*, Anneloes Smitsman and Jean Houston masterfully use the fictive power and world-creating artistry of the sacred creative imagination to weave a spell-binding story which reveals the deeper mythical—and liberating—nature that lies hidden within seemingly ordinary, nonfictional reality. Encoded within the story they tell—which is truly our story—is a living transmission that activates and awakens our evolutionary potential, helping us to remember who we are and what we are here to do. This trilogy is a true gift to humanity that I cannot recommend highly enough."

~ **Paul Levy**, Author, *Dispelling Wetiko* and *The Quantum Revelation*

"Written by two visionaries, evolutionary leaders, and master storytellers, rather than fictional, this book is *imaginal.* It speaks to our deepest longing and seeds our greatest belonging. With Jean Houston's and Anneloes Smitsman's profound and empowering guidance, it calls us to remember the truth of who we really are. And it invites us to embody lives of meaning and purpose as co-creative evolutionary partners within a revealed and living universe. Soul food indeed!"

~ **Dr. Jude Currivan**, Ph.D. Cosmologist, Author,
The Cosmic Hologram, Co-Founder, WholeWorld-View

"I have long had a personal rule: Read anything Jean Houston writes. *The Quest of Rose*, written with Anneloes Smitsman, confirms this commitment. This prescient work comes at a critical moment in human history, when we are besieged by tremendous challenges that may affect the continued existence of our species. We cannot afford to ignore this magnificent work!"

~ **Larry Dossey**, M.D. Author, *One Mind: How Our Individual Mind Is Part of a Greater Consciousness and Why It Matters*

"Anneloes Smitsman and Jean Houston deliver an engaging narrative in which profound realizations seem to pop off each page. These stellar intellects bring to life a mythic journey of personal and societal transformation. A delightful weave of edifying and enduring wisdom; beautifully crafted; and a testament for evolving human potential, the *Future Humans Trilogy* will revision and advance the path you take."

~ **Dr. Jeffrey K. Zeig**, Ph.D. Founder, The Milton H. Erickson Foundation

"These are epic books for our unprecedented times! The *Future Humans Trilogy* is unlike any other books you are likely to read. It is breathtaking in its scope, enlightening in its depth, and uplifting in its message. It seamlessly weaves together quantum physics, cosmology, mythology, spirituality, psychology, history, and more, with gripping impact. It is the one 'must read' book for everyone of all ages and backgrounds concerned with how we navigate our way through this chaotic transition time accentuated by the COVID pandemic."

~ **Prof. Dr. Alexander Schieffer**, Ph.D. Co-Founder, Home for Humanity, Adjunct Professor, Da Vinci Institute, South Africa

"The *Future Humans Trilogy* immerses us in the life of one young COVID survivor, Rose, and her quest for deeper meaning after her brush with death. Through Rose's vivifying dialogues with her evocative grandmother, Verdandi, and her peers, we participate actively in her unfolding discovery of the Cosmic architecture of life. We engage side by side with Rose in activating our imaginal cells and expanding our states of consciousness through Grandmother Verdandi's potent exercises to unfetter our quantum powers. We not only share the mythic initiation journey of Rose, but learn with her how to transform our own lives and become the future humans we need to be to create the future world that works for all. This is THE paramount book series for our times!"

~ **Dr. Rama Mani**, Ph.D. Co-Founder, Home for Humanity,
Convenor, Enacting Global Transformation.
Centre for International Studies, University of Oxford

"This astounding *Future Humans Trilogy* is a work of pure genius that inspires one to 'Know Thyself' as a multi-dimensional architect of the 'future possible.' Anneloes Smitsman and Jean Houston brilliantly bring to life our true essence as Cosmic, activating forces of evolution, by equipping the reader with the tools, codes, keys, patterns, practices, and principles to birth a collective metamorphosis out of the chrysalis into a luminous future. This is one of the most important books of our catalytic time of change and should be available for all people and in every educational institution as an architectural guide to creating a world that works for all."

~ **Diane Williams**, Founder, The Source of Synergy Foundation

"How can the enduring mysteries of science and spirituality as well as matter and consciousness, be engaged with sustained and vivid imagination? With our worlds on the edge, *how* we learn can be more important than *what* we learn if we are to boldly and faithfully innovate a future of belonging and flourishing. This soul-stirring book, studded with transformative principles, perspectives, possibilities, and practices, courageously seeds our collective will towards generating possible worlds."

~ **Aftab Ome**r, Ph.D. President, Meridian University

"*The Quest of Rose* is a powerful book to help you navigate these personal and global challenging times. Rose's quest will inspire you—ringing with integrity, authenticity, wisdom, and truth. Anneloes and Jean provide practices following each section that will guide you beyond what you thought possible for your life. This first book of the *Future Humans Trilogy* quenches the thirst for what our heart desires for ourselves, our children, our children's children, and the children of other species for now and for future generations."

~ **Dr. Anita Sanchez**, Author, *The Four Sacred Gifts: Indigenous Wisdom for Modern Times*

Foreword

It is fitting that *The Quest of Rose*, the first in the *Future Humans* trilogy, is told as a story. With so much of our world in crisis at present—with our climate and ecology, our economies, our health and safety, even our basic freedoms now under threat—we desperately need a new story to live by.

As Joan Didion famously wrote, "We tell ourselves stories in order to live." Although a patchwork of influences—religious, political, economic, scientific, and philosophical—creates the narrative of our beliefs about our world and our place within it, modern humans now look to science as the primary author.

The scientific model creates our perception of how the Universe operates and what it means to be human, and from there we fashion our world.

Although we think of science as a collection of timeless, immutable truths, science is itself just a story, a constant work in progress, with old chapters discarded with every ground-breaking discovery in the laboratory.

Despite a constantly evolving story line, most of what we have come to define as our human capacity and experience derives from ideas that were formulated more than 300 years ago, based on the discoveries of Isaac Newton and amplified by the theories of Charles Darwin in the 19th century.

Newton described a very well-behaved universe of separate objects operating according to fixed laws in time and space, and Charles Darwin's theory of evolution created a *leitmotif* of competitive individualism, a heroic struggle for dominion over hostile elements and a share of strictly limited resources.

Both were stories that defined and indeed idealized separateness. The crises we now experience on many fronts, the vague feeling many of us hold that despite our undoubted technological mastery of the Universe we are nearing an apocalyptic end of days, are both symptomatic of this false view of who we really are and also its logical conclusion.

In this book, Rose's quest is, on the deepest level, a heroine's journey to find a more authentic human story. A near-death experience (fittingly, from COVID-19), during which she glimpses a deeper and truer reality—the extraordinary unity of all things—sets her off on a voyage of deep inward discovery, not simply to find out what on earth happened to her while she hovered between life and death, but also what it truly means to be a human being.

During Rose's search for the meaning of her experience, she arrives in largely uncharted scientific territory. Coupled with the extraordinary dialogue she maintains with her wise and farsighted Icelandic grandmother, Verdandi, Rose marries many of these new discoveries with powerful, timeless myths and archetypes to fashion not only a new scientific story, but a completely new and more sustainable view of the world.

Rose begins to understand what she deeply experienced for herself: The Universe is a sentient, unified, and interdependent entity, with consciousness its main driver and digitized information the alphabet of its universal and holistic language.

She learns that time, rather than a one-way arrow, exists as an ever-present "now," so that the future is constantly creating and refining the present.

From these radical new insights, she comes to understand the power that she—and each of us—possesses to "activate and attract" our future into a higher order of reality.

"Life doesn't constrict us. It doesn't hold us back," her grandmother exhorts her.

In fact, the truth is, as Rose ultimately realizes, life actually *isn't* like our present notion of it at all. Furthermore, absorbing the implications of all these scientific revelations must inevitably lead to a very different individual and collective way of being.

The Quest of Rose is a remarkable hybrid of a book on multiple levels: both individual journey and highly palatable introduction to innumerable scientific breakthroughs, both page-turning fiction and practical non-fiction workbook.

Each chapter not only furthers Rose's journey, but also offers summaries of key insights and experiential exercises for the reader to further their own path to self-actualization—so that we can become our own "Cosmic architect."

In that sense, Rose's journey is our own hero's journey. By discovering insights and practices as Rose learns them, we respond, as Rose's grandmother Verdandi puts it, to "the lure of our becoming," the journey all of us must embark on, but most especially at present, during this pivotal moment in our human history.

Verdandi explains that this journey has never been more essential: "It seems like we've landed in our own real-life, myth-making experiment right now in these present times, as we're handed crisis after crisis."

That *The Quest of Rose* marries the mythic with the scientific results from the fortuitous partnership of two extraordinary minds: Dr. Jean Houston, futurist, visionary, academic, advisor to global leaders, and one of the primary architects of the Human Potential Movement; and Dr. Anneloes Smitsman, author, visionary scientist, and systems architect of evolutionary change.

This extraordinary collaboration has produced a bold and highly original work that invites all of us to take our place in the new "Renaissance" by finding within ourselves "the passion for the possible."

"Seeing your life as a larger story puts you back on your feet and helps you to get on with living. Yet seeing your life as a great story can fill you with passion, and give you codes to access new ranges of possibilities, and grant you a mythic life and a higher purpose," says Verdandi.

Jean Houston has decades of experience acting as what she refers to as an "evocator." Originally meant to be a soldier who calls troops to arms, the word also refers to a scientist who helps to set off the growth of a tiny embryo. Dr. Houston has spent much of her life charging tens of thousands of people around the globe with the urgent necessity of reaching further than their current grasp in order to find—and make good use of—their highest potential.

Dr. Smitsman's original research has relentlessly delved into revolutionary ideas and brought radical new scientific truths to light. And her background as a creative force of systemic transformation in education, economics, governance, and ecology has resulted from a marriage between her scientific originality and her extensive experience in the spiritual and mystical realms.

The Quest of Rose is ultimately a work of profound hope during these tumultuous times, by offering a powerful new definition of ourselves and a vision of unlimited future possibility.

But this trilogy also means to be an incitement to radical transformation. And there may be no turning back. Once you are caught up in Rose's revelations and begin to understand the deep truths within them, a new way of your own being must be born.

Accept its siren call and take this journey with Rose. Allow this brilliant new story to unleash the imaginal cells of your own extraordinary potential and become the future human you were always meant to be.

~ **Lynne McTaggart**, June 2021

Lynne McTaggart is an award-winning journalist and world renowned author. She is one of the central authorities on the new science of consciousness, and the editorial director of What Doctors Don't Tell You, one of the world's most respected health magazines. She is architect of the Intention Experiment.

Table of Contents

Introduction

Welcome to *The Quest of Rose*, the first book in the *Future Humans Trilogy*. As you'll soon discover, this is no ordinary book! You are about to embark on an experiential journey, shared as an allegory, that will shift your consciousness to the new and ancient possibilities of our future becoming. You'll join the quest of the future humans of a new era, which is really our own quest into the heart of reality to discover the fundamental unity of life.

This new era has long been foretold by the mystics, philosophers, and poets of our time, including the French theologian and philosopher Pierre Teilhard de Chardin who called himself a "pilgrim of the future." We, too, consider ourselves to be "pilgrims of the future," and the Universe has a way of introducing such pilgrims to one another in the most unusual ways (read our epilogue at the end).

In the case of Jean, it happened when she was fourteen years old. After receiving news that terribly upset her, she was running to Central Park in New York City to clear her head when she literally ran into Teilhard de Chardin and almost knocked the wind out of him. Thankfully, he took it all with great humor as she helped him to his feet. About a week later, while walking down Park Avenue with her fox terrier, Champ, she met the old gentleman again. This began their friendship over a period of three years. It was only after his passing that she learned that "Mr. Tayer" (as she had called him) was the famous Pierre Teilhard de Chardin. Although this book is not about their meetings, Teilhard is part of this book in the seed he planted seventy years ago, and in particular, through the following conversation.

During one of their weekly walks in the park, Teilhard suddenly fell to his knees, overcome with wonder. "Jeanne, look at the caterpillar. Ahhhh! How beautiful it is, this little green being with its wonderful, funny, little feet. Exquisite! Little furry body, little green feet *on the road to metamorphosis*. Jeanne, can you feel yourself to be a caterpillar?" Teilhard exclaimed.

"Ohhh, yes!" Jean replied, as a pimply faced teenager.

"Well, then think of your own metamorphosis. What will you be when you have become a butterfly, un papillon, eh? *What is the butterfly of Jeanne*?" Teilhard smiled.

"I'll travel around the world and will help people," Jean replied passionately.

The following serves to illustrate how we each carry the seeds for our own metamorphosis inside us. Then, when we least expect it, a stranger, a bump on the road, or some unexpected event, becomes the catalyst, after which, time has a way of bringing us full circle and returns us to how it all began. There, as we return to the beginning, we receive the seeds for a *new beginning*, and so it also happens for the characters of *The Quest of Rose*.

Here is how things have come full circle for us. In May 2020, Anneloes had proposed to Jean that they work with the butterfly metamorphosis as the core theme for our trilogy. At that time, she had no idea of the conversation that had transpired between Jean and Teilhard. Twelve months later, while writing this introduction, Anneloes became aware of a strong and loving presence in her living room, combined with a persistent nudge for her to find out what Teilhard had actually said to Jean during some of their talks. As she learned about their caterpillar moment, she was delighted to discover how the seed for their trilogy had been planted all those years ago by Teilhard's questions! True to her word, Jean did indeed travel the world, and has helped an enormous number of people as an evocator of the lure of our becoming and a midwife of souls, as well as a world-renowned scholar and one of the principal founders of the Human Potential Movement. She continues to travel, teach, lecture, and help people today at the age of 84. In our epilogue, you can learn about the way we both met, and the promises we had both made that manifested through this trilogy.

Join us now through *The Quest of Rose,* where we discover the keys, tools, and ways for becoming the future humans of a new era. Future humans are people like you, us, and many others, who are embracing our own metamorphosis to explore the question: *What is the butterfly of me?*

As you'll soon discover, the anticipated potentials of a more enlightened future are not merely imaginal, nor is the imaginal merely imaginative, or just happening in our minds. These future potentials are actual potentials in consciousness; Cosmic information that exists in a particular state, which we can access and activate when we discover the Cosmic Keys for doing so. This truly is a mythic journey for living a mythic life.

The Quest of Rose weaves together real-life events that are at the forefront of what's happening in our world right now, with cutting-edge insights from the new sciences, indigenous wisdom, and consciousness teachings for discovering the greater possibilities of our future becoming. We chose to give fictional names to the characters in this trilogy, yet have presented these characters as real-life people we can all relate to, and who share a deep passion to become the required change that makes the difference.

The stories and experiences of these characters also include some of the most intimate and life-changing visions, mystical insights, and transformations that we have each lived over the course of our lives, as well as the many funny and awkward moments. Toward the end of the book, you'll also find a summary of the essential insights of the new paradigm sciences with references for further exploration.

Each chapter comes with a specific Cosmic Key of Consciousness for activating and developing your future potential. This book includes nine such keys and twelve transformative practices, together with an integration section at the end of each chapter for application in your life.

Guidelines for the Practices

The practices have been designed to safely activate the new consciousness states of your future human potential. You can benefit from these practices by simply reading the story, and you may also go deeper by applying these practices to your life, and by going through it with others who are also reading or listening to *The Quest of Rose*.

The practices range between 5 and 45 minutes, and can be repeated whenever required. There is no fixed order for these practices; you can create your own sequence. However, we recommend that you read the book in sequence, since each chapter is designed for specific activations and realizations. The following guidelines are recommended for receiving the full value from these practices:

1. As mentioned, you may go through these practices by yourself or together with others. When practicing with others, please respect each other's privacy and do not counsel each other. Allow for new insights and realizations to emerge naturally and as a consequence of the practice itself.
2. Create a quiet and safe place for going through the practices without interruptions. Give yourself the time and space to integrate your inner

changes and to support yourself during times of transformation and healing. It is recommended that you drink a glass of clean water after each practice to support your body's integration.

3. Don't force or push your process; let it unfold and emerge naturally. The deep work happens from the roots, which is often invisible. Honor and trust in the natural cycles of your inner growth, and lovingly acknowledge each step along the way.
4. Remember to ease expectations and tensions with laughter and humor. This is one of the most effective ways for healing and transformation.
5. Audio recordings of some of the practices are available via futurehumans.world. You can also record your own voice by reading the practices out loud and then listening to your voice (with your eyes closed). Furthermore, you can ask a friend, partner, or family member to read the practices to you and you can enjoy the experience together. Please make sure that your voice (or the voice of the person reading this to you) is calm and soothing, and allows time between the words and sentences for you to experience what is shared.
6. Write down (or record) your experience in a personal journal for keeping track of the inner shifts and changes while going through the trilogy. This may include dreams, visions, ideas, feelings, thoughts, and new realizations that are emerging.
7. The practices have been designed to safely explore the new consciousness states and support a deeper healing and transformation. If, however, you need additional medical or personal healing support, please consult a professional therapist, coach, or physician.

CHAPTER 1

The Call of the Quest

Transforming Our Life with the Key of Conscious Choice

Rose hears the strained voices of the medical staff as they work intensely to save her. They sound faint and far away.

"Another overactive immune system."

"Blood pressure?"

"She's slipping away."

"Get ready to start the heart..."

"Seems we lost a cousin of hers who came in with her yesterday with the same viral symptoms."

Where am I? Why is it so light? Have I died? Rose no longer feels the weight of her body, nor the fever raging inside her. Everything feels surprisingly calm and peaceful now. *No, wait. This can't be...It's not my time. Mother Universe! Whoever you are, there must be another option! I'm not ready to die. My life has only begun!*

A week ago, Rose and Otto attended a party with their university friends in Amsterdam. They debated, hugged, and danced until late into the night. Early the next morning, she and her cousin were rushed into the hospital ICU with severe viral symptoms of COVID-19.

Otto had experienced problems with an overactive immune system since he was a child, so things got worse very quickly for him. The internal bleeding in his lungs could not be stopped. It was impossible to save him. Rose doesn't know this yet. She's drawing on all of her strength and focus to get through her own crisis.

Her parents in the United States are informed of Otto's death and of their own daughter's critical situation, but they're unable to fly over due to the pandemic restrictions. Upon receiving the news, they immediately notify

Rose's brother and promise they'll keep him apprised of any developments. Lucas is concerned about his sister, and naturally sad to hear the news about Otto. It will not be possible for Otto to have a regular funeral or memorial service with friends and family; he'll be cremated alone in the coming days. His family is in deep shock and simply cannot believe how things happened so fast. Will Rose be next?

Rose's last conversation with her cousin was about the escalating troubles and growing violence in the world, and whether humanity is worth being saved. Otto was a remarkable young man, full of life and always positive, looking at the bright side of every problem. He'd already overcome many health obstacles from an early age. He and Rose had made wild plans for creating a better world together.

Everyone in the ICU focuses on bringing Rose back from the brink. Her temperature is dangerously high and her lungs are filling with fluids. The medical staff work around her with quiet intensity.

"Pulse?"

"Irregular."

"We're losing her."

Rose drifts into another realm where she seems to be part of a unity that is all and everything, yet intimate at the same time. The experience feels more vivid to her than her ordinary world. *Look at all of these little lights. Where am I?*

A reassuring voice enters her consciousness. "Let yourself be embraced by the Universe, my girl."

Grandma! Is that you? I can hear you! Am I in Iceland?

"Trust. Relax. Feel the loving arms of the Cosmic Mother around you," the soothing voice continues. "She'll protect and guide you through the darkness. You're safe in her arms. Just let go now, and join her. All is well. You're going to be fine."

A wave of relaxation washes over Rose. She hears another voice. It's not the voice of her grandmother, but an evocative voice that sounds very familiar. The voice is luscious, like music. Within it are the sounds of all creation, with an insistent beauty and harmony that feel as caring and personal as a mother's kiss.

Are you the voice of the Universe? Rose knows that she must follow the voice. Strong yearning and curiosity take over, pulling her energy toward it.

The medical team at her bedside notice a slight, positive shift in their patient. Rose's fever drops slightly. Her breathing becomes less shallow. Her muscles relax. This could be a good sign, but the virus is unpredictable. The doctors know that this could also mean she's about to slip away. Just as they dare to take a cautious breath of relief, Rose's heartbeat becomes erratic.

"We must put her into an induced coma immediately," one doctor advises.

"Too risky," another doctor argues.

"She's running out of time. We must act now if we're going to save her."

They discuss their options in earnest. Rose drifts far away from the doctors; far from the hospital; far from her body's struggle to live. She's riding a Cosmic wave on the new rhythms of her heart. The beat quickens, slows down, then quickens a little more as waves of light and sound pull her further into the other realms. Dying and living happen simultaneously.

On the next wave, she sees her entire life in one flash. She watches the last months of her life unravel, like an astronaut from space who is seeing the earth for the very first time.

So that's what my recent dreams about roads that suddenly stop were all about. There's no future for me on this road. What turn am I supposed to take?

Over the past few months, her dreams were already preparing Rose in subtle ways for certain endings; nudging her to new possibilities which she couldn't see from the road on which she'd been travelling. She now understands that a new choice is required, but she has no idea of how, or what, or where.

In an instant, she sees her physical body back in the ICU and realizes what's going on. She hears what the doctors are saying about her condition, even though she's not physically inside her body.

Mother Cosmos, please help me! It's not my time! I don't want to die!

Another Cosmic wave enters her consciousness, moving her away once again. She's carried into the valley of death where she becomes aware of all that is dying and collapsing in our world, and within herself. To her surprise, this realization isn't painful. As she tunes in further, a luminous vision opens up. The world that is dying is held within a huge Cosmic cocoon, surrounded by patterns of light that mimic the fluttering wings of a butterfly. These patterns are activating new life. Her body is inside this cocoon. There appear to be others there, too. Many others. It feels like a great womb that is generating a new becoming. *It's incredibly beautiful! What does it all mean?*

The vision continues. As she explores the inner walls of the cocoon, she realizes that it's part of a luminous Cosmic Tree, with branches and roots that extend out to form whole new worlds and realities. Her consciousness unites with this magnificent Tree of Light; totality itself wells up from the unfathomable depths within her. She becomes aware of the entire Universe, from its beginning to end, all within a single breath. She realizes that one day this universe, too, will come to an end, just like the one that preceded it. *So that's what my dreams were showing me. The end of the road does not mean the end of the journey...*

From within the Cosmic Tree, she experiences how consciousness is continuous. Universes are born and die, worlds and planets are born and die, forms come and go, yet the journey continues. She remembers how our universe began as a little seedling within the Cosmic Tree, and there are plenty of other seeds there that are yet to be born. One particular little seed catches her attention. It radiates with a pulsating light that somehow feels connected with the pulse of her own heart. *What's that?* she wonders.

The voice answers inside her. "This is the seed of your future choice: the choice to renew your life from a new cycle of time. It is a new code that has not yet been born."

Rose is intrigued. She wants to move closer to this little seed, but her consciousness is once again drawn back into her physical body on the hospital bed. The doctors are still debating whether to induce her into a coma to stabilize her condition. Everything inside her screams, "*NOOOO!*" but she's unable to speak. She drifts back to the Tree with a new understanding. *My old life is dying...and my body, too, unless something changes quickly...*

The Future Choice

"My future life...the choice of my future life...my future human choice...I choose this seed...this seed...I choose my future life..." Rose mumbles softly. She shakes her head against her pillow, and clenches her sweating palms.

The nurse is worried, not sure whether her patient is having hallucinations from the fever. Rose moans. Her entire body stiffens, then relaxes with a deep exhalation of breath. The doctor turns to look at the heart monitor. Nothing. No pulse. No breath. She flatlines. The nurse prepares the reanimation machine. There is no sound. Everyone in the room waits anxiously; seconds feel like an eternity. Suddenly, Rose inhales with a sharp, quick breath.

"She's breathing!"

"She has a pulse!"

"Come on, Rose, you can do this!"

The monitor's rhythmic bleeps resume as Rose's heart starts pumping again, just in time. The nurse sighs in relief.

While her physical body resets itself, Rose enters the future seed of her new cycle of time: her choice for this new cycle. *This is not only a new cycle for me, but also for the world*, she realizes. This and similar seeds exist within the Cosmic Tree as sacred potentials for the times when universes shed their old skins, the times also known as periods of renaissance, when one era completes and another begins. This particular new cycle of Rose's choice is not only about a new renaissance for the world, it's also the beginning of a far greater cycle, which Rose has yet to discover.

Rose is carried into the future possibilities of her new life. The codes of her new choice turn into visions, dreams, whole new experiences and sensations. Her body responds immediately. Her fever goes down. Her pulse becomes steady and strong. The doctors and nurses look at each other with shining eyes and relief; they even smile behind their masks. She's made it through. She's on the other side now; on the road to recovery. One nurse remains with Rose while the doctors rush off to their next patients who've just been brought into the Intensive Care Unit.

While her body sleeps peacefully, Rose is deeply in her Cosmic journey. She discovers consciously for the very first time what has been there all along, yet has been hidden for most.

Ohhh, this is incredible. So all this time we could have created a world of abundance and prosperity for everyone, together with life? This is the real architecture of the Universe. This is what space-time truly is, and this is how we manifest the future. The Universe is also a womb. This changes everything! These futures are already here...in these seeds, the inner codes of life! That's why the old world is dying. The Keys of Consciousness...the Cosmic Keys...the Keys...I need to remember this.

Rose is carried in a stream of revelations. She returns to her "inner Rose": her Cosmic self. The seeds of her new life activate within her, like the imaginal cells of the butterfly. Her caterpillar self has completed its purpose. Her body begins to heal deeply and repatterns itself.

Rose slowly awakens. As she opens her eyes, she enters the world from a whole new time…

New Beginnings

A few days later, Sophia calls to see how Rose is doing. She is one of Rose's closest friends. Both women are in their mid-twenties, and they love to explore the mysteries of life together. Sophia is studying in Amsterdam to become a medical doctor. She's of mixed Dutch and Australian Aboriginal origins; a natural beauty, and most intuitive. She's as tall as many of the Dutch, with a golden, honey-brown complexion, beautiful brown eyes, and thick, wavy hair. The two friends met during a violin concert many years earlier, mesmerized by the performance of the Bach Chaconne. They loved the concert so much that they were both inspired to take violin lessons.

Rose puts her friend on speakerphone and takes a sip of hot chamomile tea from the cup that the nurse has brought to her. "Oh, Sophia," she sighs, "I'm feeling so much better now compared to a few days ago. I almost died! Or maybe I really did die. But then I received a miracle. I came to understand things about the Universe that may change everything. It all still feels like a dream."

"I'm so sorry you got that sick, Rose, but it sounds like you received something amazing. Have you told your grandmother yet?" Sophia knows how close Rose is to her grandma Verdandi in Iceland. Sophia likes Verdandi, too. In the past, the two young women enjoyed many deep conversations with the wise, indigenous elder, who carries knowledge of the ancient healing ways, as well as a delightful sense of humor.

"Not yet." Rose blows on her tea, takes another tiny sip, then continues. "I felt like she was with me the night I almost died. The doctors told me that my pulse and breathing stopped for several seconds, but then everything in my body seemed to reset. I can't recall any of that, but I do remember the most incredible dreams I had during that same time. I called out to the Universe for help when I thought I might not make it through the night. I was so weak with high fever, and there was terrible pain all over my body. I could hardly breathe. I kept drifting in and out of consciousness, as if I was moving between different realms. When I feel a little better, I'll share more of the details."

"Yes, you should rest now. That's the best way for your body to heal. I'm so glad you're still with us. You always have the most remarkable experiences, even in the midst of a crisis!" Sophia recalls many of the adventures she's had with her friend, but there has never been one that came so close to death.

The two women end their call. Rose leans back into her pillows and wishes she had something interesting to read. She silently vows to purchase some new books on cosmology and quantum field theory to add to her collection at home the minute she's able to do so. Her recent experience has piqued a renewed interest in these subjects.

Rose graduated with a degree in biology from a university in New York several years earlier. After that, she had moved to Amsterdam where she started working in a bookshop while she tried to figure out what she really wanted to do with her life. Although she loves the study of nature, she's interested more in the experiential understanding of life. Her direct tuition from the Cosmos has now begun in earnest. As her dad, a therapist, often tells her, "The real knowing is the path of revelation; the path of direct inner tuition."

The Bend in the Road

"Oh no, not Otto!"

Tara, Rose's mother, speaks quietly on the other end of the phone. "I'm sorry, honey. I know this is a blow for you. I didn't want you to find out from one of the nurses, so I thought I'd better call and tell you myself."

"Why? Why couldn't they save him? When did this happen?" Rose tugs a tissue from the box beside her hospital bed. "I can't believe it. Last thing I heard, they'd moved him to a floor for people who go onto the breathing ventilators."

Her cousin had been admitted to the same hospital a few days before Rose.

"It's very upsetting. He was a good man. I know how close you two were."

Rose remembers the mischief she and Otto had gotten into together over the years; their plots for tricking the world into transforming itself into a better version. *Otto. No. Too young to die.*

"I'm sure he can still feel you from the other side of the veil," Tara continues.

"Do you really believe he can hear us, Mom? He often said jokingly that if for some bizarre reason he were to die before his time, he would journey to the 'Cosmic puppet masters' and put pressure on them to give humanity a serious upgrade."

Tara smiles. "That sounds like Otto."

"He said that humans are the joker card of the animal kingdom, with just enough free will to make us believe we can direct our own destiny, and not enough to steer our destiny clear of hazards. I wish I could talk with him now," Rose says with a catch in her throat.

"The Universe works in mysterious ways, love. We don't always know why things happen the way they do. It's hard to accept sometimes when life throws us an unexpected curve."

"That reminds me of a conversation I had with him a few weeks ago. He may even have predicted his own death."

"Really?" Tara asks. "How so?"

"We were talking about all of the apocalyptic changes happening in the world right now and wondering what we could do about it. He said, 'Each of us can choose to become a tipping point for a better world.' Then he quoted one of his heroes, Buckminster Fuller: 'Make the world work for a hundred percent of humanity, in the shortest possible time, through spontaneous cooperation, without ecological offense or the disadvantage of anyone.' That should be our focus."

"Beautiful."

"Yes," Rose continues, "I asked him how we could become a positive tipping point. He answered, 'Life works in mysterious ways. You never know how the Universe will prepare you for your right role. Sometimes the road you're on suddenly curves around a sharp bend. Those who don't know that the road continues past the curve may think the path ends there, but the sudden twists and turns are just part of the journey of life.'"

Tara nods. "On some deeper level, Otto may in fact have been preparing you for this sudden turn in the road. Reminding you ahead of time that when he's no longer physically with us, his spirit lives on past the bend."

"Thank you, Mom. It makes it a little bit easier to come to terms with his death, although I miss him so much already." Rose brushes a tear from her cheek. "But maybe he's right where he needs to be now. Maybe he's even our best hope if he manages to reach those puppet masters he was joking about."

"I'm sure he can hear you, my darling. You two have the strongest bond.

Nothing can come between that, not even death. Now go and rest some more. I'll call again soon."

Rose pictures her mother far away in the United States, unable to fly to Amsterdam due to coronavirus restrictions.

"I wish you were here."

"Soon, love."

Trust in the Process of Life

"Good morning! How are you feeling today?"

Sophia's cheerful voice on the other end of the phone lifts Rose's spirits.

"I am getting better every day. They told me that if my temperature remains normal, I can go home by the weekend."

"Great news. This sudden recovery of yours is so amazing, especially when the docs said they weren't even sure you were going to make it. Nurse Tom told me your heart stopped. Do you remember anything that might explain how you came back to life?"

"Yes, I was given the possibility of a new choice from my future. The future of a different cycle than my old life that ended that night. I had no idea that was even possible."

"Me either."

"I guess the Universe heard my plea and showed me how to heal myself."

"That sounds wonderful, but how?" Sophia has always been fascinated by life after death, ever since her own father was declared dead after a heart attack for several hours, and then miraculously returned to life. The experience changed his life forever. Sophia was born a year later. Her dad often jokes that he had to almost die to find Sophia's soul deep within the stars, and bring her to Earth with him. Sophia's mother had attempted to get pregnant for many years with no luck. Soon after her husband's near-death experience, she became pregnant with Sophia, who is their only child.

"While my body was dying, I entered into an altered state and everything became clear with a clarity I've never experienced before," Rose explains. "In this altered state, I received strong visions. One of the visions was about a tiny seed that carried the codes of a new future inside the Cosmic Tree of Life. As soon as I connected with this seed, everything changed. I realized how to heal myself with these future codes. It felt similar to the birth of the butterfly within the dying body of the caterpillar. Before this, I'd always focused on trying to repair my life by keeping my old body alive. Once I understood how my body is not this shape, but the process of life that created it, I understood what rebirth is truly all about. From then on, it was like a deeper inner knowing woke up within me. That knowing guided me through the valley of death, which then transformed into a magnificent womb of life."

"Wow. That's incredible, Rose. You healed yourself from the future! That's such a liberating way of working with the power of time. Nature has always shown us how to heal through transformation by trusting in the deeper process of life."

"Yes!" Rose loves the fact that Sophia is so curious and intelligent. She can discuss anything with her friend.

"A snake also grows its new body while still within the skin of its old body, and the imaginal codes of the butterfly activate within the dying body of the caterpillar," Sophia says. "It reminds me of the 'second birth' that some of the mystics speak of. It sounds so similar to what my dad went through. How were you able to access this power of renewal and birth?"

Rose thinks about that. "It all happened so fast. Maybe my body was never really dying from the virus, but was actually renewing and transforming itself together with this virus."

"Interesting."

"Yes. The doctors may tell you I was dying, but from my own experience, it felt like my future life was already awakening within my body. Maybe the high fever was necessary as well, because it provided the fire for the transformation. Maybe the virus had a key role to play in all that happened."

The Key of Conscious Choice

This thought is a revelation. Rose enjoys sharing with Sophia because it helps her to clarify her own thoughts.

I'm beginning to realize why the Universe has given me this experience. I want to tell Sophia about the keys I discovered in the architecture of the Universe, Rose thinks to herself, *but maybe not yet. I need more time to integrate that first. Those keys have activated within me, and may guide me to whole new discoveries about the Universe I've been studying in books for all of those years.*

Rose says aloud, "We don't have to physically die and leave this life in order to start a new creative cycle in another place or body. We don't have to break everything down before we start something new. We already carry the futures of new possibilities inside us. It's just that many people don't know how to activate the seeds for these possibilities. We have the power to renew our lives, just like the caterpillar and the snake you mentioned. We're nature, too. The key is being able to access the state of consciousness of the choice that awakens the future potentials inside us. You can't renew your life from your old realities."

Rose's voice rises in excitement. "Each choice carries a state of consciousness, so much so that a choice can carry an entire world. If part of our life is dying or sick, then something inside us is already seeking to be reborn! As a new choice; a new experience for life to evolve!"

Sophia pipes in, "So, maybe…in some bizarre way…the coronavirus crisis is actually an attempt for life to renew itself? I mean, given that we're all being cocooned—"

"Quarantined."

"Yes, restricted from moving, and challenged to release our old, unsustainable ways of living. We're like hungry caterpillars that are continuously and voraciously consuming more and more, to the point of collapse. But we can't remain caterpillars forever, right? That's what nature tells us. It's time to transform so we can learn how to thrive as lighter creatures, like butterflies."

"Exactly."

"But, Rose, how do you enter the state of consciousness of your choice?" Sophia asks. "Can we learn this? Or does it just happen when the necessity for change reaches a critical point?"

"Now that is the golden question, Sophia." Rose laughs. "My grandma told me that the magic seems to happen when the readiness of time and the necessity of change marry with the power of our future choices. The power of our future choice is not the choice *about* our future, but the power *from* our future."

"Well, there's an interesting thought. So it's the higher potentials inside us that are part of the Cosmic realities that stimulate new growth and evolution?"

"Yes. Grandma also said that we need to be ready and available for those transformative opportunities. We need to be prepared so we can recognize the opportunities when they come along."

"Yeah, and they often come when you least expect it," Sophia says.

"Isn't that the truth?"

The two women laugh.

"I'm so grateful for all the guidance I've received from both her and my grandfather, and my parents, as well. My grandmother especially, and she also loves deep discussions. Ever since I was little, we've been able to share like that. She's a really good listener and she offers helpful insights. And I'm grateful for you, too, Sophia. It's nice to be able to discuss all of this with you."

Cosmos as the Architecture of Wholeness

Rose reflects silently on her discovery of the living architecture of the Universe. It reminds her of the fractal patterns she discovered within the growth patterns of nature when she was studying biology. She enjoyed studying the infinitely complex patterns that repeat in a self-creative and self-replicating manner, through all dimensions of life. She first discovered the fractals in the ways flower petals grow and open as unfolding spirals. She then discovered the same patterns in the way trees grow, and in the weather patterns. Even within a little twig, the potential of the whole tree is already there.

Even as a young child, Rose's favorite fractal patterns were in broccoli and cauliflower, with their florets arranged in such exquisite geometry. As part of her study at the university, she discovered that rituals too are fractal, like the rhythms pounded out by an African drummer, and the fertility and harvest rituals performed by ancient shamans; even the courtship habits of peacocks and prairie dogs. Some even go as far as suggesting that fractals are the habits of nature, appearing as laws.

Curious to learn more, Rose studied the Fibonacci number sequence, also known as the "Golden Rule," wherein the next number is found by adding up the two numbers before it. This sparked her interest in sacred geometry and the architecture of living systems. Yet, it was not until her near-death experience a few days ago, that she experienced for the very first time how the Universe grows and evolves as a single unified entity.

"Something else happened during the night I almost died, Sophia. I don't know yet how to put all of this into words and concepts. All I can say is that this huge universe in which we live, which looks so incredibly diverse and vast that it's hard to see what we may have in common with the stars and planets in, or even beyond, our galaxy, is in fact a single unified entity of life. My grandmother was right: The Universe is a living being, and she, he, or it is aware of us. The Universe revealed many things to me about its architecture. I came to know this architecture as Cosmos."

"Ah!" Sophia exclaims. "Like the Greek word 'Kosmos'? That means 'ordered wholeness.'"

"Yes, exactly. I discovered hidden keys that could radically change the way we design, govern, and evolve our world."

"That's so exciting."

"Of course, those keys aren't hidden from nature, but they seem to be hidden from the human mind," Rose says.

"Maybe that's because we still understand so little about the Universe as a single entity? You know, Rose, this reminds me of what that physicist, David Bohm, spoke of when he referred to the Universe as 'an undivided wholeness'; the implicate order that is within everything at all scales of existence as an undivided flowing movement. Remember that?"

"I do. He also mentioned how this wholeness expresses as ever more subtle implicate orders, like a kind of 'super-implicate order.' An architecture of wholeness. During my visions the night I almost died, I experienced this architecture of wholeness, deep inside the Cosmic Tree. I realized how it manifests in our world as fractal potentials and evolutionary codes, which become expressed through the aesthetics, beauty, and natural wonders of our world. This same architecture has inspired our greatest artists, musicians, composers, designers, storytellers, inventors, and sages. Not only is the Cosmos ever-present as the eternal now, it's also the source of our deepest creativity."

The Future as a Cosmic Magnet

Sophia takes a moment to reflect on what Rose has just shared. "Ohhh!" she exclaims. "So that's what is meant by the 'power of now'! The Cosmic presence is always in the now. The 'now' gives you access to all forms of time, including past and future, all happening simultaneously. Amazing! So the Cosmos never leaves, which means that we have never left the Cosmos. We are the Cosmos looking into this world and the world looking back at itself as the Cosmos. A great unity and oneness that is the nature of the evolutionary jump from the future that we really need for this time." Sophia gets more and more excited as she shares her insight with Rose.

"Exactly, Sophia. You got it." Rose grins. "That's one of the keys I received during my near-death experience. The Cosmos is our own awareness. We see from the Cosmos into the world, yet mostly without realizing it. The very act of seeing, of being self-conscious, of being able to choose, is the presence of the Cosmic architecture within us. The Cosmos is the architecture of consciousness. Can you see how realizing what this implies can change everything?"

"I'm trying to follow along and understand everything you're sharing with me, but I don't quite see how this changes everything," Sophia confesses. "But in listening to you, I get a whole new appreciation for how my skin, organs, cells, bones, and all of my bodily functions are the living expressions of this Cosmic architecture. I wonder what this implies for healing a person from cancer or viral infections or any other diseases and illnesses?"

The two young women are silent for a moment as they consider this.

"It seems you really did re-enter our world from the future," Sophia says. "It may take decades before science is able to understand what the Universe shared with you."

"You could be right."

"You know what? I'd like to experiment with some of the things you've talked about today. I'd like to start with my own body, by focusing my awareness as the Cosmic presence on any areas within myself that need healing, repatterning, or optimization. Then I'll enter the consciousness of the higher order choices by connecting with my future self. This is exciting!"

"It is!"

"This conversation has opened up a whole new world of possibility for me. Thanks so much for sharing all of this. I can't wait to talk more about these concepts, but you're still recovering, and you must be tired. Go rest now, my sister."

"Alright." Rose doesn't argue. Her friend is right: She's exhausted. "I'm so relieved that you're open to hearing about all of my discoveries. I feel closer to you than I would to a real sister."

"It's my pleasure. Hey, with my medical background, I'm all over this. I can't wait to start experimenting. Using the power of choice to access infinite realities within the field of consciousness? What's better than that? It means that the future is no longer what happens because of the flows of time. Unexplored Cosmic potentials can inspire whole new inventions! Entirely new ways of being! I love this."

"Me, too. Now I know why my grandmother always says that the future is our 'lure of becoming.' I never really understood that fully before this. Cosmic magnets attract us into higher orders of reality."

"This is a lot to think about, Rose. My head is swirling."

"I know! Mine is, too," Rose laughs. "But it's fun."

"I agree. Let's talk again soon."

Defining Moments of Choice

The doctor enters Rose's room with a big smile. "We're so pleased with your progress that we're releasing you, Rose. Tomorrow, you can return home."

"That's wonderful news! Thank you."

She misses her apartment. She's been in the hospital for nine days. The time has passed slowly. Her friend Peter sends her an article on her phone from *Time Magazine* by Justin Worland, titled "One Last Chance: The Defining Year for the Planet." The title lands deeply for her and reminds her of a conversation she had recently with her grandmother.

"Rose," Verdandi said, "you have to elect yourself to become the required human for this renaissance time. Renaissance times are mythic times, as it was for Athens in the 5th century BC and the late 14th century. What's required now is truly a mythic task. Never before have the stakes been so high for ourselves, society, and our planet. The sheer scope of breakdown and breakthrough, beauty and ugliness, the unexpected as the expected, the upside down, topsy-turvy nature of things that previously had been ordinary and unchanging—all of these elements bring us into the planet-wide life of a story that's unique and previously unknown, always surprising, and therefore mythic. This is happening to all of us, simultaneously, around the world, regardless of culture or context, economics or ecology, science or spirit. It's as if we've landed on the unknown, other side of the moon of ourselves, and we have little or no training or mentoring with which to meet the immensities of this challenge."

As Rose recalls her grandmother's words, she realizes what a huge difference it makes for her, knowing that she can now call the help of the

Cosmos as a loving guide and mentor. Her thoughts turn to Otto. She closes her eyes.

"Dear cousin, if you can hear me from the other side of the veil, know that I love you. Enjoy your time in the stars."

A Happy Day

Today's the day. Rose sits on the edge of her hospital bed, waiting for the release paperwork so she can finally return home. The birds outside her hospital window are chirping happily while the morning sun's rays gently land on her cheeks, filling her body with gratitude. Everything feels new for her, like the first day of a new life.

Nurse Tom arrives with the paperwork. "Leaving us so soon, Rose? I guess some people will do anything to get out of wearing our stylish hospital gowns for another day, huh?"

She laughs. "I won't say that wasn't my highest motivation for getting out of here."

"We're going to miss you." Tom hands her a pen and adds, "But everyone's thrilled that you've recovered. Some days are really tough around here. You've been a bright light. Your story gives us hope."

"You've all been amazing. Above and beyond." Rose signs the papers and hands everything back to the nurse.

"Before you go, may I ask you for a little favor? You seem to have found a remarkable way to heal your body, since you recovered much faster than any of our other COVID-19 patients. Would you mind letting us in on your healing practice so we can share it with them?"

"Of course. I am happy to help in any way I can."

"Great. Here, you can use my phone to record it."

"You can also use this practice for other healing purposes by making slight adjustments," she explains. Rose takes Tom's phone and records the practice that she learned from her grandmother.

A Practice for Self-Healing

"Give yourself 10 minutes without any interruptions to go through this healing practice. Make yourself comfortable, either seated or lying down.

Relax your body as much as possible. Relax your attention, and let go of any tensions. Just let it all go for now.

"Become aware how the Cosmos is always present within you as your own awareness. You see from the Cosmos into the world via your awareness. The Cosmos is alive in you as the living architecture of your body and innate wholeness of life.

"Give the Cosmos permission to support you through this practice in a way that is for your highest good and pure health. You can send this permission by simply holding the intention in your heart to receive the Cosmic support that is here for you now.

"The Cosmos answers your intention by gently weaving a beautiful healing cocoon around you and your personal space. This healing cocoon is perfectly designed to support you with the vibrations, patterns, healing serums, and wisdom that you need. It provides you with optimum support to safely heal, repattern, and evolve with ease and clarity.

"Feel the Cosmic healing cocoon safely embracing you like a warm, loving hug. It shields you from outer harm and interferences, while providing you the support to safely surrender to your inner growth and transformation. It also draws out and transmutes any harmful patterns and toxins. Those may be physical, mental, emotional, or energetic toxins. It transmutes them all from their root cause.

"Feel the toxic and harmful patterns being thoroughly transmuted. The energy repatterns, heals, and evolves your body, mind, and spirit to create your optimum health and wellbeing. An inner liberation takes place. You may experience this as tingling sensations or the sensation of little currents of light moving inside you, creating balance and wellness.

"Hold the intention that this healing support can repair and enhance all of your genes, cells, tissues, organs, and inner systems. Feel the wonderful sensations of this serum of healing that now flows through your veins, and circulates to all of your cells. Wherever this serum enters and touches, your health is revitalized; a greater clarity and deeper alignment naturally emerge. It now becomes easier to access your innate abilities and future resourcefulness as this healing serum continues to naturally clear harmful patterns. Even viral or bacterial patterns are transformed now by this serum, so that you can all evolve together into a healthy symbiotic relationship.

"The pattern of greater health and wellness initiates a deeper collaboration within your whole self, including your genetic codes and the codes of bacteria and viruses. All work together now for your full health and wellbeing, supporting your vitality. Feel the genius of this collective collaboration of your whole system coming together.

"Rest a few more minutes in the experience of your greater health and wellness. When you're ready, gently come out of this practice by opening your eyes, being fully present here and now."

Going Home

Rose finishes the recording and hands the nurse back his phone.

"Wow! Thank you. That practice will be so helpful. My whole body is tingling just from listening," Tom says in a warm voice. "Please stay in touch. Send us a message once in a while so we know how you're doing."

"Tom, I can't thank you and the others enough. You're all my heroes. One day I'll come back here with fresh flowers and Dutch apple pie to thank you all in person. I promise to stay in touch."

"No need to thank us, Rose; that's why we're here. We're just so glad you've recovered. That's the greatest gift." Tom smiles. "I'd better get back to my other patients."

The moment to return home has finally come. Rose takes one last look at the bed where she's been for all those days and almost died, and then turns and walks through the door to start a new chapter of her life.

Integration - The Key of Conscious Choice

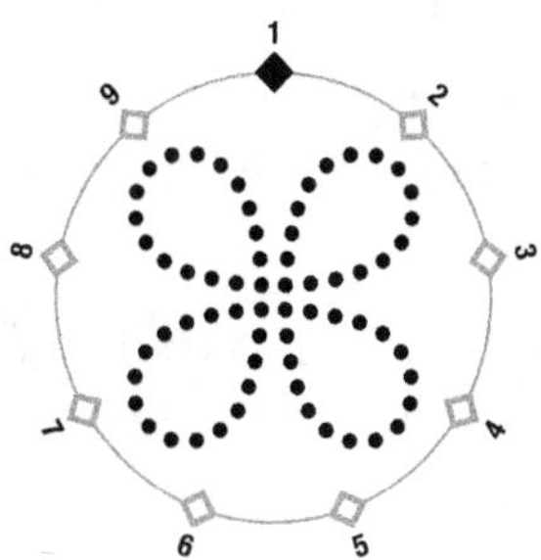

This is truly your story as well as Rose's. Join her now to connect with your future human potential. Her choice for a new cycle of life can be your future human choice. How does the necessity of change and the call of a new cycle, a new spring, live in you?

During her near-death experience, Rose received many essential keys for accessing and applying her Cosmic powers. The most important key she discovered for shifting her consciousness to a higher order of reality is the Key of Conscious Choice.

> *The Key of Conscious Choice helps you to recognize how each choice is a state of consciousness to effect change. Your future human choice activates and awakens the consciousness of your future human potentials.*

To support your discovery and integration, here is a summary of the essential ideas that have been shared with you in this chapter:

- The end of the road doesn't mean the end of the journey. Sudden twists and turns are also part of the journey of life.
- The world that is dying also contains within it the future seeds of a new world. Life continues past the bend.
- Consciousness is continuous. Universes are born and die, worlds and planets are born and die, forms come and go, yet the journey continues.

- Your body is not your physical shape, but the process of life that created it. Understand this deeply and you will realize the keys to rebirth.
- We are living in a renaissance (rebirth) time; one era completes and another begins. This is not only a new renaissance for the world, it is also the beginning of a far greater cycle.
- The valley of death inside the cocoon is a hospice for the caterpillar, yet a womb for the butterfly that is forming and being born from this cocoon.
- We each carry within us the possibility of a new choice from a new future cycle. It is from this future choice that we can heal and repattern ourselves and our world.
- You can't renew your life from the old realities. Enter the consciousness of your future potential to make the new choices that will evolve your life further.
- If part of your life is dying or sick, then something inside you is already seeking to be reborn as a new choice and a new experience for life to evolve.
- The power of your future choice is not the choice about your future, but *the power from your future.* Your future is the higher potential inside you that is already part of the Cosmic realities that stimulate new growth and evolution. Your lure of becoming is a Cosmic magnet that attracts you into higher orders of reality.

CHAPTER 2

The New Mythos

Exploring the Mythic Realms with the Key of Imaginal Power

It's been several weeks since Rose returned to her small apartment in Amsterdam. She's still integrating the powerful visions she received, along with a deepening curiosity to continue her conversations with the Cosmos. Now that she's experienced how each choice that she makes has its own life, and even its own realm of possibilities, she no longer wants to use that power in a way that limits her options in life. The bookshop has closed temporarily as a result of the coronavirus regulations. Even if it were to open again later, Rose doesn't want to return to her old life. She will, however, keep her violin lessons because they bring her so much joy. She holds the keys to form a new path, and this time with entirely new allies, including the Universe Herself.

Einstein's Advice

Rose happily takes a sip of the green smoothie in front of her.

"Thanks for calling, Grandma. I miss you. I also miss your cardamom gooseberry cake."

"You funny girl. I miss you, too. We were worried about you when your mother told us what was happening. It's wonderful to hear you sounding so strong."

"I had a lot of time to think in the hospital. Remember that story you told me one time about Einstein?"

"You mean the one where I told you I was sure he moussed his hair to make it look like that?"

"No." Rose laughs. "The story about the children who asked him how they could become intelligent like him? He told them, 'Read fairy tales!'"

"I remember. And when they asked how they could become more intelligent than him, he replied, 'Read more fairy tales!'" Verdandi chuckles.

"Well, Einstein was also a musician and he used his imaginal powers to unravel some of the greatest secrets about our universe, right?"

"Right."

"Do you think I can do this as well? Apparently, he had help from his first wife, Mileva Einstein-Maric, who worked out much of the mathematics of his theories. So *his* genius wasn't about mathematics or even hard core science. Rather, his genius, as he always said, was in the power of his imagination."

"Yes! And thus, his ability to enter the Universe," Verdandi affirms. "There he could intuit the deeper architecture that sustains and evolves the Universe, just as a fine composer can intuit and evoke the music of the spheres, making it possible for all to hear and feel that."

"That's what I'm thinking."

"Yes, you've got it, Rose. Merely listening to Bach or Handel or Mozart can bring a person directly into Cosmic consciousness."

"Isn't it exciting?"

"Absolutely! Though I've often wondered if the Universe secretly prefers banjo music."

"Or bagpipes."

"Exactly. Why make a choice when you can have it all? That's the perk of being the Universe." Verdandi chuckles. "I like the way you think, my girl."

"Well, you're the one who taught me."

"No wonder I like it so much."

Verdandi has always encouraged her granddaughter to develop her imaginal capacities. From the time Rose was little, she'd given her specific exercises to practice her imaginal powers to envision the answers to her questions. From time to time, she would draw from her shamanic training to show Rose how she could connect with the non-human worlds, including the world of the elves, giants, and trolls that are so prominent in Iceland. She explained to Rose how all worlds, human, physical, spiritual, and nonhuman, are made of imaginal strands of consciousness that keep us connected with the great universal Dreaming. The imaginal realm is present in every molecule and atom, as they dance between different states of existence.

Rose was a bright child, eager to learn. She practiced using and trusting her imaginal powers by connecting with these imaginal strands that live in the landscapes of her dreams, visions, and intuitions. Verdandi taught her to use her senses to extend her natural receptivity beyond the domains of her mind to connect with the Cosmic dimensions of life. She often reminded Rose that the imaginal goes beyond the imaginative, as it includes the Cosmos and the transformative powers of the Universe in the way we think, perceive, and respond.

Rose takes another sip of her smoothie. "Grandma, I don't want to go back to the bookshop where I was working, even if it reopens at some point. I can't return to my old life. Everything's changed. Now that I know how powerful our choices can really be, I want to make my next choices more carefully. I want to be open to greater possibilities."

Engaging the Archetypes

"Mother Universe is your new friend now, Rosie; a wonderful friend who's always guided you throughout your life. Involve her in your questions about what to do next, then be open to the answers."

"Thanks for understanding, Grandma. These days it seems like we're constantly asked to choose: 'Be only this and not that! Make up your mind! What do you want to do with your life?' The list of what we're told we should and shouldn't do is long and boring, and it's not my list."

"I understand. It doesn't evoke the imagination of the possible, and it shows no understanding of the power of our own choice."

"You know how you often talk about archetypes as the personification of universal forces that are sometimes also portrayed as gods, goddesses, deities, and beings with higher powers?"

"Yes."

"Well, I've been wondering, is Mother Universe also an archetype? And should I include these archetypes in my explorations of my new life?"

"Mother Universe is the Mother archetype of the vast universe that has birthed our world," Verdandi explains. "This Mother, as well as the Father archetype, is within the structure and relationship of every atom, as well as life as a whole."

"I think of the archetypes in the myths and stories you told me when I was a child."

"Learn to partner as a co-creator with those archetypes so you can discover how to build bridges to the very source levels of your life. Think of archetypes as the connective pattern for the way things grow and evolve. We each have unique archetypal forces in our life that help us to realize our true potentials. By engaging these archetypes in our lives, we actually help *them* to grow and evolve as well."

"Really? The archetypes grow and evolve as well? That's interesting," Rose says.

"Yes."

"Ohhh, so if archetypes are part of the deeper mythic structures of our lives, then there might even be whole *new* archetypes that belong to my future life!"

"Yes!"

"And there may even be whole new archetypes that belong to the new era we're entering into?"

"That's right. And it might be that Einstein's brilliance came from his archetypal understanding of the laws of physics, not as dry rules at all, but as creative codes for greater possibilities. The laws of physics he discovered are also great universal archetypes that belong to the architecture of the Universe, which you have come to know as the Cosmos. The Cosmos plays the role of the great Architect: the ordered wholeness that is indivisible. Imagine and connect with the future possibilities that call you forth. Enter into these greater possibilities with your imaginal powers. When you do this, they receive a place in our world. You become the place for their manifestation in this world and time. Your imaginal powers are the key to your mental fertility. Make your explorations 'sensory rich.' See them! Smell them! Feel them! That way, the future becomes our power for renewing and evolving ourselves and our world."

"It's a lot to take in," Rose says.

"Yes. And to think I just called to see how you were feeling."

Verdandi laughs with her granddaughter. "More about this another time, my girl. Enough of this talking on the phone. If you feel up to it, why don't you take a walk in the park? Get outside and drink in the fresh energies of spring."

"Will do, Grandma."

Living a Mythic Life

It's a beautiful spring day in the Netherlands. Nature is in full bloom. The sun warms Rose's body. She breathes deeply. It's the first time since her return from the hospital that she's been able to go outside. She turns the corner to make her way to the park when she bumps into Sophia.

"Sophia!"

"Look at you! Outside and walking around? This is wonderful."

"I'm feeling better every day. Are you busy? I'm on my way to the park and I'd love it if you could join me."

"I could do that," Sophia says. "With the coronavirus restrictions, we can still go out in nature, as long as there are no more than two people together."

"Great. How are your studies going?"

Sophia makes a funny face. "It's a challenge, but I'm highly motivated."

"You'll be an outstanding doctor."

"Thanks, Rose."

The friends walk in silence for a minute, enjoying the blossoming trees in the park.

"You know, Sophia, since I received this second chance at life, I really want to live a *mythic* life. I want to be free to live and explore all of my passions and abilities—as a scientist, storyteller, musician…I'm all of those things—and I can't live in a limiting box of rigid formulas and societal expectations anymore. It just doesn't work for me."

"I don't think it works for anyone, really."

"Why do we limit ourselves to confined choices when we can be so much more?"

"Well, isn't that obvious? People use their choices to limit possibilities to confirm their belief in a limited world that is set up to make 'either-or' decisions. That way they can blame it on life when their greater dreams don't manifest because 'life forced them to choose.' You are living proof that life doesn't constrict us. It doesn't hold us back. For you, either-or options are not an option at all. You see it as a false choice because you don't believe in duality."

Sophia adds, "Believe me, I know the world of labels and dogma and how constrictive life can become when trying to fit into other people's expectations. As a young woman of color, I'm often labelled and categorized."

"Why do we do that?" Rose asks. "Why do we play small when we can be so much more? Grandma Verdandi often tells me that during these renaissance times we need a new mythos to engage people's passion for the possible. It seems like we've landed in our own real-life, myth-making experiment right now in these present times, as we're handed crisis after crisis."

"I agree with you. Especially you. Few people get to tell their story of entering the valley of death and coming out the other side. Now *that's* mythic. Ever since you told me about your experience, I'm more interested than ever to learn all I can about that. I'm even asking the doctors I know if they've had any terminally ill patients who've made miraculous recoveries, and if so, if they'd be willing to talk about it. There's so much more to life and death than what most people think."

"There's so much fear around that subject, too. But it's not scary at all."

"Oh Rose, I'd love to talk more about this, but I'd better get back to my studies."

"I understand. I'm happy we bumped into each other. And what a gorgeous day, huh? All of this fresh air has done me a world of good."

"Me, too. I'll talk with you soon."

Rose enjoys the easy walk back to her apartment. She feels invigorated rather than tired, so she decides to call her grandmother back.

The Need for New Narratives

"Rosie! You're back from your walk so soon?"

"You know me. I have more things I'd like to discuss with you."

"Well, let's hear it, my girl. What's on your mind? Hold on a second, these cats need their lunch."

"I can hear them."

"Yes, it's their kitty opera to make sure I put enough food into their bowls. They'd eat fifteen times a day if they could get away with it. Just like your grandpa. Now where were we?"

"I want to know how we can create a new story for our world. I'm tired of hearing all these stories of conflict, lies, violence, and division."

"Yes, it can be disheartening. That's why I turn off my television. Except for *Jeopardy*."

"There must be a way we can create a better story about what it means to be human. The Universe showed me how incredible life truly is. That incredibleness lives in every cell of our being, yet people either don't realize that or they ignore it," Rose exclaims.

"If you don't like our current world story, then start telling a better story, even before it becomes reality. Live a better truth from the reality of your choice. Inspire the change. What you appreciate, appreciates. Devote time, attention, and intention to this coming of the higher plan for our Earth and the species she carries."

"But there's so much destruction—"

"Don't shake before the passing disasters," Verdandi advises. "Co-create with the Cosmos a higher pattern and the new earth story! It already exists in the imaginal realm. During this time when death and collapse are stirring the very foundations of our societies, a rebirth of the self is an absolute necessity right now. You are that story. You are living this yourself right now. Culture, religion, and the politics of our beliefs are all calling to be newly reimagined."

Verdandi continues, "This is the time of the new conception that will birth the new era. We're living in a potent time of renaissance! Rebirth! This is the revival of our souls from the potential of our greater future. The future that brings to life new patterns and possibilities that unlock the hidden treasures of our minds. This is an act of mythic creation through the divine act of re-mythologizing our story: to release the purpose, plan, and greater possibilities of our lives. It's absolutely thrilling!" She pauses and adds, "Do you know what else is thrilling?"

"What?"

"This loaf of homemade rye your grandfather just pulled out of the oven. It smells like heaven. Dagaz! Bring me the butter!"

"Stop! You're making me drool."

"I'm giving you an incentive to visit us."

"I'll visit you as soon as I can. Save me a piece of bread."

"I can't promise that." Verdandi chuckles. "Look, Rosie, the very dynamics of our current time are regrowing us to greatness and inviting us to take our place with Percival, Penelope, White Buffalo Calf Woman, the Lady of the Lake, Quetzalcoatl, Isis, Athena, Mary, and even Buddha, Jesus, Mohammed, and Krishna! This is the most exciting time to be alive! Your name in this newly emerging myth belongs to this list as well, dearest, along with every other person who's part of the re-mythologizing of our story and world. Each of us is being called for this mythic task, and we're up to it. We're made for these times." Verdandi pauses to let that sink in, then adds, "Trust me. I know things."

"And you're living a mythic life, Grandma. You embody that."

"You'd better believe it!"

Verdandi's unique perspectives are sourced in long traditions of indigenous wisdom from Sami and Norse traditions, combined with her extensive knowledge of world mythology. Born in Norway, she later moved to Iceland when she married Dagaz. She became well-known as a seer and wise woman; a mystic who knows how to open the inner portals to the Cosmos, guiding people through the mythic landscapes of their souls.

Seekers from all over the world come to her to receive initiations. One of these visitors referred to her as a "female Merlin" one time, but added that instead of doing magic for people, the wise woman showed people how to access their own creative powers.

Verdandi had loved Merlin ever since she was a young girl in Norway when she sat beside her mother and listened to tales of King Arthur. The visitor's comment delighted her so much that she named her newest dog Merlin. The dog was eagerly welcomed into the family that already included two cats and two dogs. Verdandi adores creatures of all kinds and communicates with them telepathically, even those in the Spirit World.

Her name, "Verdandi," loosely translated in English, means "present." The old Norse mythology speaks of three female deities called "Norns" who live at the roots of "Yggdrasil," the Tree of Life. These Norns are said to govern the destiny of the gods and the humans with respect to all things past, present, and future. The Norns, called Urðr, Verðandi, and Skuld, also look after the Tree of Life by bringing water and soil from the sacred well, "Urðarbrunnr," and pouring this over its roots. It is said that this is necessary to keep the sacred tree strong and healthy. The Norn Verðandi is responsible for all that governs our present, including our process of becoming here and now.

Verdandi surely takes after her name, as this has been her role for many people, including her granddaughter, Rose. Her appearance is striking, with a strong "otherworldly" charisma and warm, brown, magnetic eyes that always feel welcoming. Her natural, long hair consists of different colors: dark brown, a reddish auburn, and white. The white streaks of hair remind Rose of the beautiful snow of Iceland.

"As soon as we can fly again, I'm coming to see you," Rose promises her grandmother.

"I'll hold that intention, Rosebud. The sooner, the better."

The Role of Myth

The next day Rose calls her grandmother again. Her grandfather, Dagaz, answers.

"She's walking the pack," he tells her. "Well, I say that, but it'd be more accurate to say the dogs are walking her. But she's feisty, that one. Being out in this weather with three big dogs doesn't faze that woman one bit. Hold on, they're coming in the back door as we speak. Good to talk with you, Rose. Here she is…"

Dagaz hands the phone to his wife.

"Hello, Rosebud!" Her grandmother's voice is a comforting balm. "It's a blustery day here, but my furry friends insisted that we get some exercise. They're smart that way. There. My coat is off, my boots are off, Dagaz has the kettle on, and I'm ready to talk. How are you?"

"I've been thinking more about our conversation from yesterday. When you speak of myth, it's alive for you, Grandma. It's so different from the way my teachers in high school and professors in college spoke about mythology."

Verdandi smiles. This is her favorite topic. Loki the cat leaps into her lap and settles himself as Verdandi speaks. "Mythic stories live in everyone and hold great promise. They provide the deepest nourishment and strength for the soul. Especially during times such as we find ourselves in right now, as you and I discussed. It's myth that tells us where we are, what we could be, where we should be going, and how to face the challenges that will meet us. And finally, also how to get back home and bring our hard-won gifts into time and society."

She strokes Loki under his soft, gray chin and continues, "Myth is fundamental to the very genesis of our existence. That's why I often refer to myth as the 'DNA of the human psyche.' This is also why I, and others like me, have taken on the task of exploring the mythic terrain within ourselves. We've studied the myths of many times and cultures, and then brought all of these forth into books, talks, and dramatizations, which can help in the telling and enactment of these great, fertile stories. We do this in such a way that the individuals joining our quest move from the personal to the universal, and thus, can live out the myth with all of its power and passion.

"What we've found," Verdandi continues, "is that such immersion in the myth reveals the codes that have been lying dormant and need to be put back into practice. We're the heirs of this richness, which is there, not just to be recovered, but to bring its many parts into the weave of a new story; a re-genesis of myth for the betterment of all."

"That's exactly why I want to know more about it. 'A re-genesis of myth for the betterment of all.' I love that. So the Cosmic codes and seeds that I saw in my visions from the Universe are also mythic codes?" Rose asks.

"Oh yes, Rosie, very much so. They're the seeds from the Cosmos for a great new story that's being born from within you, calling you to experience these new possibilities in your everyday life. We've been relying too much on secondary myths. You know, those quickie tales and truncated stories found on television and in popular movies. Great stories, as encoded in myth, give us direction and divinity. Myth at its best is always about growth and transformation; the movement from an outmoded self and condition to one that encompasses the higher form of what could be."

Rose starts to realize how this mythic understanding can help her discover and share the deeper realities of what she has been going through this last month. This way of living and sharing her story is far more profound than simply looking at what happened.

"Thanks, Grandma. This helps me to make sense of the transformations I'm going through."

"Remember, your view of your life *as a story* often determines how life will treat you. If you see your life only as a small, trivial story, you may fall easily into inertia and defeat. Seeing your life as a larger story puts you back on your feet and helps you to get on with living. Yet seeing your life as a great story can fill you with passion, and give you codes to access new ranges of possibilities, and grant you a mythic life and a higher purpose."

The Key of Imaginal Power

"But *how* do we change the mythic patterns in ourselves and in our world? Especially when these patterns are so deeply engrained in the structures of our psyches?" Rose wants to know.

"We live in a truly unique time right now. Up until recent decades, I doubt that anyone could have done much more than alter certain details of their pattern. But now that we've entered this time of whole system transformation, when *everything* is deconstructing and reconstructing, our mythic structure is also changing. To change the dominant myths, we need to guide people into the realms of their own psyches first, so they're able to access their power to change their own essential story," Verdandi explains.

Rose recalls her recent near-death experience. "When I entered the valley of death, I was somehow able to access my power of conscious choice. I saw how each choice, as a state of consciousness, is also a coordinate within the landscapes of consciousness that belong to different possibilities. Before that, I'd never really considered the conscious states of my choices. Instead, I'd choose whatever I felt like in that moment without ever really considering what my choice would close or make possible."

"Each choice is a state of consciousness and contains its own codes of consciousness, dearest. A choice is a seed for the future and can powerfully set the trajectories for many years to come. When you realize how your choice takes place *in consciousness*, and how the Universe is a body of consciousness, you start to understand how we each are also a 'mything' link for evolving life. Why don't you ask Sophia and your other friends what narrative ignites their inner fire and passion for the possible?"

"That's a great idea. We talk a lot about creating a world that works, but not from this mythic perspective. For most of us, myth is something we read about in stories or see in movies, especially those movies about superheroes and legends."

"Yep. Good ol' Spiderman."

"We're never really encouraged to look at our own lives as mythic."

"Without this deeper lure of becoming, people will remain asleep within the systems that keep them from accessing their mythic abilities." Verdandi adds, "Education and media today are alienating people even further from the true power of their psyches. The key is to live our lives with mythic vibrancy through the use of our imaginal powers. The mythic vibrancy of those who inhabited the ancient stories, partnered with us, can create the new maps for our time. The maps of the ancient traditions no longer fit our personal territory to the degree they once did, because of the radical change of our time. Yet the process of map making and finding our moral compass for navigating through life-threatening situations is at the heart of the mythic structure."

"I really need a new navigational system, Grandma. It's impossible to go back to the way I lived before. My old life died that night in the hospital and I don't know how to navigate my future from where I am now."

"Release yourself from the old maps, Rosebud. Trust in your inner compass, just like you did the night your old life died. You found your way to your new seed of life. You went through a 'jump time' moment, which happens when myth is recreating itself from the stuff of personal experience. For the development of your psyche, this is monumental. Give yourself a well-deserved pat on the back. You're developing whole new inner structures in mind, brain, and psyche that are granting you abilities and perspectives that have never been explored before. No small feat!"

"Is that why I also need a lot more rest now?"

"Yes. You're doing a lot."

"The other night I dreamed that my old house burned down and I decided to make my new home directly under the stars. It felt like a powerful metaphor for this burning down of my inner structures and the death of my former life."

"Yes, and while our world is on fire and our Earth is running her own parallel fever, this burning down of the old maps and archetypal structures of our societies is taking place everywhere. Yet this is precisely what provides the conditions for the emergence of new mythic stories. Just like the phoenix rising from her ashes. She needs the fire for her rebirth."

"Grandma, what do you think is the most important human power that we need to develop to re-mythologize our world and create a new story?"

"Our imaginal creative powers, sourced from the ancient wisdom of our heart, Rosie. As you know, the imaginal goes further than the imaginative, since it also engages the deeply creative realm of the Cosmos itself. Imagination happens at the level of your own mind and physiology. By partaking in the larger and infinite bodies of being and knowledge of the Cosmos, you find the keys for invoking the transformative powers of the Universe.

Verdandi continues, "The Universe renews itself from the imaginal realm of the Cosmos, which is like the imaginal cells of the butterfly that are awakening in the skin of the dying caterpillar body that's in the midst of its metamorphosis. The future already exists as a Cosmic potential within our own imaginal selves, which activates the possibility, as well as the transformative powers, for realizing these possibilities. Remember the mystic, Meister Eckhart?"

"Yes."

"He once said, 'The eye through which I see God is the same eye through which God sees me; my eye and God's eye are one eye, one seeing, one knowing, one love.'"

"That's very profound. It gives me something to think about."

"This is the true essence of the imaginal state of consciousness, which is far beyond where imagination can take us. All of the great mystics were also the most creative people, overflowing with ideas and revelations precisely because of their ability to enter into this state of deep Cosmic union, the direct experience of our oneness with the great Oneness."

"That's beautiful, Grandma. I understand what you are saying. I know from direct, personal experience that the imaginal realm is real; that it's not just happening in our own minds. Not that we know what 'mind' is, in any case. The doctors couldn't explain my sudden recovery. It wasn't because my immune system fought the virus. I know this so deeply. Instead, I feel like the relationship with the virus shifted the moment I entered my future choice; like it all got repatterned. Once I understood how this virus is also part of the totality, I entered the possibility of a symbiotic relationship with the virus. I actually feel like its codes can even further enhance my abilities somehow. Sophia wants to learn more about her own imaginal powers. Do you have a practice I can give her?"

"I do. Let's go through it together right now so you can share it with her. After that, go and rest, my girl. You're still in the process of building your new body. Call me later this week and I'll give you a story-writing exercise to help you to discover and enhance the mythic structure of your new life choice. For now, make yourself comfortable and let's go through this exercise."

Rose relaxes her body and tunes into the comforting sound of her grandmother's voice.

Practice for Connecting with Your Imaginal Powers

"Begin by accepting that there are realms of existence and modes of being that extend beyond your personal mind. You already have imaginal power. We all do, as does life, in all of its expressions. Your imaginal power is your direct Cosmic connection, which naturally connects you to the larger realities from where you draw inspiration, guidance, vision, and an intuitive sense of direction, as well as your ultimate transformation.

"The imaginal realm extends beyond what is more commonly known as the 'imaginative' realm that is associated with the act of imagination, and sometimes fantasy. The imaginal realm includes the Cosmic dimensions that are not merely mental. It also includes the transformative powers of the Universe in the way we think, perceive, and respond.

"Become more conscious now of your imaginal powers and how you share this power with life and the Universe. Once aware of your imaginal capacities, you can begin to utilize these capacities more consciously to effect the appropriate change in your life and the world around you. You're ready now to begin this practice.

"Close your eyes and take a few deep breaths. Relax yourself completely and let go, then let go some more. Become aware of life inside you: in your breath, in the warmth of your heart, in the flow of your blood, in your pulse, in your feelings, thoughts, intentions, and even your questions. Life is always inside you. You are life.

"Acknowledge how this same power of life is also within nature: in the plants, animals, oceans, our planet, and the whole Universe. Your life force and nature's life force are the same, and are deeply connected. The power of renewal, healing, transformation, and rebirth that are intrinsic to life are also within you. Each of these powers are also imaginal powers, intrinsic to life and within you, granting you the capacities to self-create, self-renew, heal, learn, develop, and evolve.

"Hold the intention now to connect directly with your potent imaginal powers. Feel your imaginal powers awakening and activating inside of you. You may even experience this as a wonderful sensation that spreads through your body as your imaginal powers awaken within you. You're performing an imaginal process. Welcome to a new way of being and exploring.

"Your imaginal power is your direct access to the creative powers of the Cosmos. You may call upon this power, enormous as it is, whenever required.

This power yearns to join you and brings profoundly new ways of being and doing to your life. Let your ability to access and direct your imaginal power grow even more. Feel your imaginal powers grow and glow within you. As they grow stronger, they are naturally optimizing and enhancing your creative abilities, as well as your capacity to envision and intuit. Sense your healing power and your transformative powers. You only need to think of your imaginal power and it naturally activates. Your imaginal powers are drawing you forward to the higher realization of the path of your destiny.

"Place your hands over your heart and connect with the powerful imaginal genius of your beautiful heart. Ask the heart to guide you and to infuse your imaginal power with boundless love and wisdom. Stay there for the next few moments...

"Now you are ready to connect with the imaginal powers of the Universe. Ask the Universe to support you with the transformative powers that help you to create, invent, and manifest the experiences and the opportunities that support your higher path and purpose. Feel the surge of these powers as they flow within you. Feel them energizing, igniting, and bringing new life and purpose to your life on the planet at this time. Know that you are partners to each other in the great theater of evolving life. Stay there for the next few moments...

"Now you're ready to connect with Mother Earth and ask for her support as well, which she graciously grants. You can even ask her how you can support her too, as her creative partner in evolving life. Hold in your heart the intention of abundant, creative goodness and wellness for everyone. See the world and your own life in an optimum state of being: thriving, healthy, happy, and prosperous. When you are ready, open your eyes, stretch your body, and be fully present here and now."

The Imaginal Touch of the Universe

The next day Rose runs to her front door when she hears the knock. Sophia is right on time.

"Come in, come in!" Rose closes the door behind her friend. "I have ratatouille in the oven and I thought we could have a nice salad, too, but before we eat, I have something to share with you."

Rose shares the practice she'd received from her grandmother the day before. Sophia relaxes on the couch and listens to her friend's voice take her through the process. When they finish, she opens her eyes.

"Well?" Rose asks. "What do you think?"

Sophia takes a moment before speaking to form her thoughts into words. "Powerful stuff. I really got how the Universe is truly alive in me, and in all of us…everything." Sophia sits up. "You know, as a doctor-in-training I'm always exploring the life force that flows invisibly through all of our veins and cells, like universal currents of consciousness. But mainstream medical science rarely, if ever, acknowledges our life force."

"You're right. Imagine how their approach to medicine would transform if they did."

"It would change everything."

"Want to help me make the salad? We can keep talking while we do that."

"Sure."

Rose pulls an assortment of fresh vegetables out of her refrigerator. Sophia washes lettuce in the sink, while Rose slices the cucumber.

"I've always wanted to help people," Sophia says as she separates the leaves and dries them on a paper towel. "Ever since I was a child, I've wanted to make the world more caring and humane. That's why I'm working so hard to become a doctor. I want people to be healthy and vibrant so they can enjoy life."

"You've had that goal since I've known you. Now that you've experienced more directly how your imaginal power is also your direct communication channel with the Universe, do you think this could help you as a medical doctor?"

"Interesting question, Rose. Want to know a secret?"

Rose sets a few carrots next to the cutting board and gives Sophia her full attention.

"I like to speak with the bodies of my patients directly," she says. "I become very quiet and focus my energy, then I put my hand on my patients. When I do that with a pure, loving intention, it feels like I'm touching the Universe in flesh."

"Did your grandmother in Australia teach you to do that?"

"Yes. It works with animals, too. In my mind, I ask the body to tell me what's wrong or out of balance. Sometimes when I do this, I get information about the root cause of the issue, as well. Then I encourage the body to heal the areas of concern."

Rose nods. "They sure never teach you that in medical school."

"No, but I've found that by talking with the bodies of my patients, I can gain better insight into the areas I should be focusing on. I've had success with this countless times, but I've never discussed it with my peers."

The timer on Rose's stove goes off and she pulls a dish of bubbling ratatouille from the oven.

"Look at that. Good job, Rose."

"Thank you. I'm famished. Let's eat."

Rose sets the ratatouille on a hot pad beside the salad, and the two friends sit down to enjoy their lunch.

"You've outdone yourself, Rose. The table looks so pretty with the colorful tablecloth and fresh flowers. And cloth napkins! This is so much better than grabbing a quick bite in the cafeteria at school."

"I'm glad. I appreciate you taking the time to get together when you're so busy, so I wanted to make it special. And to celebrate the fact that we're meeting in real life, rather than on the computer or phone," Rose says as she passes her friend the balsamic vinaigrette for her salad.

"I know what you mean," Sophia agrees. "It seems like contact between human beings is primarily digital these days. Now, when we need each other most."

"Yeah, machines can never replace human contact."

"Not if our imaginal powers are our powers of contact to other dimensions, spaces, and times, they can't. Human touch is essential. It's so much more than just our physical touch. Our touch carries the fingerprints of deeper contact; our touch connects us beyond space and time; our touch can open us up to our interbeing. Our bodies and minds are made to touch each other and be touched with feelings, words, imaginations, and the qualities of the living field of the Universe that comes alive in our relationships with one another," Rose says.

"You're right. We're connected in ways that machines and technologies can never understand."

"Many of Grandma Verdandi's imaginal practices affirm that. We're connected with each other beyond time and space by virtue of our imaginal touch. Life isn't just a simulation or computational process. The Cosmos touches every aspect of our lives as the presence of our own awareness. Our awareness is an awareness that touches life. It's not a sterile entity that only observes." Rose stops to eat a few bites, then continues.

"What would a world without this imaginal touch look, feel, smell, taste, and sound like? How can we heal with this touch? How can we possibly bring new futures and unborn potentials into being without this touch? I have so many questions!" Rose pokes her salad with her fork. "Thanks for listening. I don't mean to get all worked up. Be glad you aren't inside my brain these days because those are just a few of the questions I have running around in there. It's been a lot to take in."

Rose doesn't know how to further express all of her concerns verbally, so she places her hand on Sophia's arm and looks her into her friend's eyes. In that moment of real contact, Sophia understands how profoundly Rose has been touched by the Cosmos during her experience of life after death, and that she needs her close friend to help her to integrate it all.

"It's okay, Rose," Sophia says quietly. "You don't have to try to figure all of this out right now. You had an extraordinary experience and it's changed you in some really big ways. Just know that I will always love you as your friend and sister, no matter what."

"Thank you, Sophia. There's so much I want to share. I just don't know how, yet."

The Holy Grail of Communication

"What intrigues me," Rose continues, "is how the Universe is able to communicate with us, especially when it's so vast. How can something so enormous and infinite communicate with humans here on Earth, when we're so tiny and exist in this form only in fleeting moments from a universe perspective? How did the Universe even understand what I needed when I called for help in the hospital?" Rose pauses and laughs. "See? I told you I have a lot of questions."

"You've always been curious," Sophia says. "I'm glad you have questions. It means you're thinking. Go on, let's hear them."

"What if this living architecture that I experienced from the Cosmic realms is a vast universal communication system? What if the Cosmic architecture is the architecture of communication at the meta-level of design?"

"Rose, if you've discovered the keys to that, then you may just have discovered the Holy Grail of communication," Sophia grins.

"Maybe that's exactly what it is: the Holy Grail of communication! The communication of immortality!"

"Actually, I was joking about the Holy Grail," Sophia smiles.

"Well, I'm not. Think about it. Here's the Holy Grail, revered for thousands of years as a sacred relic or a divine power that holds the key to immortal life. Some people believe it's the cup that Jesus drank from during the last supper in which his blood was collected during his crucifixion. Others believe it's an emerald stone that contains the power of immortality. It's also known as the alabaster anointing jar that Mary Magdalene used for anointing Jesus with oil. And this connects with some of the druidic legends in my family where it's said that the anointing of a king happens not just through sacred oils, but also through the womb of the high priestess who carries the bloodline that can transmit the powers of immortality."

"You mean the bloodlines of Jesus Christ and Mary Magdalene? They had children?" Sophia asks with wide eyes.

"Yes," Rose nods. "I mean, it's highly controversial, of course, and there are similar bloodlines in other spiritual traditions, but yes, it appears that Mary Magdalene was pregnant with his child or children, according to my family. Their bloodline is said to have continued in Europe, where Mary fled after his crucifixion. Mary, according to our traditions, also served in the role of high priestess. What I learned from my family is that the womb of certain high priestesses, like those from the Merovingian bloodlines, can become like a Grail for transmitting the power and blessing of immortality. When this high priestess anoints the prince to become a king, she marries him to the non-human worlds. She can also transmit the blessing of immortality as a healing and fertility blessing by the power of the awakened Holy Grail inside her. But that's really a story for another time," Rose laughs.

"Wow, okay, so you're really serious. That's amazing. And how does Cosmic architecture connect to the Holy Grail?" Sophia asks her friend.

"Because the Cosmic architecture is immortal, and shows us how this is not exclusive to certain bloodlines. It's the foundation for all physical life, while originating from realms that exist outside of the dimensions we know as space-time," Rose explains. "Finding the Holy Grail has long represented the quest for immortal life to regain the vision of eternity and realize our divine powers. Although, superficially, it may have appeared as a quest to gain access to a relic that can produce miracles, the deeper search has always been about understanding who we are, where we come from, and how to transcend our mortal life. The Cosmic architecture might well be the best hidden Key of Immortality. It helps us move beyond the secrecy and exclusivity that has long divided humanity!"

"The communication of immortality...The timeless universal language from the worlds beyond the veil..." Sophia smiles, taking in this new information.

"Exactly. And why not? I know it may sound pretentious, but what if the Cosmos wants us to discover this? Almost every problem I can think of arises from gaps in communication and wrong patterns of communication. Manipulation is able to divide people precisely because we're not communicating through a universal language, and we're not speaking the Cosmic language of immortality. No wonder harmful viral programs can so easily hijack our computers and communication systems."

"I hear you, Rose. I agree with everything you're saying, but I doubt that the people who benefit from those communication gaps would be willing to listen to you. It would alter their game too much. Most of our political and economic systems are built on this communication gap. It's designed to keep the divisions between people alive."

"I admit it won't be easy," Rose says, twirling her fork between her fingers. "But maybe that is precisely why we are *mything links.* We can start by making the invisible visible. I'm thinking back to my cousin Otto and some of the conversations we shared about Buckminster Fuller. My cousin loved to quote him all the time. 'Ninety-nine percent of who you are is invisible and untouchable' was one of his gems. And, 'We are called to be architects of the future, not its victims.'"

"Imagine becoming an architect of a whole new civilization!" Sophia exclaims.

"A civilization that speaks the universal language of the Cosmos," Rose adds.

In making this declaration, a shiver of passion flows through Rose's entire being. Her body is really warm now; her heart is glowing. She continues, "I'm convinced that the Cosmos *is* the Holy Grail of communication. We don't have to invent this; we only need to realize and apply it. This can revolutionize the way we grow, develop, and evolve our world and future. The Universe is our greatest ally. It's alive in each of us. As my grandma Verdandi always says, 'We are the Universe in a local biodegradable space-time suit!'"

"A *sacred* biodegradable space-time suit!" Sophia pipes in. "You know, when we give allopathic drugs to our patients, there's often the risk of the medication taking over the communication system of the body, and this creates dependencies on those medications. Allopathic interventions are necessary at times, but as doctors, we must remember that they don't heal the systemic communication problems of the body. Those systemic problems often take the form of illnesses, allergies, cancer, or immune system disorders. If, medically, we can somehow engage the Cosmic communication capabilities of our bodies and minds together—really make those conscious connections—we may have discovered a major key for unlocking our natural healing capacities. Our bodies will know what to do."

Rose nods. "We need to learn to tune in and listen."

Evolution as Narratives That Connect

The two friends clear the dishes from the table.

"That was delicious. Let's wash these dishes," Sophia says.

"It's okay, I'll do them after you go. Let's sit down. Would you like to hear some music? I treated myself to a vinyl record player and a few new records the week before I had to go into the hospital. I know it's kind of old-fashioned, but I like the way the music sounds far better on the record player than on the computer or my phone. Sometimes I even join in on my violin."

"I'm so happy you're still taking lessons. I play my violin, too, when I want to unwind after a long day with patients."

Sophia sits on the couch with a fresh glass of water. Rose lowers the needle onto a record already in the machine, then settles herself in the chair across from her friend.

"Sophia, I feel deep inside my heart that there's something vital and important about understanding our universe from the perspective of communication. And its architecture as the Holy Grail of communication in particular." Rose listens to the music for a moment. "Did you know that many of the great mystics have shared how the world is created as a great song? Isn't that interesting? Even the word 'universe' has the word 'verse' in it."

"What a beautiful thought."

"When I went to the other side of the veil, I experienced the structures of space-time and the ways our atoms have formed; the precise informational patterns that are finely tuned to make life possible. Since that experience my whole notion of solidity and what is 'matter' has shifted."

"That makes sense," Sophia says.

"I experience everything now in a state of relationship...of interconnectedness. All of nature is designed to communicate: plants, animals, insects...even our climate systems. Nothing can function or evolve without communication at the most basic levels. Even the bacteria and viruses in our bodies are chatting away as we speak. Our cells are listening to our thoughts. Life is communication. Our whole universe is a vast communication system. Now that I've experienced this, I think that mainstream human systems are completely out of tune with the narratives of life. We've reduced evolution to this awful model of struggle for survival on a planet of scarcity, by competition and dominance. Our mainstream economic systems are still built on this limited narrative that breeds divisive competition between people and a politics of dominance through economic control over scarce resources. This narrow way of believing feels totally alienated from the deeply collaborative and co-creative narratives that I experience within the living architecture of our universe. Evolution is a story of wondrous collaboration and co-creation in ways we haven't even begun to imagine. Sure, it also includes competition, but not in the ways we as humans have made this our modus operandi."

"I agree with you, Rose. And our mainstream education systems aren't much better. This reduced, narrow version of evolution, from the old mechanistic view of life, is still the backbone of modern education."

"When education could be so much more! It could be vital and alive! Get the students out of the classroom. Instead of sitting at desks all day, let them move around outside and have meaningful explorations and experiences."

"Sadly, the soul has been taken out of nature and also medicine. The way we learn about the human body at medical school is so mechanical and matter of fact, with its focus on treating symptoms and illnesses, rather than promoting the improvement of health and immunity as a natural process of life."

"So many of our current ways of doing things on this planet feel out of whack that it starts to become overwhelming, and yet..."

Rose feels a flash of future possibilities in her heart; transformations that are not only possible, but required. She jumps up and says in an excited voice, "Let's become the new story, Sophia! Let's make it so exciting and nurturing and...*wonderful,* that people can't help but join in."

"How?"

"We'll evoke people's 'passion for the possible,' as my grandma always says. We'll invite children into the wonders of nature, so they can experience what life is truly all about. Oh, this is good. I want to be part of co-creating systems and cultures; a partnership where taking care of our planet and one another is the most natural and obvious thing to do."

"How would we do it?"

"We need to make taking care of our planet far more personal, sexy, and attractive. Instead of saving trees for carbon capture and to fight climate change, let's tell the story of saving trees because they are living beings like you and me. Their lives are important. We need them and they need us; we're connected."

"It's true," Sophia agrees. "I always feel better when I'm around trees. A world without them is a world that I want no part of."

"Trees make the world amazing, lush, vibrant, fascinating, and just awesome. And water!

Instead of stopping the pollution of our waters because it spoils our drinking water, let's tell the story of how water is life, and life is worth saving and caring for. Water connects us, too. We're born from water. Heck, sixty percent of our bodies are made up of water."

"Changing our narratives to create a more positive future may actually help heal our bodies as well, Rose. Negative, limited narratives impact our bodies. If people are subconsciously and consciously told all the time that in order to evolve and progress, we need to compete and fight for scarce resources, what does that narrative do to our bodies? We're constantly telling our bodies that life is not safe, which increases our adrenaline to dangerous levels. Our stress hormones are on high alert all the time." Sophia shakes her head.

"Even more so now with the way this whole virus crisis is being handled," Rose says. "How are people internalizing all of these fear-based narratives? Our bodies are literally sick of the stories we feed ourselves."

"I agree with you. Let's create better narratives, where all of us are safe in life and cared for by the Universe, even in the midst of death and collapse."

"Can you imagine what a relief that would be if we internalized that truth instead? 'I am safe.' 'I am cared for.' 'The Universe loves me.' All of that daily stress and fear would just melt away. It's so liberating."

"And you, Sister, are a living example of this new way of telling our story of life and evolution."

"Thank you, Sophia. I'm excited about this. The Universe has already given us the architecture to communicate unity, belonging, and wholeness. Let's just do this."

Sophia nods. "I'm already thinking of how I can apply this to whole new health and healing protocols for my future patients." She adds, "That reminds me of something that evolution biologist, Elisabet Sahtouris, wrote about in her book *EarthDance.* She mentioned that the sexual communication system of bacteria is based on trading DNA genes. She wrote that these tiny beings actually created the first world wide web of information exchange.[1] Imagine what could happen if our computers learned to communicate and trade information with the intelligence of bacteria!"

Rose laughs. "I'd say it's about time!"

"Yes, and remember that Deepak Chopra book *Metahuman*? When he wrote that we're always communicating with immortality, yet we're mostly unaware of it? He said that wholeness is immortal and communicates with mortal life as time, space, matter, and energy."[2]

"I do remember that. See why you're such a beloved friend, Sophia? Who else can I share these perspectives with?"

"Yeah, and all on my one-hour lunch break!"

Integration - The Key of Imaginal Power

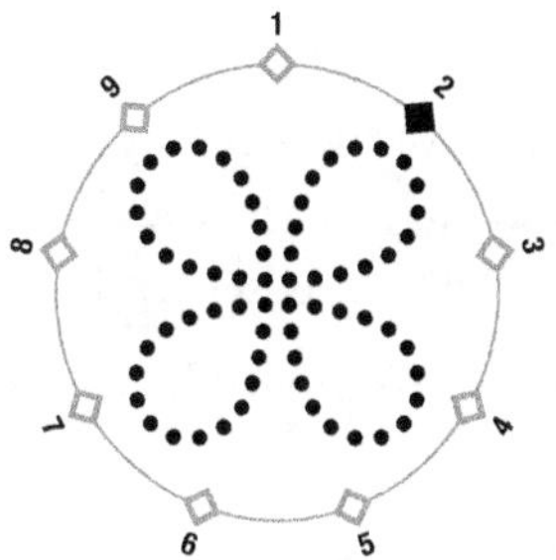

How do all of these new ideas and revelations of Rose live in you? What does it evoke in you to realize how you are imaginally and physically part of the great Cosmos? To know and realize how the Universe lives in you and that you evolve each other co-creatively? To know that you have direct access to its architecture as your own inner architecture? Through this chapter we've explored the Key of Imaginal Power for accessing your Cosmic powers and developing your future human capacities.

> *The Key of Imaginal Power is your direct access to the imaginal realm of the Cosmos from where you can experience and engage the future possibilities of the unified field of consciousness. Through this key you learn to access and apply your imaginal powers for evolving and actualizing your life and our world with the Cosmic architecture of consciousness.*

The summary below will help you to integrate these discoveries further:

- The imaginal realm is architecturally present in all levels and realities of existence as the space to dream the higher dream and evoke a greater future.
- You can shift your states of consciousness by using your imaginal power.
- Trust your imaginal powers and use your senses to extend your

natural receptivity beyond the domains of your mind to connect with the Cosmic dimensions of life.

- Explore your archetypal forces in the way you grow, learn, develop, and evolve. Archetypes are the connective patterns for the way things grow and evolve. We each have unique archetypal forces in our life that help us to realize our true potentials.
- Your imaginal powers are the key to your mental fertility. Make your explorations "sensory rich." That way the future becomes your power for renewing and evolving yourself and our world.
- Life is the art of connective multiplicity. Use your choice accordingly, as a connective power.
- If you don't like our current world story, then start telling a better story even before it becomes reality. Live a better truth from the reality of your choice. Inspire the change. What you appreciate, appreciates.
- Myth is like the DNA of the human psyche. The mythic story lives in everyone and holds great promise, which provides the deepest nourishment and strength for the soul. What is your mythic DNA? What narrative evokes and inspires you?
- We are each called for the mythic task of transforming and evolving our world, and we are made for these times. What are the mythic tasks that you have said yes to?
- Your choice takes place in consciousness and becomes manifest in the body of consciousness: the Universe. You are a mything link for evolving life.
- The future already exists as a Cosmic potential within your own imaginal self, which activates the possibility, as well as the transformative powers, for realizing these possibilities. The Universe renews itself from the imaginal realm of consciousness, and you can do the same.
- Your imaginal power is also your direct communication channel with the Universe. Have a chat with the Universe.
- The Cosmos touches every aspect of our lives. It is always present within us as the presence of our own awareness. Explore the touch of your awareness. How does your awareness touch life? What is the quality of that touch? What narrative does your touch communicate?

- The architecture of the Universe is an architecture of consciousness; a living architecture that creates worlds and realities with Cosmic fractal codes and potencies. Get creative with this architecture.
- The Cosmos is the Holy Grail of communication. We are always communicating with immortality, yet most people are unaware of it.
- All of nature is designed to communicate. Knowing this, how can you communicate from the information of immortality and communicate our great unity in diversity?
- Evoke the passion for the possible, in yourself and our world.

CHAPTER 3

Becoming Mythic in New Ways

Lifting the Veil with the Key of Cosmic Communication

Rose's profound choices of rebirth and healing from the future of a new cycle is beginning to generate fresh perspectives and patterns within her. Her quest, like that of many others, started from the necessity for change at a time when her old life could no longer carry her forward. She has now fully embraced the call of her quest, while also realizing that there is no way back to her old life. The invitation of the Cosmic architect inspires her to catalyze and evolve our world; to architect new realities and worlds with Cosmic information and the immortal building blocks of consciousness, which is the living architecture of our universe. Her passion for the possible increases. She's curious and eager to learn more about the many new ideas and revelations that are flooding her mind and dreams. She wants to live a mythic life of meaning and purpose; she's called to a greater destiny.

While these new revelations are thrilling, Rose also realizes that she needs more time inside her cocoon. Her body needs rest while former notions of herself and her life are breaking down and dissolving. Her future self is forming and taking shape inside the cocoon, but it is not yet ready to emerge. Her grandmother often reminds her not to rush. She urges her to just let it happen and trust the process of cocooning while the new is forming.

Verdandi calls and asks Rose to join her in Iceland to receive an initiation that will help her to discover more of her new powers and how to apply them.

Lifting the Veil

Rose is delighted. "Grandma, are you saying I need some kind of ritual to go further with all these discoveries?" The young woman feels a burning desire building up inside her to lift the veil and see what's next. From the time she was a little girl, Verdandi has taught her the importance of rituals. She explained how a carefully crafted ritual can enable a person to more safely enter the next key passage in one's life.

"Yes, love, that's why I am calling." Verdandi smiles. "In my meditation this morning, the Raven told me that it's time for you to start preparing for your initiation in Iceland. Until that time, some smaller rituals may help you to integrate all of the changes and transitions that you're moving through.

"Rituals illumine our transitions and are sacred practices for creating the field of possibility in which to plant our new futures and capacities. Rituals draw upon the powers of time, space, nature, the heavens, culture, community, and life itself in such a way that we know we are the vehicle of these possibilities, whether it be for rain-making, healing, announcing a life transition such as marriage, or declaring one's connectedness to high purpose or spiritual realities."

"Interesting. I had a frightening dream last night."

"Tell me about it."

"I found myself in a forest. It was dark and there was danger all around me. A teenage boy was calling for help from deep inside the forest."

"Was anyone else with you?" Verdandi asks with some concern.

"Yes, Sophia was with me. We'd found an ancient ruin, a place of worship and sacrifices. It felt like it had been used long ago for both animal and human sacrifices. The boy was being chased by two men. I desperately wanted to help him by stopping the men, but I was being held back by an invisible, restrictive force."

"Hmm. What did the force feel like?"

"It felt truly evil, like it had been unleashed from long ago, deep inside the forest. It felt like it originated from terrible things that had happened there. I don't know what had awakened these forces, but they were now roaming around in our present world and time to hunt down their next victims. I felt so scared that this boy might become the next human sacrifice. I was crying for help, but my voice got stuck in my throat and for some reason, I couldn't get past those evil forces.

"All of a sudden, Sophia, who was next to me, screamed, 'PUT YOUR RING ON! PUT IT ON NOW, ROSE!' I had no idea what she was talking about. I couldn't find a ring. I woke up abruptly because the neighbor's loud dog was barking at the garbage truck that was passing by just under my window. I felt terrified as I came out of the dream. It took me several hours to shake off my uneasy feelings. I have no idea what it all means, Grandma. Do you?"

Verdandi is quiet. She has a strong sense of what the dream is about, but doesn't want to scare Rose, or tell her more than she's ready to hear.

"Please make sure to record that dream, Rose. It confirms the importance of your initiation, and how certain things may have to happen sooner than I had hoped. You may need another initiation or ritual before you come to see us in Iceland. The archaic forces are sensing your growing powers and what's awakening within and through you. Remember your magical cape? Visualize it around you with the hood over your head to cloak your presence in the other worlds before you fall asleep. Call on the Goddess for Her protection as well, in the ways I showed you. Your soul is remembering many things. Ancient and dormant future abilities are awakening within you, but you don't know how to access and apply them yet. If this dream comes to you again, please call me. I'll send some prayers for the protection of those who called for you in the dream."

"Thanks, Grandma. The dream was unusually vivid; almost like a predictive dream, though it also felt like a memory from long ago. Strange."

Verdandi is careful not to bring more energy or attention to the dream. She doesn't want to feed it further, so she shifts Rose's focus onto a different topic.

"Rosie, do you remember the beautiful fertility ritual you created with your mom to celebrate your transition from girlhood to womanhood when you had your first menses?" Verdandi guides Rose back to her natural powers by nudging her mind to this happy time and the power of her blood that contains the bond of the unity of life.

"Oh, yes. I loved that ritual. I even told my class about it later that year as part of a school project when we were studying rituals. I was excited to share it with them, but when I explained it, the guys started to giggle shyly when I said the word 'menstrual blood,' as if I'd just dropped the scariest forbidden word. Even my male teacher looked terribly uneasy about the subject as I described the color, smell, and touch of my own menstrual blood, and my curious discovery about it coming out of my own body. Why is it still such a taboo to talk about this openly?"

"For thousands of years men have feared a woman's menstrual blood," Verdandi explains. "Some mistakenly believe it's not clean. Others feel terrified because women are so powerful during their menses. So much so, that our male shamans told us that their magic doesn't work when a woman joins their ceremony during her menses!"

They both laugh. Verdandi continues, "Unfortunately, this taboo has been internalized by many women who now feel a sense of shame around their own menses. Or they believe they are less attractive when they have their menses. Many dread that time of the month, and have no idea that it's one of the most powerful times of their cycle. Women are often moody or overly sensitive during their periods because they don't know or haven't learned how to work with the additional psychic energy that nature gives them during that time. They could use the time for going inward, like the bear who retreats into her cave. That's why we refer to this as our 'moontime.' By retreating deep inside our own wombs, we shed our old skins and cycles. We renew ourselves with the seeds of the Dreaming; the Great Mystery, which gives us visions and directions that become fertilized during our ovulation time. Female fertility is about so much more than physical pregnancy. Your mom and I really wanted your first experience of womanhood to be deeply sacred, safe, and meaningful."

"Oh, it worked Grandma. I remember standing there next to Mom in our garden. It was such an incredible moment. I held my fertility bowl in which you'd instructed me to collect the blood of my menses. I then gave it to the roots of my birth tree, where you had both planted my placenta and navel cord years earlier. Doing that gave me the deepest sense of connection. Like my own roots in life merged with the roots of my birth tree as well as the roots of our ancestors and all of life. It was magical."

"Feel that connection and power again. Feel the power of your blood and the fertility it contains. Feel how you carry within your body the fertile, life-giving powers of the Universe. Think of all those women who have come before us. Feel the bond of our love for each other as sisters, mothers, and grandmothers, and as guardians of life, the earth, and her beloved children.

All held together in unity through the sacred and ancient bond of our Mother Universe who connects us all, women, men, children, and all our relations. The family of life.

"Feel and remember how this bond of unity stands the tests of time, as well as the tests of hardships, divisions, and conflicts. It keeps our hearts connected and united with the Cosmic heart of our universe. Breathe into that bond of unity now. Let it strengthen and harmonize your energy and whole being." Verdandi uses her ceremonial voice, which has the ability to invoke the powers of the ancient ones.

"By the power of this bond of unity, may you be fully released and freed from any and all harmful forces or interferences that are restricting your natural powers and Cosmic purpose! Know yourself to be free of these forces now, while the bond of unity restores and regenerates your space and energy with the radiance of your Cosmic self." Verdandi continues by invoking the ancient healing symbols, which she draws with her hands in the space in front of her while intending for their powers to manifest within and around Rose's space.

Rose has experienced the power of these symbols many times. She feels the energy around her start to lift and clear, even though she is physically hundreds of miles away from her grandmother.

"Thank you, Grandma. That really helps. It's so powerful, I feel like myself again. The dizziness is gone now, too. I forgot how strong this bond of unity is. I remember how you told me long ago that my menstrual blood is also a protection. We have some amazing feminine powers, huh?" Rose chuckles as she relaxes into her more bubbly self.

"Good. That's my girl. Glad to see you're back." Verdandi smiles, not wishing to reveal to Rose what she suspects is still lurking around, yet now from afar.

"So, how about this ritual you mentioned earlier?" Rose asks.

"It's time to create your own rebirth ritual to celebrate your return from beyond the veil. Let it come to you. It may manifest as a dream in which you can more fully experience your future human power in a further actualized and awakened state."

"Ohh, that's exciting. Yes, I'll do that. I may also ask Sophia to join me to make it a real celebration."

"Good idea. Now onto other matters. As I mentioned before, your grandfather and I would love for you to come and spend some time with us in Iceland once the planes can travel again and you feel fully recovered. In addition to the potent initiation that I'd like to share with you from our ceremonial circle, we also want to spoil you with good food, cuddles, nature walks, and fun games."

"I can't wait! I'd love that! Is that the same ceremonial circle where you told me to do that Crane dance before?"

"Yes, that's the one. That circle has supported our ancestors for thousands of years. There are so many powers and abilities awakening with you that we just have to make sure you're not going to turn into a dragon, flying off to the old craters while rising to new levels of consciousness!" Verdandi chuckles.

"Or combusting into a rising phoenix. That would be quite a sight," Rose laughs.

"More seriously, this initiation will greatly help you to better understand how to work with the powers and the purpose they serve. Until that time, I need to make sure that you can safely deal with what's happening right now and also with what's just ahead of you on your path."

"Okay, I'll play cool until then."

"You? Playing cool? Oh, my girl, there are many things you can do, but that's not one of them!" Both women laugh at this.

"You know me too well. That's not fair!" Rose chuckles. "I wish more people had the opportunity to grow into new powers in such a sacred, guided way. When I look, I see so many people plunged into the waters of change, having to learn to swim without any preparation. So many of my friends are overwhelmed by the new sensations and shock of uncertainty in the world today. They feel like their lives have turned upside down and are out of control. Nothing is as it was. Sadly, some have even drowned before they could figure out how to navigate the waters of change. Did you know that two of my classmates from the university committed suicide recently?"

"Oh, Rose, I'm so sorry to hear that," Verdandi says gently. "These are difficult times for many people."

"I wish I could have helped them, like you're helping me now. I can't even help the boy in my dream. There are days when I feel so powerful, and then there are days like this morning when I feel helpless and overwhelmed with the enormity of all that's wrong with the world."

"If you ever feel like it's becoming too much, please promise to call me and your parents. Or call Sophia, if you want to talk with a friend instead, but do something to reach out so we can help you. You're not alone. We'll use these coming months to better prepare and equip you to work with all the changes and challenges this time is bringing."

"Thank you. That sounds wonderful. I promise to call. Now will you please tell me more about these new mythic structures of the hero and heroine's journey?"

The Mythic Codes

Verdandi answers, "As I mentioned before, myth is the coded DNA of the human psyche. It's the stuff of the evolving self that awakens consciousness and culture according to the needs of time and place. It's the promise of our future becoming. Through the mythic initiations, you begin to discover that you are a valuable character in the drama of the world soul, pushing the boundaries of your own local story and gaining the courage to be and do so much more. What has been part of the collective as our shared myths or archetypes is now finding new rivers of unique stories emerging from the passion play of our individual lives. We are mentored and informed by the ancient myths, and we're also in an open moment—a jump time, where myth is recreating itself from the stuff of our personal experience."

"Aha! So does that mean that most of the old systems are unable to guide us into the future or prepare us for who we are to become? Is that why so many people feel restless, angry, deceived, trapped, divided, controlled, used, and manipulated?"

"Exactly."

"It's painful to realize you're trapped in a world that was never designed to flourish, but only designed to take, extract, and control. That reminds me of Tim. Remember him?"

"That fellow you dated for a while?"

"Yes. That was a painful relationship. I felt trapped and anxious to get out of it. That was a tough time for me."

Rose doesn't have much experience with men, apart from a couple of flirtations and one intimate relationship that lasted for almost a year. She met Tim during her last year at the university in New York. He was studying law, and was a powerful orator who could be very persuasive and convincing. Rose had just turned twenty-two, and although she wasn't sure if she was actually deeply in love with him, she felt drawn to his magnetic personality. After almost a year of dating, she decided to end her relationship with him when a powerful dream made her realize she'd gotten herself trapped in a very unhealthy situation.

"Did you ever tell Sophia how you really felt and what made you end that relationship with Tim?"

"Not yet. Do you think I should?"

Verdandi hopes that Sophia can be a positive influence for her granddaughter in selecting her intimate partners, as she seems to have more emotional maturity and experience than Rose.

"Yes, Rose, it would be good to tell her the full story. She's your closest friend and her perspectives may help you understand a few more things about yourself. As you remember the pain you felt in your relationship with Tim, you may also want to explore the classic mythic pattern of the sacred wound that awakens our psyche to the necessity for change. Like the crucifixion of Christ, irrespective of whether it really happened in that way. The mythic pattern of the symbolic crucifixion on the cross of life is much older than the story of Christ. It's about the rebirth that happens at the center of the cross.

"The cross within the circle of life has been a symbol for indigenous people for thousands of years. The center of the cross is the place where new life enters as our old life dies. This is the place where the horizontal axis of our mundane life and the vertical axis of our spiritual life marry to bring forth a human who is a living bridge between heaven and earth."

"Oh, can't we become mythic in a less painful way? I don't want to be nailed to a cross, and I don't want Jesus Christ or anyone else to have to make such painful sacrifices. Why do we need to get wounded to evolve to higher consciousness? What if this pattern of wounding and self-sacrifice only belongs to the old mythic structures? There may be whole new options for us to evolve that we've never explored. I want to grow in new mythic ways."

"Rose, I understand that from your future perspective this old mythic pattern doesn't resonate. But first be aware of the role it served before you bring in the new future patterns too quickly. After all, you also have thorns as the beautiful rose you are."

Rose knows that her grandmother often has the long view that she doesn't yet have, hence she's willing to learn more, although reluctantly. "Okay, then. Tell me more about the activating role of pain."

"All of the classic myths have the theme of wounding at their core. Christ must have his crucifixion; otherwise, there's no resurrection. Artemis must kill Actaeon when he comes too close. Job must have his boils. Dionysius must be childish and attract Titanic enemies who rip him apart. An abundance of sacred wounding marks the core of all great Western myths and their attending gods and humans: Adam's rib, Achilles' heel, Odin's eye, Orpheus's decapitation, Inanna's descent and torture, Prometheus's liver, Zeus's split head, Pentheus's dismemberment, Jacob's broken hip, Isaiah's seared lips, Persephone's rape, Eros's burnt shoulder, Oedipus's blinding...And so it goes, on and on, wounding after wounding."

"Why are we so drawn to these stories, Grandma? We don't we even flinch or question all these terrors? And worse, why do we repeat it through our own lives?" Rose asks. "Just listening to the whole list of wounding makes me feel uneasy in the pit of my stomach."

"It might have something to do with the way the stories carry us into the mystery, Rosie. The marvel, the uncanny, and the announcement that with wounding, the sacred enters into time. Each prefigures a journey, a renaissance, a turning point in the lives of gods and mortals. From the point of the wounding, the journey of gods and humans proceeds toward new birth, and with it, the unfolding of a sensuous acuity to the needs of others that wasn't possible before. Being more vulnerable, we then reach out and extend our hands and hearts to others who are wounded. It's only at such a pass that we grow into a larger sense of what life is about, and act, therefore, out of a deeper and nobler nature.

"For thousands of years, wounding served to open the doors of our sensibility to a larger reality, which is blocked to our habituated and conditioned point of view. Pathos gives us eyes and ears to see and hear and feel what our normal eyes and ears and feelings cannot."

"I just wish there was another way, Grandma. Something less painful. A way to directly access the states of consciousness that make it possible for us to see the larger reality without having to suffer first. I'm sure this way exists somewhere in the Universe."

"Then this is part of your quest, my girl. Ask the Universe to join you in this quest, and you can be partners in creation and stewards of our future wellbeing. As our ancestors knew, this story is bigger than all of us. Bring in the future pattern of initiation. Use your imaginal powers to envision with all your sensory abilities this new future pattern for how humanity can become engaged in and committed to its self-transformation without the need for all of this wounding first. Don't answer the question now. Commit to the journey that will ready you to first receive, and then become, the answer."

The Information of Immortality

Rose feels there's something ironic about these old mythic patterns for dreaming the higher dream and accessing the higher state of consciousness to enter into Cosmic unity or effect change. Why make it so difficult and painful to connect with the deeper unity of life when Cosmic information is already eternally present in all matters of life? Can't humans just relate to the information of immortality like nature does?

The more Rose thinks about this, the more she feels like something just doesn't add up. She perceives self-harming and requirements of harm as dynamics that belong to an archaic worldview of dualism and separation. She questions the rationale of sacrificing something from the whole in order to evolve or receive from the greater whole. She simply can't accept that, especially as she deeply knows that our universe is whole and indivisible. Determined to find out other options, Rose explores how she can learn more about the information of immortality.

She wants to understand what type of information the Cosmos uses to communicate and create. She realizes that for a communication this vast and immediate, it cannot originate from or be bound by the space-time dimensions of our universe. There has to be a non-physical dimension that is within and part of space-time, perhaps even informing space-time, yet not bound by the classical laws of physics that relate to our physical realities. During her studies in cosmology, quantum physics, information sciences, and consciousness research, she learned that the word "information" has a specific meaning in each of these fields. She discovers how a growing group of scholars propose that the Universe itself is informational.

Curious to learn more, Rose reads Paul Levy's book, "Quantum Revelation," where he mentions that our material universe is itself an ever-evolving organism of living information.[3] She mentions this to her mother, Tara, who recommends that she contact her friend, Dr. Jude Currivan, who is a cosmologist.

During their call, Jude explains to Rose how what we call physical reality is literally made up of "in-formation." She explains how the science of informational dynamics, also called "infodynamics," reveals a kind of universal "alphabet" of the 1s and 0s of digitized information. This science also reveals how our manifest physical world emerges from implicit cosmological dimensions that are nonlocal and unified. Through this new scientific understanding of the nature of reality, the former dualistic notions that energy-matter and space-time are different dissolve, and we discover how each expresses itself in complementary ways, creating the emergent phenomena of our universe.

Jude further stresses to Rose that in-formation literally "in-forms" the whole world. She explains that the Universe is like a Cosmic hologram composed of digital in-formation that reveals how our universe evolves as a holographically informed wholeness, where its three-dimensional appearance is actually a holographic projection from the two-dimensional boundary of space.

Jude confirms to Rose that the Cosmic digital information is the same as the digital information of our phones and computers, where coded number combinations give the appearance of pictures, music, and videos. In other words, the digitized information or "digitized bits" used for developing human technologies is *the same as universal information*. The difference is in the way it becomes embedded and embodied.

She urges Rose to read her book, "The Cosmic Hologram," to learn more about the specifics of how our universe is able to exist and evolve as a single, unified entity, and how the one-way flow of time increases the information of our universe from one moment to another.

After the call, Rose's curiosity is sparked even further. She's determined to find out how these quantum potentials can become concrete realities within our finite universe. She feels that this is the perfect topic to explore with Sophia, who has a way of asking the kinds of questions that help Rose to articulate and bring forth the deeper knowings of her intuitive mind.

The women relax into the colorful cushions on Sophia's couch, while enjoying their warm chai drink made of vanilla tea from Mauritius with fresh ginger, cardamom seeds, cinnamon sticks, a touch of masala powder, and milk and honey.

"Remember that talk we had last week about the Cosmic architecture as the Holy Grail of communication that creates?" Rose asks her friend.

"Yes, I remember vividly. Why?"

"I've been digging a bit further into this so-called quantum 'superposition state' of information as a realm of potentiality where all possible states of information coexist simultaneously prior to being observed. It got me thinking that even the future can be considered as a state of potentiality *in* consciousness. The process of information convergence or translation from the quantum to the local state is apparently called 'quantization,' whereby information, as digitized bits, becomes encoded at the holographic boundary of space-time, with one bit encoded per Planck-scale area. Scientists now say that the Planck-scale is the tiniest physical level, as small compared to a quantum particle as it is to the entire Universe.[4] I also learned from my conversation with Dr. Currivan that the information increase in our universe is actually indicative of the way our universe is learning."

"Whoa, that's quite a mouthful, Rose. Is that the same digital information that our phones and computers use?" Sophia asks curiously.

"Yes!"

"That's fascinating. I never knew that numbers, or digits, could do that! I always saw them as abstractions of our human minds; I never realized that we live in a universe of digits." Sophia smiles. "To tell you the truth, I used to feel a little scared of numbers and math. I much prefer the concrete realities of the human body and how to help people heal. I probably would have even dropped my science units at school if it weren't for my burning desire to become a doctor."

"I'm so glad you persisted, Sophia! I never knew that Cosmic information is digital, either. It puts a whole new perspective on my dad's fascination with sacred geometry and his study of the Gematria."

"Gematria? What's that?"

"The ancient Jewish number system in the Kabbalah that translates letters to numbers and numerical codes."

"That sounds interesting. I'm learning a lot today."

"So am I. My dad always told me that I could learn anything—even the most challenging subjects—if I take my time and go step by step."

"That's a wise philosophy. And true!" Sophia sips her chai.

"You know, interestingly, our modern computers are all built from digital technologies that use a binary number system of only two digits called 'bits.' A bit is short for 'binary digit,' which is a single unit of information with a value of either 0 or 1. In other words, in a binary system, the base of the number system is two. The two values of '1 or 0' correspond to the 'on' and 'off' states that computers understand."

"You mean to say that when I give my computer an instruction by typing letters on my keyboard, it's programmed to read the letters as combinations of digits?"

"Yes. I'm certainly no expert in this field, but what I've learned so far is that the way we've currently developed most of the standard computers is by binary code, which is the 1s and 0s. For example, our computers don't know our human alphabet or the meaning of 'A.' Computer language translates the letter 'A' as the binary number: 1100 0001. We don't think in numerical codes. At least average humans don't." Rose chuckles.

"Okay, I get it. So we create interfaces for translating one type of language system into another?"

"Exactly."

"Does this mean that the universal language of the Cosmos is also digital, or mathematical, out of which we create meaning, culture, and human language?"

"Yes. Think of digital codes as the Source codes out of which nature creates fractal growth patterns, genetic codes, and sequencing, and we, as humans, create meaning, understanding, art, science, and culture, as well as our profound spiritual insights about the nature of reality. A 'bit' is a unit of information, which becomes an 'it' in our experience and perception. The problem with us humans is that we often get lost in translation. It's like we have our Cosmic interface set on 'duality mode' by only reading the information of life from a binary, dual, state, instead of the quantum state of qubits. Just look at all the political and economic systems we have of winners and losers and zero-sum game competition."

"Hold on a second, Rose. Slow down. What are qubits?"

"A qubit is the basic unit of quantum information. Quite different from the classic binary state of bits where information behaves in an 'either-or' and 'on-off' mode."

"By 'classic state' do you mean like us being two distinctly different physical beings with our own autonomy in our own local reality? Where I am not 'Sophia and Rose,' but I am 'Sophia and not Rose?' How does that all change in a quantum state?"

"The qubit state is a state of both-and, and not the classic state of either-or. In a quantum state, we are Rose and Sophia and the earth and the Cosmos and the whole of life being able to experience our concrete local reality, and simultaneously, our unity with everyone and everything. Quantum physicists refer to this quantum state as the quantum superposition state. Remember, how digits in the binary state of classic bits have a value that is either '0' *or* '1'? The fascinating thing about qubits is that they have a value that is either of these, or a quantum superposition in any combination of the two states as '0' *and* '1.' They're the best way to describe what multiplicity is all about, and how diversity remains unified at more fundamental levels of reality."

"Ha. I like the sounds of these qubits. It sounds far more interesting to see the world as a qubit than as a binary bit," Sophia laughs.

"Yes, and there's more!" Rose takes a deep breath. "Dr. Currivan also confirmed in our call that qubits are the informational building blocks of possibilities which become embedded within the informational state of probabilities. Whereas digitized bits manifest or are observed as a single state, which means they exist in that dual 'on-off' or 'either-or' state, qubits can be superposed in any combination of the two states and have this fascinating ability to exist simultaneously in many states of the superposition. This radically changes their information processing capacity compared to classical digital information processing. Hence the prediction that quantum computers are going to completely transform the way we communicate, store, and analyze data."[5]

"That's amazing. These qubits are shapeshifters!" Sophia bursts out. "Like the 'clever' men and women in our tribe back home in Aboriginal Australia. These shapeshifters can really play tricks on your mind. First, they appear to you as a fierce warrior from ancient times to warn you. Next, they appear as the snake that crosses your path. Then, just when you think you've moved to safer ground, they sweep your lunch off your plate as the mischievous kookaburra bird. Later that evening when you tell them what happened, they laugh and laugh, and tell you they've seen it all, and that you'd better enjoy your dinner before the dingo fetches it!"

Rose laughs. "Oh, Sophia, you tell the best stories. Why study quantum physics if we can spend a weekend with your family in Australia?"

Sophia grins. "I agree, but let's get back to what you were sharing."

"I've come to realize more and more that the imaginal realm I experienced during my near-death experience is far more real than I previously thought.

It even precedes our experience of reality as the building blocks with which realities are made. Can you imagine architecting our world and experiences directly from the building blocks of consciousness?"

"It gives me happy chills. It's like the famous saying by the Persian mystic and poet Rumi, 'The Universe is not outside of you. Look inside yourself. Everything that you want, you already are.'

"My Auntie Yindi, the one who taught me so much about our traditional knowledge, told me that the spiritual knowledge of the Dreaming can't be perceived directly, but it lives in the Dreaming stories, the songlines, and the land as the primordial creation forces that form the mountains, waterholes, rivers, oceans, and the earth, as well as each of us."

Rose nods. "That's similar to what my grandmother taught me. She said that even if the Cosmic information can't be perceived directly, it can be entered into, like all the great mystics have experienced. She mentioned how everything is consciousness, including space-time and energy-matter."

Sophia looks off dreamily. "Why are we making it all so complicated to understand these fundamental realities that our ancestors knew in their hearts? They didn't have to learn all of this; they just knew and experienced it."

"Perhaps in their time it wasn't necessary to understand the unity of life in a scientific manner. Living from unity was sufficient. But I believe that it's not sufficient now, especially with the rate of our current technological developments. If modern science and technology would consider both space-time and energy-matter as forms of information, we could advance in creating whole new technologies and systems that mimic the informational architecture of consciousness. Imagine how this could radically shift our view of matter and the way we grow and extract resources?"

"You've got a point there, Rose."

"I strongly feel that by exploring the various states in which information appears, whether it appears to us as dual or as a quantum superposition state, it'll give us whole new insights about the dynamic and creative nature of consciousness itself. Look at our model of 'modern' progress. We've been stuck in duality mode for hundreds of years. We've been creating harm to our world and planet because we've been approaching life mechanistically. We separate medicinal substances from the plants that grew them. We remove animals from their natural habitats and grow them as meat in factories, ignoring the fact that they're sentient beings. We turn our sacred sites into mines for extracting rare minerals from the earth, taking gold from the stones that grew them, and so forth."

"Yes," Sophia nods. "And what about taking children away from their families and the land that grew us for thousands of years, like what happened to many of my aunts and uncles who are part of the 'stolen generation' in Australia? So many Aboriginal children were forcibly stolen from their families and put into colonial schools to create so-called 'civilized' people and breed out the Aboriginal genes from humanity's stock. Can you believe this went on until the 1970s?" Sophia shares with tears in her eyes.

"It's sickening." Rose sighs deeply. "It's similar to the residential schools in the United States where so many indigenous children were taken.

"We must affirm that other ways are possible and required for growing and developing our world and our humanity. But we can't access these possibilities if we don't grow our consciousness first. We've got to realize and honor how life is unified and interdependent. As my mom's friend, Uncle Phil Lane, often says, 'The harm of one is the harm of all, and the honor of one is the honor of all.' If we're in a renaissance time, then we owe it to the future generations to make the most of the opportunities this period of time affords us."

"I agree, Sister. You've inspired me."

"You too."

"Hey, I have an idea. Let's watch that science-fiction movie we've been wanting to watch all week. I need some distraction to lift my spirits and relax my mind. We can't solve all these problems from our couch, and perhaps there's nothing to solve once we resolve our own disconnect from the nature of reality."

"You're right. Bring on that movie!" Rose smiles. She cuddles one of Sophia's soft, fluffy animal pillows, and the two friends relax into their movie.

Information as the Creative Tools of Consciousness

The next day Rose calls Verdandi in an attempt to share some of these new insights with her as well. Verdandi asks Rose for creative metaphors to help her understand what she wants to talk about.

"Cosmic information is creative, Grandma. It's like an architect tool that consciousness uses for building whole worlds and realities. Just like you use healing symbols that none of us can see, but which activate specific potentials and properties of consciousness. Those symbols are also Cosmic information, able to communicate and create realities simultaneously. Or perhaps Cosmic communication really is the high art of creation, like those sacred words you invoke that are so powerful."

"It's true. Thank you for relating it back to something that I do and am familiar with. That helps. It also confirms what my elders have always taught me: The Universe is unified and one.

"Mystics have said that the world was created by 'the word,' but not just any words. What I'm hearing from you is that consciousness uses a specific type of alphabet for constructing physical realities and worlds, right? Is that correct? An alphabet of digits and numerical codes?"

"Yes, precisely. Our physical world is digital, yet not in a computer-generated sense, and not like these theories that say we live in a universe simulation of consciousness. Consciousness is far more dynamic and creative than a mere simulation; it's not just algorithmic or a mathematical formula. These Cosmic digits form patterns for the way things grow, develop, and evolve, which are studied by physicists, biologists, and mathematicians, and also by economists and social scientists when they analyze the growth patterns of human behaviors. The Cosmic digits also form part of the creative languages of sacred geometry, art, and music, to name just a few."

"I see where you're going with this now, Rosie. I see how these same Cosmic digits you're talking about are also within the ancient mystical texts that we use, coded in numerical and geometric formulas that contain the hidden knowledge of the Universe. The initiates were trained to read and embed these codes to keep this knowledge safe. It sounds like you've discovered the creative language of consciousness that many of our greatest inventors, composers, chefs, writers, and other creatives have worked with, even though they wouldn't refer to this in terms of digits."

"That's it exactly, Grandma. Each person translates and uses these digits for different purposes, yet at the foundational levels of reality, those are always the same digits. Bach and Mozart created majestic compositions with these digits. Einstein used them to describe his discoveries of the laws of physics. The famous painters Rembrandt and Salvador Dali used them for unique light and dark effects that stretched our minds out of the ordinary ways of seeing the world. Culinary maestros like chef Nigella Lawson and chef Mauro Colagreco use the digits to create culinary feasts that engage the full enjoyment of our senses. Writers such as Jane Austen and Joanne Rowling use digits to build narratives that capture our hearts and transport us to magical realms where the adult in us is free to play with wizards and witches. Sports heroes use the Cosmic digits to master what we can do with our bodies, and the list continues. See what I mean? It's so creative. I just love it!" Rose laughs.

"It's wonderful, Rose. I understand now why the digits you discovered have become your best friends. What you're telling me is that as human beings, we're encoded and potentized in the same way that our universe is."

"Yes! And we can bring this to life in the most wondrous ways."

"We must also remember, however, that digits expressed through the creative human mind can also become weapons of mass destruction, exploitation, slavery, and brutal regimes of power-hungry politicians. Our creative power is a universal given, yet what we do with this is our human responsibility to realize."

Personalizing Our Relationship with the Cosmos

Verdandi is always guiding Rose to make her discoveries relevant and personal. She helps her to become aware of how, and in what way, the information she's discovering is empowering her or not.

"Rose, these discoveries are exciting, but an abstract relationship with the Cosmos as an architect of digits may not be sufficient to help you solve the enormous tasks that are ahead on the path you've chosen. Ask the Cosmos to appear to you as a persona. Let's do that right now. Close your eyes and connect with the Cosmos like you usually do. Now ask the Cosmos to appear to you as a real person with real qualities. See those lovely Cosmic qualities as a face. Hear those wise Cosmic qualities as a voice that is just right for your order of understanding. Then tell me what you see and hear."

Rose closes her eyes. She's silent for a moment, then says, "I see the Cosmos as a person with four faces, like those Indian gods. Each of the four directions has a different face: happy, sad, stern, and funny. It's starting to spin. It's morphing into a rather confused face…then a hilarious face…then a sweet face like a child. Oh! Now the face is seductive. It's blowing me a kiss! Its facial program can't decide what it's going to be. Or maybe it's testing my facial recognition abilities? This isn't working, Grandma. It isn't staying still long enough to just show me one face."

Verdandi chuckles as she imagines what her granddaughter is seeing right now. Rose doesn't think it's funny. In fact, she's rather annoyed.

"Oh, sweet girl, can't you see what's happening? Try it again and focus on the voice this time. Ask the Cosmos to speak to you in a voice that you can recognize and personalize. Tell me what happens."

"All I hear is one of those casino machines that spins the numbers until it goes 'bingo.'" Rose crinkles her brow. "Please, Cosmos, this isn't working for me. Can't you show up as the Lady of the Lake with a beautiful melodious voice? Or Merlin with a nice mysterious voice? Or a wise elder with a deep voice, or a wonderful child with a delightful, playful voice?" Rose is quiet for a few minutes. Verdandi is hopeful that this time it might be working. But the Cosmos has a different plan for what it wants to teach her granddaughter.

Suddenly, Rose exclaims in an agitated voice, "Really? You've got to be kidding me. You're making this my job? But why do you always appear so mythically when Grandma asks you? For her, you show up as the most incredible characters. Then when I ask you, you give me this? I feel like I'm the subject of a huge Cosmic joke."

"What happened?" Verdandi asks lovingly.

"I did exactly what you told me to do. Then the Cosmos handed me this interface and told me that I was to design the face of my preference myself, and to enjoy the new mythic realities where ready-made faces are no longer up for order."

Verdandi smiles as Rose continues, "That this is a higher order where architects assemble their own Cosmic faces and characters. I should have known by now that this future human business has certain consequences. Now we even have to design our own reality characters." Rose has a sharp intake of breath. "Oh wow! I see my own face now, and hear my own voice! Ahh, so that's what the Cosmos wanted me to understand. I get it now."

The Key of Cosmic Communication

Verdandi is very pleased that Rose has had this experience and now understands. "Could you hold on a minute, love? Dagaz needs me in the kitchen. He's making the most wonderful bean soup."

"Of course," Rose says.

"He's such a character. He sings while he stirs in the ingredients. He says it makes the soup taste better. I'll be right back."

Verdandi goes to the kitchen, and Rose reflects on all that she and her grandmother have just discussed. She hears the rumbles in her own tummy, reminding her of the physical realities of her life.

Her thoughts go back to the idea that Cosmic information is the original information that was here before the beginning as immortal fractals of the totality we can co-create with. She recalls her vision in the hospital, of Cosmic units of information that form part of our inner and outer worlds and report back to the totality as tiny, invisible Cosmic agents. More unusual thoughts and questions enter her mind.

Is it possible for the Universe to learn from us via these Cosmic units? Is the language of the Cosmic architecture the language that mystics and inventors such as Plato, Leonardo Da Vinci, and Hildegard of Bingen used to enter into Cosmic unity and discover the hidden knowledge of the Universe? Is this the primordial language that makes it possible for trees, birds, rivers, humans, bacteria, planets, molecules, atoms, stars, and consciousness as a whole to communicate directly with themselves while being parts of one another?

Verdandi returns to the computer and notices how Rose is in a state of deep reflection. "All fine, love? It's probably time for you to eat as well, eh? Dagaz is such a fine husband, but he never seems to remember the specific herbs that go into that soup. I must have told him a thousand times already. Or perhaps it's just his excuse to call me into the kitchen for a kiss."

Rose smiles. She adores the long and deep love that her grandparents share. "I miss your soups, Grandma. They always make me feel cozy. Just thinking about your soups puts me into that state again."

"We'll be together again soon, dear girl. Now what else is on your mind? I have 10 more minutes and then I need to go and join Dagaz for our delicious lunch."

"That sounds great. I'm getting hungry myself. Grandma, do you think that someone like Einstein knew this informational language of the Cosmos?"

"Okay, give me a minute to switch from soup to Einstein." Verdandi pauses for a moment, then continues. "Einstein was brilliant at unlocking a far greater totality of understanding of how the Universe works from a simple formula. And similarly, from the totality, he was able to put this back in the form of our human mathematical language of equations and formulas.

But his real genius was in the use of his imaginal powers, which gave him the intuitive understanding of the way our universe works, far beyond the science of those days. If Einstein were alive today, I'm sure he would have told you that we can all become intelligent like him by developing our imaginal powers."

"Do you think I can communicate with viruses by using this Cosmic language of life? Viruses are mostly combinations of genetic codes, and codes are digital. I believe I can, but I'm not sure doctors would believe what I did in the hospital."

"Trust yourself, Rosie. It doesn't matter whether anyone else believes in what you did. You know what you did, and so do I. For you, viruses are not enemies, but evolutionary catalysts. This perception is the first bridge for being able to communicate with viruses."

"That's it exactly! Viruses have always played a major role in our evolution by triggering the process of epigenetics; changing the activities and sequencing of the genes. There's even research that suggests that human intelligence would never have developed, if not for the role of viruses. Viruses learn with us and can become part of our body. Did you know that some ancient viruses have actually become part of our human genetic make-up, and are now acting as 'double agents' by helping our cells to tackle other viruses that can be harmful to our bodies?"

"That'll give me a good lunch story to tell Dagaz. I'll tell him that his intelligence is from a virus. I married a virus!" Verdandi laughs.

"Please tell him he's a nice virus!" Rose grins. "But seriously, viruses are truly evolutionary agents. They're not our enemy. Even the coronavirus may well be a catalyst for a deeper evolution of our species that one day may prove to be useful and necessary."

"Dagaz will like the sound of that. He's been building up a whole theory of why this is happening, which I am sure he'll gladly share with you when you come to visit us.

"I agree with you, Rose. It's entirely possible to communicate with viruses and bacteria, just like you're able to communicate with the Cosmos. I saw how you were able to shift the effect of the coronavirus inside your body, even if most of it happened subconsciously. Once you entered into that Cosmic state of unity, you were able to activate the future potentials of a beneficial relationship with everything that forms part of your body.

"There's one more key I'd like to share with you, especially since you had

that dream yesterday where you weren't able to make yourself heard. And then I really must stop for lunch. Are you up for another key?"

"Of course!"

"This is the Key of Cosmic Communication, which brings you in touch with the universal languages and immortal information that the spiritually oriented mystics, architects, priests, scientists, philosophers, and alchemists work with. This might also explain your fascination right now with the hidden Cosmic codes behind the numbers and digits. This knowledge used to be concealed and reserved for initiates only, to the point that many old mystical texts included errors on purpose to ensure that common people could not decode or misuse it. Now times are shifting. We've entered the time of the revealing; the time of revelation. The Key of Cosmic Communication is all about communicating from the Cosmic state of *unity consciousness.* Remember how each choice is also a state of consciousness, which influences the way your choices manifest in life? The same is true for the state of consciousness through which you communicate."

"Whoa, I like this key! Tell me more."

"These are the times when I wish you were physically here with me so I could show you in the ways I've always taught you. We could take the dogs and get out into nature together for direct, experiential understanding. But I digress…

"The key is to know whether you're in a state of duality, like you explained to me earlier when you spoke of the binary digits, or whether you're in a state of unity, in which case you'll recognize that behind all phenomena that appear as dual, there's a third principle. Just like there's the quantum principle behind the dual appearance of those digits you spoke of. The unity state of consciousness is also referred to as 'trinity vision.'

"From trinity vision, you see with hindsight, insights, and foresight as one," Verdandi explains. "Just like you have two physical eyes and your third eye as the spiritual eye that integrates the dual information of your physical eyes, the trinity helps you to see the true nature of reality in all that appears or behaves as dual."

"Grandma, do you remember that nightmare I told you about just before the coronavirus entered my body? The one I had the night before my fever spiked really high? In my dream, there were three monsters that were headed straight for me. Just as I was about to scream, a protective figure jumped in front of the monsters and beheaded one of them. As soon as the monster was beheaded, it would materialize again and multiply. It happened each time one of the monsters was beheaded.

"After that dream, I started to feel progressively worse. The night in the hospital after my fever went down, the dream came back again. This time I told the protector in my dream not to behead any of the monsters. They then transformed and ceased to be a threat.

"Sophia sent me an article by a Dutch virologist, Berend-Jan Bosch, from the University of Utrecht in the Netherlands. It showed how the coronavirus has a crown-like structure, hence its name 'corona' meaning 'crown.' The corona crown sits on three spiked enzymes that are interwoven. When the body tries to defend itself, it sends an enzyme to these three interwoven crowns, which chops off one of the heads. The beheaded viral stem then transforms irreversibly into a spear that pierces through the cell membrane. This enables the virus to enter into the cell. Once inside, it duplicates itself."

"You've got your answer right there, Rose. Your body's initial defense reaction of 'beheading' weaponized the coronavirus by seeing it as 'other' and therefore, a threat. Later, you learned to keep the trinity of the virus intact after you experienced the state of Cosmic unity when you went to the other side of the veil. Duality attacks 'otherness,' whereas unity integrates it. The difference between a parasitic or symbiotic world has its origins in us."

"That's profound. That would mean that our state of consciousness literally changes how information appears to us. It also implies that the only way to communicate with or from the information of immortality is to be in a state of non-duality because that's the state of immortal information. It's permanently in the non-dual quantum state of unified possibilities."

"Good, my girl. Now I must stop and eat. Can you relax this afternoon? Have some fun. Remember, you're still inside your healing cocoon with so many inner changes and transformations happening. I suggest that you also spend time with your feelings and not just all of these dazzling new ideas. Honor your process and your body, too. This might be the perfect time to reach out to Sophia to complete that chapter of your life when you felt trapped in your relationship with Tim. Let her know what really happened. We can talk again in a couple of days."

Getting Out of Strangled Relationships

The next day Rose invites Sophia to meet her for coffee. The café offers take-out service as well as tables outside that are socially distanced. The young women sit with their lattes and croissants and enjoy the cool spring air.

"This is relaxing," Sophia says with a smile. "My morning felt so overloaded, it's good to take a short break. How are you feeling, Rose?"

"I've been thinking about my former relationship with Tim lately. There were some things I never told you. I talked with Grandma Verdandi about it briefly yesterday and she suggested I talk with you so I can complete that chapter of my life and heal the feelings. Would that be alright?"

"Of course! You're like my sister. I was so happy when you found the courage to break up with that guy. He really had you looped into a very toxic dynamic."

"He did."

"He was always trying to undermine your belief in yourself while at the same time positioning himself as the savior for all your problems. Your world and circle of friends started to shrink smaller and smaller. I was worried about you."

"Thanks, Sophia. It took me quite some time and a lot of tears to realize what he was truly doing to me. I just couldn't believe that someone who kept saying he loved me would want to purposefully break me down like that."

"What he did to you was a classic manipulation pattern. He started by making you feel like you were the most wonderful, special woman in the whole world. 'Only *he* could see and appreciate your beauty and genius! Only *he* could ever understand you.'"

"It's true."

"He was creating intimacy with you by making you feel like he was the best thing that ever happened to you."

"You're right, Sophia. In the first few months of our relationship, I felt like I was walking on clouds. I felt so special. Then the attacks started."

"I remember. He started to tell you how disappointed he was with something you said or did. That maybe he'd been mistaken about you; that you weren't as special and intelligent as he thought."

"So I worked harder to please him and regain his approval."

"That's when he knew he had you in his claws. He knew he could control you. Then came the victim attacks to make you feel guilty. I remember how you called me one night, crying in total confusion because you couldn't understand what you'd done wrong."

"I remember that night. It was awful. I felt like my whole world was crumbling. I didn't know left from right anymore. I thought that maybe what he was telling me was true. Maybe I really did have some formidable blind spots that I couldn't see. Maybe I was a manipulative, controlling person. I didn't realize that he was the one manipulating and controlling me."

"That's right. Then he offered to 'guide you to the light.' He became your savior, so you'd feel grateful that he stayed with you, despite you being such a 'bad woman.' He had you in a place where you'd start to defend him in front of others. You never let on to anyone what was really going on."

"Yes, that was the worst time. I remember my dad and I got into a huge fight because I was mad that he would question Tim. I can see now that this is precisely what Tim wanted: to isolate me from the people who love and know me."

"What broke the spell for you, Rose? How did you get out of that toxic relationship?"

"The big 'aha' moment happened when I was listening to an interview with Maya Angelou. She said, 'Love liberates.'"

"Ahh. Beautiful."

"The moment I heard those words, it burst the balloon of lies. I realized then that my relationship with Tim was not based on love. I suddenly saw all of the fear, manipulation, and control dynamics. I closed my eyes and asked, 'As Love, what would I do? Does this relationship build me up or break me down?' I knew that what we had was definitely not love. Love doesn't distort reality; love doesn't create dependency; love doesn't isolate or manipulate a person. 'Love liberates!' I got sucked in, not wanting to see that perhaps his intentions weren't that noble. I fell for his classic devil trick that made me feel special and promised me the world."

Sophia sips her coffee and takes a moment to reflect. "To tell you the truth, Rose, during the whole time you were with Tim, I found it really hard to reach you. It felt like you weren't open to me; like you were no longer interested in spending any time with me. Was that true?"

"I'm sorry, Sophia, I didn't want you to feel like that. I felt torn. I wanted to spend time with you, but Tim kept telling me that you were jealous of my relationship with him. He said I should be careful not to be influenced by you. I didn't dare tell you this at the time because I was afraid of how you might react. I started to close myself off from everyone. Even my family, not just you. I threw myself into my studies and into my books in the hope that the storms would just blow over, but they didn't."

"I understand. Thanks for telling me, Rose. We've never really spoken about this before. Is that also when you started to get those dreams about death?"

"Yes, part of me wanted to die. It felt easier to slowly slip away and start a new life elsewhere than to confront Tim. I didn't tell this to anybody, but I started to progressively feel more and more numb. I didn't realize that my closing down also meant that I was weakening my connection to life."

"I'm so sorry, Rose, I had no idea it was that bad."

"There's more. A few weeks before I ended the relationship, I woke up from a really scary dream. In the dream, a huge python had entered my apartment while I was sleeping. It slithered over me and then got on top of my body. I thought that if I remained very still and calm, the snake would just move away by itself. I became still as a Zen monk, waiting for the snake to move. But it didn't. Instead, it seemed to like my body's warmth. Then it started to feed off my energy.

"I decided to try a different tactic. I believed that if I fed the python with my love, it would remain peaceful and not attack me. This didn't work either. Before I could realize what was happening, it had managed to curl around my neck and was slowly tightening its grip.

"None of my strategies worked and I felt terrified that I hadn't been able to protect myself. I woke up shocked in the midst of dying in that dream. I realized that I was getting strangled in my relationship, and that my passive approach of giving more love was getting me killed."

"Oh Rose, your dream contains so many powerful messages. Look at what's happening in our world today. So many people feel strangled and trapped. Perhaps all we've done is feed this deadly serpent of the old ways, rather than proactively getting ourselves out of the traps. I really hope that your insights about the Cosmic architecture of life can somehow help us access and apply the powers we need to use instead. We need to use the keys that life is giving us to get out of these old narratives."

"You're right, Sophia. I realize now that I was also responding from the old female pattern of the old story. By passively feeding the abuse in the hope that 'being nice' would get me out of trouble, I enabled it as well."

Sophia takes her last sip of coffee. "Do you have time for a short walk? Let's go to the park and continue our conversation there."

Welcoming the New Mythos

Rose and Sophia walk to the park, which is close by. It's one of their favorite places, with its old trees, flower gardens, and small pond.

"Rose, don't move!" Sophia whispers. "Tilt your head to the left very slowly. Do you see it?" A small, white butterfly has landed on Rose's shoulder.

"I see it! She's beautiful!" Rose says softly. The butterfly takes a few steps and flutters off. Rose grins. The butterfly's visit fills her with delight.

"Do you mind continuing our conversation about Tim?" Sophia asks her friend.

"No, not at all."

"How would the heroine or hero of the new mythos have dealt with the situation you were in with Tim? How do we, as the new heroes and heroines, get out of traps, threats, and manipulation? If you had fought Tim as a man who took advantage of you and tried to break you down, it would have brought you back to the old mythic structure of attacking the enemy."

"I agree."

"Could it be that by seeing Tim as a symptom of all that's wrong with the world, and by recognizing your learning in all that happened, this moves you to the new mythic structure that focuses on the deeper transformations of our world? It seems to me that this isn't really about Tim, but what he represents."

"You're brilliant as always, Sophia. I spoke with my grandma just yesterday about dual and non-dual communication, and how duality responses get us further trapped into reactive patterns. Now you're saying the same thing, but in a different way. We need to look for the *third* principle by seeing that this isn't about Tim, but about the larger system of what doesn't work. Just like the COVID-19 crisis is only a symptom of everything else that's sick and wrong with our world. In my dream, I was passive by not facing the python directly.

Instead, I enabled it to strangle me. I became part of the problem, instead of the solution."

"Exactly. So let's get proactive and realize that there are no victims here. It is time for us to take up the leadership call for whole system change. This new story of co-creative partnership that you've been talking about is so much more exciting. Let's really welcome the new mythos in our lives."

"One more thing, Sophia. These new mythic structures of the hero and heroine's journey are really challenging us to enter into an entirely different relationship with all that we consider threatening. In the old mythic structures, 'the threat' or the 'the wound' became the catalyst for awakening the hero's mythic abilities. In the new mythic structure, it's our own ability to transform this dualistic notion of 'fight and conquer' that awakens our transformative powers for this renaissance time. We need to explore 'third way solutions,' rather than regressing in old dualistic reactions. We must become 'future creative' in the midst of crisis and breakdown, rather than using the might of movie superpowers. We must call forth the higher order choices that empower us all by entering a state of Cosmic unity by will, instead of going for the old superhero pattern of saving those poor, helpless humans. We must develop our future human capacities through empathy, inclusiveness, and love, while enhancing our communication abilities by communicating from the Cosmic architecture that connects us all. We must develop our moral passion for doing what is right and necessary, and not what is popular and expected. We have a lot of work to do, my sister."

"You're right, Rose. And the list is long: viral pandemics, uncontrollable fires, our climate crisis, racism, terrorism, the rise of populism, the social divide and polarization of our world. Imagine approaching each of these crises with our future human capacities! Our new *mythic* abilities. We need to pause and think before reacting. So much can change by responding differently. I'm glad we were able to talk about this." Sophia checks the time on her cell phone. "Oops, I'd better get back to class."

"Thank you for meeting with me today, Sophia. It feels so good to have these discussions with you."

Our New Response Abilities

While walking back to her apartment, Rose experiments with different states of consciousness and how they shift her sense of the world, as well as her response abilities. Life is a powerful teacher. *It's fascinating how each state of consciousness creates a different reality,* she ponders. *We literally in-form the fields of life around us through our intentions, thoughts, feelings, postures, beliefs, and expectations. We truly are the living information of consciousness.*

On the other side of the street, a young boy struggles to ride his new bicycle. His fingers grip the handlebars tightly as he tries desperately to steer straight. The boy bites his lip. His cheeks are flushed, and his eyes are close to tears. Rose's heart overflows with empathy for this little boy as she remembers those days herself. She used to return home with burning, bleeding knees from riding too quickly around the corners of her street. She wants to help him, but doesn't know how. She sends the boy a wave of calming love and calls out to him gently, "Relax your grip and look up! Don't look down at your feet. Let your legs do the work. Have faith and trust! You can do this!"

The boy is too stressed to look at Rose, but he hears her instructions. All of a sudden, he relaxes his posture, puts his chin up, and finds that magical, sweet spot of balance while letting his legs do the pedaling. His dad sees the change in his son and quickly shouts, "Thank you!" to Rose with a big smile, before running behind the boy as he happily speeds away on the bike.

Entering her apartment, Rose remembers a webinar from the night before, and how differently that had gone. She'd felt overcome with defensiveness after getting into an argument with one of her former classmates about the state of the world earlier in the day. She couldn't find a way to get out of the troubling impasse, so after a while, she just shut down emotionally and left the webinar before it ended. She now realizes how slipping into a state of judgment and defensiveness actually inhibited her creative capacities and pulled her into an antagonistic debate that went nowhere. Her dad had warned her that we can't access our inner resourcefulness or learn when half of our brain functions are shut down, which is what happens during times of fear or stress.

Excited about her discoveries, she decides to call her older brother, Lucas. It's been a while since she's spoken with him; he's usually very busy with his children and his job, especially now that everything has moved online. During their last call, they'd had a passionate discussion about the state of the world and what could be done about it.

After some chit chat and superficial updates on personal matters of life, Rose asks: "Hey, bro, what if the state of our world actually reflects our state of mind? Maybe we can catalyze whole new possibilities, but it requires that we enter into the heart of the storm and shift our state of consciousness to where the winds are most turbulent?"

"Are you saying that we enter the consciousness of the storm and merge with it?" Lucas asks.

"Yes. Then we shift it by consciously activating the future potentials that lay dormant in the storm. We need to call upon the higher order of realities; to activate the attractors that can gravitate the forces of change to new constellations, new directions, and new configurations."

"Sounds like you've been talking with Grandma Verdandi a little too much. How often do you two talk to each other these days?" Lucas says grinning.

Rose is used to his teasing. "We talk almost every day," she tells her brother. "She's my pillar of sanity in so much madness. You should call her more often, and Grandpa, too. I'm sure they'd be delighted to hear from you. They always ask me how you're doing. My standard reply is, 'He's busy. Very, very busy.'"

Lucas laughs. "Well, it's true. But you're right, I'll call them soon. And regarding you merging your mind with the storm of the world? You always have the wildest ideas! How do you plan to do that? And what guarantee do you have that the storm won't overtake your mind? Its force may be far stronger than the power of your mind."

"But is it really stronger than the power of my mind if I tune my mind to Cosmic consciousness? What if the consciousness of the world is composed of the same Cosmic information as my personal consciousness, and my inner state of consciousness can remind the inner state of the world how to move through this crisis? What if the true nature of our crisis is caused by tremendous amounts of energy that are trapped in our outdated modes of thinking because we hardly ever tune our minds to Cosmic consciousness?"

"Are you serious?"

"Yes, I am. Think about it. All this energy of our sun has now become trapped in the lower biosphere of our planet because we pumped the air with fossil fuels that trap the radiation of the sun. To make things worse, we've cut the trees that are nature's technology for capturing the carbon emissions from the atmosphere by storing it safely in their roots. Now all of this potential energy becomes destructive because it's no longer embodied in the natural systems of life. Ninety percent of this trapped heat is absorbed and stored in the oceans, which is leading to a dangerous increase in ocean temperatures all over the world. The equivalent of this excess heat is around 3.6 billion Hiroshima bomb explosions.[6] Just imagine what could change if we could learn to utilize this enormous amount of energy for our collective transformation? Instead, it takes the forms of hurricanes, cyclones, heatwaves, fires, extreme weather events, drought, earthquakes, violence, conflicts, war, and more. Show me how this doesn't reflect the state of consciousness of humanity? We've been in this troubled state for thousands of years. Our history books are filled with stories of war, conflict, and division."

Lucas listens to his little sister. He admires her, but has a more pragmatic mind than Rose. He's currently working as a marine engineer on renewable energy solutions. "I see your point, but I don't think we can resolve this by simply shifting our state of mind. Especially because 'mind' as a substance is also not an energy state that can embody that excessive amount of energy you just spoke of." He pauses. "It does raise an interesting idea about the radicalization of our world, however, because we're not embodying our transformative capacities, and as such, they turn destructive. Just like the free radicals in our body."

Rose smiles. She can sense an opening in her brother's mind. "While walking home earlier, I saw a small boy who was learning to ride his bike. He reminded me that we can't change direction by trying to control what's happening and stopping everything. When you ride a bike, you have to keep moving to stay upright. Maybe the same is true for our world. We can't control the events we've set in motion, but we can learn to steer the direction if we can tap into the powers of what has become unleashed and connect them to a state that is unifying and transformative."

"That sounds logical. How would you propose we do that?"

"I don't know yet," Rose answers, "but I do know it has something to do with entering the fire through a higher state of consciousness that is non-dual, rather than trying to fight or control it. Fighting this crisis and trying to 'combat climate change' isn't going to work, and neither is declaring a war on the coronavirus. There are other ways, other possibilities, that we have never collectively explored. Ask Grandma. She has so many interesting ideas. She says it has something to do with the renaissance dynamics of our time."

"Okay, will do. Right now, Olaf is reminding me that we have to walk our dog."

"Give that sweet boy a kiss from his auntie and tell him I'll call soon."

"Good to talk with you, Rose."

"You, too. Bye for now." Rose ends the call, happy that she had the chance to speak briefly with her brother.

She feels fired up now, and is in full creative mode. Or, as Verdandi would have said, she is "in a state of heartful knowing that opens up a whole band of intelligence that is connected with our capacity to take creative action." She's determined to become the solution for all that isn't working. The necessity of change is activating and awakening the seeds of her future human purpose. She feels that this is our moment of choice; the call to become mythic in whole new ways. She wants to discover how, together with the Universe and the vast wisdom of our planet, we can heal and transform our world. It's been a long day and she is looking forward to a good night's rest.

Just before falling asleep, she tunes her mind to Cosmic consciousness and enters into the consciousness of the major problems of our world, just like she suggested to her brother. She becomes aware of how, within every challenge, there's a potential solution that requires a new or different state of consciousness. She asks herself how future humans might view all of these challenging problems. She enters deeper into her imaginal state of consciousness, and starts to experience herself within the heart of these issues. She notices how merely being there in this Cosmic state already in-forms new realities to activate and emerge, transforming the state of the problems.

In that moment, Rose realizes profoundly how in the new story, our existential threats and the energy of destruction become the fuel for our transformation and enlightenment. She sees how the new story is awakening in the heart of humanity, igniting our world soul to rise up from the ashes of what didn't work. She realizes how future humans know how to embody and work with the primordial forces of transformation. Their consciousness no longer gets trapped into the old duality modes; they embody the consciousness of wholeness and communicate from the immortal and unified state of Cosmic consciousness. They understand what makes life and each of us flourish in all of our diversity and splendor. She drifts into deep sleep, until she finds herself in a most unusual dream…

Integration -
The Key of Cosmic Communication

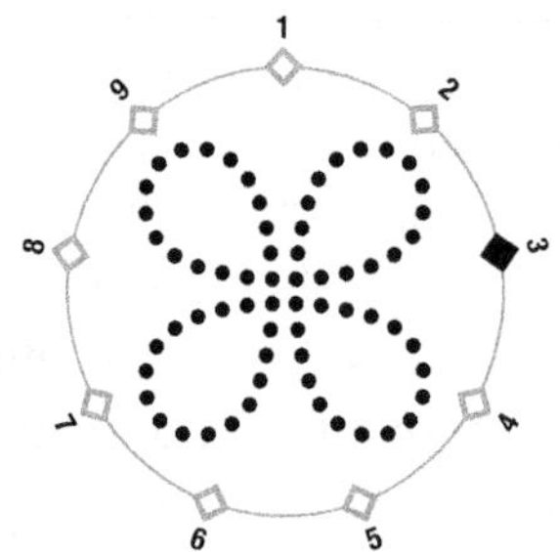

Through this chapter we've explored the Key of Cosmic Communication through some of the ground-breaking ideas from the new paradigm sciences, including cosmology, quantum field theory, and the science of infodynamics. We will continue to share more of these insights in the coming chapters.

> *The Key of Cosmic Communication helps you to realize how your state of consciousness influences the state of information that you communicate, whether you communicate from duality or unity.*

The summary below will help you to integrate these discoveries further:

- Life is a unified reality. Cosmic communication in-forms all levels and realities of existence from the nonlocal Cosmic state of unity and wholeness. Cosmic information is eternally present in all matters of life as the building blocks of consciousness. You can build your reality and experiences from wholeness by tuning your mind to the unified state of Cosmic consciousness, just like nature does.
- The informational architecture of our universe is a Cosmic hologram composed of nonlocal digits (numerical codes) that create and communicate simultaneously by in-forming reality. In other words, Cosmic language is an alphabet of digits (numbers) that in-form how life manifests and evolves from deeper implicate orders of reality that are nonlocal.

- The quantum superposition state is *the realm of potentiality* where all possible states of information coexist simultaneously, prior to being observed. The "future" is literally an informational possibility state in consciousness.
- Cosmic information, as the building blocks of consciousness, can also be experienced as archetypal structures.
- Both energy-matter and space-time are complementary Cosmic information, forming and in-forming our physical universe. By exploring the various states in which information appears, whether dual or as a quantum superposition, the dynamic and creative nature of consciousness itself becomes revealed.
- Dual states of consciousness create dual patterns of information that collapse into either/or options that can eventually turn into oppositional dynamics. Unity states of consciousness are in the quantum superposition state of information of simultaneous possibilities. This is the informational state of what we call "futures."
- Human beings are Cosmically encoded and potentized in the same way that our universe is. You can bring this to life in the most wondrous and creative ways.
- Behind all phenomena that appear as dual, there's a third principle: the unity state of consciousness. You can access this through trinity vision using hindsight, insight, and foresight simultaneously. Trinity vision helps us to see beyond duality by connecting our physical eyes with our Cosmic inner eye.
- The physical world with binary information and dual appearances is simultaneously a Cosmic world in a superposition state of simultaneous possibilities, as are you.
- Duality states of mind collapse the field of possibility, which can create experiences of otherness and division. You cannot heal yourself or our world from a mental state of duality. Duality responses get us trapped into reactive patterns. Enter a state of unity consciousness to see beyond the veil of dual appearance. All that is two is three in aspect, unified at deeper levels of reality.

- The new mythic structures develop our renaissance capacities for transforming dualistic positions and activating our future potentials by:
  - Initiating third way solutions.
  - Becoming future creative in the midst of crisis and breakdown.
  - Calling forth the higher implicate orders of future possibilities in the midst of change and chaos.
  - Communicating from a state of empathy, inclusiveness, and love.
  - Engaging the connective patterns and informational codes of the Cosmic architecture of consciousness that are within us all.
  - Developing our moral passion for doing what is right and necessary, and not what is popular and expected.
- The necessity of change activates our future human purpose. This is our moment of choice. We can rise to the challenge and become the required humans of a new era. We can heal and transform our world in partnership with our universe and the vast wisdom of our planet.
- The new story is awakening in the heart of our humanity. Future humans know how to embody the primordial forces of transformation. Their consciousness no longer gets trapped into the old duality modes as they embody the architecture of wholeness and know how to communicate from Cosmic consciousness.

CHAPTER 4

The Cosmic Compass

Navigating for Wholeness with the Key of Trinity

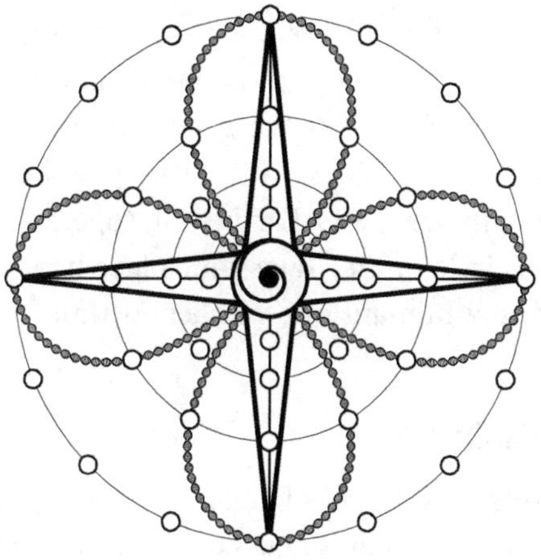

Rose is dreaming. She experiences a Martin Luther King moment as she speaks in front of a huge crowd of millions of people in her dream. They've gathered to declare the beginning of a new civilization; one in which humans are committed to steward our world more wisely and with a lot more fun and joy.

"Elect yourself! Rise up from the graveyards and terror of all those thousands of years of suffering, slavery, and violence. Become the required future human for a new story, a new time, where we stand united in the great circle of life. The count is on us. Remember who you are and why we are here. Shake off those blankets of forgetfulness. You know your truth. You know who you are. Ignite your passion with the flame of love that was kept alive by Nelson Mandela, Mahatma Gandhi, Martin Luther King, Mother Teresa, Joan of Arc, Ruth Bader Ginsburg, Malala Yousafzai, and all those who fought and are fighting for our liberation and the healing of our world. This is the same flame that lives inside your heart. With this flame, ignite your moral passion for doing what is right, not what is easy and expected. Love liberates. Ignite the healing of our world.

"Divest from the currencies of greed and separation. Unplug the fuel of hatred and violence and invest in our future with the currencies of justice, truth, and compassion. Put *care* first, not money first. In this world, there is no place for the old story of prey and predator, winners and losers. In this new time, we stand for everyone together. We are the future humans; the architects of a world that works for all of us. A world of plenty, beauty, and care. A world we call home.

"Together we will transform the old, sick systems. Together we will change our story in favor of life. This is your moment of choice. You hold the power! You make the difference! With this life-given power, elect yourself now for this new world and this new story. This is the new hero/heroine's journey where men, women, children, and Earth walk together, hand in hand with the Cosmos and the circle of life. Take your place now as this world comes alive in you as the future humans of a whole new time."

The Lake of Consciousness

As the dream progresses, Rose goes back in time to a poor city in Europe at the early beginning of the former Renaissance period, somewhere around the 14th century. She watches the hardships and desecration of life, and notices how the smell of death is literally everywhere, with burning bodies and mass graves. Deadly diseases are a normal part of life for this town. The terror of ongoing violence and life-threatening situations are visible in the hollow eyes of the people. Children are crying and hungry; many don't survive the plundering and mass slaughters of their cities. Here the laws of the predator rule. You are either the hunter or you are hunted. Life has no value, and for those less fortunate, their lives are up for sale to the highest bidder.

Rose is semi-conscious in her dream and doesn't understand why she's dreaming this. She reaches out for the Cosmos and asks why she's been brought back to this time. The Cosmos responds by guiding her to the water of the collective unconscious.

Her dream landscape shifts and she sees a beautiful large lake. As she puts her hands in the water, she becomes aware of the dreams, hopes, and disappointments of humanity. The water holds all our memories of all times lived. As she puts a drop of this water on her lips, she notices that it tastes salty like tears. *Is this an ocean of our tears?* She marvels at the vision. She dips her hand into the water once more and becomes aware of the inner lives of people as if she were inside their hearts and minds.

She watches a little girl who's about to go to bed. The child hugs her fuzzy dog and whispers into his ear, "Night, night, Max. You understand me. Adults never listen." The little girl is already learning the difference between the adult world and the world of the child. She doesn't understand why the adults don't take her ideas and suggestions more seriously.

Rose is curious to learn more about this incredible water. As she connects with its qualities, she becomes aware of an endless compassion and deep empathy. The water equally embraces all emotions. It doesn't reject any feelings that enter it, no matter how painful. The water loves so deeply because its eternal nature is unchanged by what enters it. The water is in a permanent state of pure awareness; it notices the impermanence of life and the tides of change without getting engaged. The water is pure compassion. Its nature cannot be poisoned. All is known, seen, felt, understood, and heard by this water as it mirrors perfectly our essential wisdom nature and the eternal qualities of consciousness.

The Cosmic Compass of Wisdom

The water calls Rose to enter it fully. As she enters the water with her whole being, it shows her an object at the bottom of the lake that is rising up to the surface. She sees a luminous, golden compass with a glowing light that is not from this world. As she moves closer, the compass becomes larger and transforms into a sphere. The compass invites her to enter its sphere.

Once inside, Rose notices how the coordinates inscribed on this compass are not the spatial cardinal directions that she knows as north, east, south, and west. Instead, these are the coordinates of our essential wisdom nature that point to the directions for actualizing our consciousness. *Is this our inner compass? This must be our Cosmic Compass that guides us through life and helps us become who we truly are.*

Curious to learn more, Rose moves to the center of the compass where she notices a little black dot. While holding her hands above the black dot, her inner center begins to vibrate and glow. She feels deeply in touch with her inner purpose, and relaxes as she experiences her own inner unity.

The Center Point speaks to her, and says, "My purpose is to remind humanity of the all-pervading wisdom qualities of consciousness; the ever-presence of your eternal nature. I am also the coordinate of your own Source point for existence; your inner point of unity, and how this manifests through the various Source codes that you bring to life through your purpose here on Earth."

Rose thanks the Center Point and continues through the sphere. She moves to the east coordinate. As she enters the east, she feels a great clarity emerge from within her. This clarity is helping her to discern what is real and what is not. This clarity feels very similar to how she experiences her future consciousness. The east coordinate speaks to her and says, "My purpose is to help humanity with the mirror-like wisdom qualities of consciousness; to realize the true nature of your experiences and how to surf the tides of change. I am also the coordinate of your future potential, illuminating your path forward in life."

Rose thanks the east and continues her discovery by moving to the south coordinate of the compass sphere. As she enters, she feels a deep unity and connectedness with all of life, and in particular, how her life fits within the larger unfolding of our planetary evolution. The south coordinate speaks to her and says, "My purpose is to help humanity thrive with the wisdom qualities of equanimity; to remember how life is always interdependent and our fundamental nature is the same. From the perspective of consciousness, we are each of equal value. I am also the coordinate of your stewardship potential, guiding you to live in right relationship with all dimensions and expressions of life."

Rose expresses her gratitude and continues to the west coordinate. As she enters, she becomes aware of the sacred darkness within her. She feels ancient, as if she has always existed. The darkness carries endless compassion. It understands the root causes of our suffering. The west coordinate speaks to her and says, "My purpose is to help humanity realize the wisdom qualities of discernment; the path of liberation through the power of love. I am also the coordinate of your sacred will that is fueled by the sacred flame of love that has the power to purify and harmonize all desires."

Rose is grateful for the information and continues now to the north coordinate. As she enters, she experiences a great state of accomplishment, as if all has already been completed and achieved. With relief, she realizes that she truly can trust in her own inner wisdom, knowing this Cosmic

Compass is part of her inner nature and guides her to thrive in life. The north coordinate speaks to her and says, "My purpose is to help humanity realize the all-accomplishing wisdom that guides the path of self-actualization. Through this wisdom you will discover the steps and actions that lead to true success, and how to develop the perseverance and right actions for fulfilling your purpose. I am also the coordinate of your Cosmic destiny, helping you to realize the multitude of roles and personas in the great play of consciousness, and how to realize your deeper destiny with the Cosmic story of life."

Rose's heart fills with gratitude. She feels deeply peaceful and attuned to her inner essence. She moves once more to the Center Point of the compass where she notices eight points as she looks out from the center into the world. The eight points speak as one voice: "We are the eight directions for your inner and outer growth and development. We will help you to balance your path, knowing when it is time to go within and rest, and knowing when it is time to expand and move into action. You can connect with us as your inner values, helping you to choose, and guiding you to grow, develop, and evolve."

A little bird outside the window wakes Rose from this magnificent dream. The light from the sun is just peeking over the horizon. It's still very early in the morning. She thanks the Cosmos for showing her where and how to connect with this inner compass that is part of our inner architecture. She decides to explore how to work with this compass often to discover more of her own wisdom constitution. She reflects on her dream and notices that it feels familiar to her, like the Medicine Wheel teachings of her indigenous relatives.

Our World in Moral Crisis

Later that evening, Rose watches the news on television, which shows her one sad story after another. "What is wrong with humanity?" she keeps murmuring to herself as her stomach tightens. Reports on murder, rape, torture, lies, deceit, violence, robberies, diseases, climate disasters, pollution, corruption, greed. The list is endless. Some people starving to death, while others are revolting for change. Millions are dying in the most horrible circumstances; animals are slaughtered for mere consumption; trees are cut at alarming rates; rare minerals are mined for our endless consumption. Then the advertisements pop up, showing happy people demonstrating how technologies, pharmaceuticals, and superficial solutions will solve all of the viewer's problems. These ads are followed by change gurus who promise a life of purpose by following their methods. They offer to sell the viewer meditation gadgets that can enter them into a state of "superconsciousness" in less than 5 minutes. The contrasts are enormous. *Or maybe it's all part of the same pattern?* Rose wonders.

Disturbed by the manipulation and severity of our destructive human tendencies, Rose thinks back to her dream with the Cosmic Compass. *What could change*, she ponders, *if humanity were to implement this compass in our governance, constitutions, economic systems, and education? Are people ready for the change that's required?*

Still feeling disturbed and unsettled, she gives her grandmother a call and shares what's on her mind. Verdandi listens attentively, as always.

"Rosie, what the caterpillar calls the end of the world, the master calls a butterfly. Those were the famous words of Richard Bach. Are you a caterpillar or a butterfly?"

"I'm both, Grandma. Without the caterpillar, the butterfly wouldn't be born," Rose answers, not quite sure where Verdandi wants to go with this.

"Very good! Knowing that without the old time, the new time would not be born, how can you help this transition? How can the horrors of what you have seen and heard on the television help to activate the inner codes of the new possibilities for our evolution within the world that is sick and collapsing? Remember that each character plays their role. Even someone like President Donald Trump activated in people the call of democracy by threatening to take it all away from them."

"Grandma, did you know that not every caterpillar is able to complete the metamorphosis to become a butterfly? The critical turning point is the linking up of the imaginal disks that hold the genetic codes of the butterfly within the skin of the caterpillar. If those imaginal disks don't link up, the imaginal cells will never form. The imaginal cells are required for growing the butterfly body from the mush of the dying caterpillar body."

"Excellent point, my girl. Now let's apply this. Linking up is the work of community building and network weaving. It's the work of developing the social membranes and capacities of our new time. The mush of our dying body of time is the activation for the new butterfly time. This activation is already happening right now, and has been happening for many years, perhaps even decades. We need to take flight in the air of the new story. As the butterfly cross-pollinates from place to place and flower to flower, so do we, if we have the will and the willingness to be part of this extraordinary moment in time."

Rose feels her passion activate again as she replies, "Yes! And I can be the rose and the butterfly! I'm part of the new emerging story that embodies our transformative capacities."

"Yes, you are. And what you saw tonight on television reminds you that our world is in a moral crisis and that's why we're in a climate crisis and social crisis. Humanity's moral values have severely eroded. We've normalized violence for thousands and thousands of years, justifying it as a part of evolution that's necessary for progress.

"Work with the coordinates of your inner compass to navigate through all of these contradictions, Rose. Find your North Star. Become like the mirror of the ocean of consciousness in which everything gets reflected, yet the mirror itself does not become what is reflected. Spend some time with your inner compass for 10 minutes a day. Ask it to guide you and to reveal to you what is yours to learn, heal, realize, and act upon."

The Key of Trinity

"Grandma, is that the North Star that our ancestors used to navigate the oceans? A constant beacon of light to give direction? I wonder what our moral North Star can be in times like these when people can't even tell the difference between fake news and reality? People argue about anything these days."

"The North Star is our Polaris. Now more than ever we need a common Polaris that can guide us through this difficult time. We knew the North Star by many names: Stella Polaris, Stella Maris, Leiðarstjarna, Niqirtsuituq, the Fire Star, the Emperor, the Chief Star, the Star That Does Not Walk Around, Dhruva, and many more. In fact, Polaris is a triple star system."

"That's fascinating."

"Remember when we talked about the trinity before?"

"Yes. I remember that when we see from unity, we see the trinity behind the appearance of duality. We need a Cosmic Polaris that can show us the way to true north."

"Exactly, Rosie. So what does 'true north' mean to you from your future human perspective?"

"It means having a clear understanding of the architecture of our possible future with a strong commitment toward its realization. It also means having the moral passion to do what is right and necessary. With those three elements in place—architectural understanding, commitment, and moral passion—I'm convinced we can do this."

"Excellent. So that's your Polaris. Your *triple* star system. What does this architectural understanding entail for you, Rose?"

Verdandi is guiding Rose toward a deeper comprehension of the many ideas and feelings that are bubbling to the surface of her mind. Rose answers with excitement, "We start with the Universe, which reveals the Cosmic architecture of life. From the cosmological architecture of our living systems, we can improve all of our human communication and economic systems. We can design new codes and guidelines that embed the fractal potentials of the Cosmos in the way we grow, develop, and evolve our world. Codes that communicate inclusiveness and diversity, instead of exclusion and division.

"I have so many ideas for how we can do this! I'm already looking for the communities and platforms where people share similar ideas and passions. I'm convinced that the key to real transformative change starts by developing our architectural understanding of the cosmological potentials in all living systems."

Verdandi can see that a profound realization is happening for Rose. "It sounds like you've accepted the invitation to become a Cosmic architect, my girl. Welcome to your new purpose. Now you'll discover the many ways in which all that you've studied and learned before can be put to good use for the tasks ahead. Just like the caterpillar body is put to use to build the body and life of the butterfly. Life has prepared you well. Humanity has now evolved to the point that we can take a monumental leap forward in the way we design, resource, and govern our world. This is a great time to accept the invitation of living your life as a Cosmic architect. That's what being a future human is all about: to architect our realities and worlds in partnership with life and the wisdom of the Cosmos."

Evoking Moral Passion through Wonder

Rose is letting the moment sink in. She realizes that indeed she has accepted living her life as an architect, and not just a bystander or someone who merely rides the waves that others create. Being a Cosmic architect goes even further than being a change agent. Many of her friends call themselves change agents, but for Rose, it's not about creating change, unless change is architecturally purposeful for building a world that works for everyone.

Verdandi smiles as she witnesses this profound shift in her granddaughter, who for so long has been looking for her purpose, and her way of being in life. "Rose, why do you care so deeply about this possible future that you experienced so profoundly when you went beyond the veil?"

Rose takes a moment to reflect before she answers, "For sure it's not this wounding business of the old myths. In fact, that makes me feel rebellious. I'm not playing that game. My activation is beauty, joy, love, harmony, curiosity, and wonder."

"Which of these qualities evokes in you the deepest passion and commitment?" Verdandi asks.

"Wonder. I love to find the hidden treasures of life. To experience the awe and 'wow' of the greater mystery. I love those moments when the veil falls away. The 'ohh,' 'wow,' and 'aha' moments. I'm an explorer who loves the experience of discovery. Routines and predictability bore me. I get really engaged when I feel a sense of wonder."

Verdandi laughs. "Well, my darling, then don't complain anymore that the Universe has hidden and veiled its secret knowledge. Remember Easter Sundays when you were a little girl? You used to bring me your own chocolate Easter eggs so I could hide them for you. You were always fascinated by hidden things. It seems your archetype for getting involved is the magical child. When the magical child becomes wounded, she can lose her sense of wonder and close her heart. That's why most of the adults don't believe in fairy tales anymore."

"That's interesting. Maybe we should create a Cosmic Compass game for humanity so people could discover the Cosmic architecture? We could include all kinds of fun rewards and riddles. Players could have fun discovering their own architect potential and a whole new experience of what morals can be used for. That would be amazing!"

"Great idea. Morals aren't boring commandments to be followed. That's the old religious dogma. We've evolved way past that now. At least I hope so. The discovery of our inner compass as a moral compass can be a journey of wonder. You can think of a moral as in the moral of a story; its deeper teaching. Life is wondrous. In fact, the word 'wonder' in the Dutch, Norse, and Germanic languages means 'miracle.'"

Rose's eyes sparkle like stars as she asks, "So doing the right thing and feeling hugely attracted to the miraculous can link up?"

"Of course, love. For people to do the right, moral thing in this time of greed and distrust is nothing short of a miracle itself. It's precisely from this sense of wonder and the miracle of real change that people would be willing to open their hearts again. We can't open or soften the human heart with dogma and threats. Populist leaders are gaining so much influence in our world because they know how to play on people's desire to see their lives transformed, and to make their countries great again.

"Hitler gained so much influence because he spread the myth of a united nation for the 'Übermensch,' the 'higher, civilized, chosen' people. Work with your archetypal inclination for wonder. Help people to see the real miracles of life."

"I'll do that, Grandma. No wonder religious dogma doesn't inspire people's moral passion for the possible. It doesn't give any space for discovery. If the Universe had given me a lecture on its architecture, I would probably have stopped listening after just a few minutes."

Life as a Cosmic Comedy

Verdandi chuckles. "Now there's a thought. Can't you just see the Universe standing behind a tall, wooden podium, wearing long, dark robes smelling of chalk dust, adjusting its spectacles and giving lectures about the nature of reality...to an empty room?"

Rose laughs. "And if any brave students did try to sit through the lecture, they'd be nudging one another and whispering, 'Why the heck did I sign up for this class when I could've taken a pottery class?'"

"'Or Home Economics? They bake cookies in there!' That would be your grandfather."

The two women laugh.

"Hey, Grandma? One more thing before I go. Does the Universe have a sense of humor? Do animals laugh as well? Do trees experience us as funny creatures, hiding in clothes?"

"That's a funny question in itself, my darling. As you know, I laugh a lot. I find life quite hilarious. There's an old Apache tale that says the Creator made human beings able to do everything: talk, run, look, and hear. He wasn't satisfied, though, until they could do just one more thing: LAUGH. And so, man laughed and laughed and laughed. And the Creator said: 'Now you are fit to live.'"

"What did the Creator do to make them laugh? Show them a giraffe?"

"Hmm. Maybe so."

"We laugh a lot when we're together, don't we? I always have so much fun with you. I love your unique, funny way of seeing the world."

"Comedy and humor are a wonderful spontaneous upwelling of the discovery of the unexpected universe within and without ourselves, and then the cockeyed reinvention of that universe. It's God's job rendered hilarious. Putting together the unlikely and the improbable from the unseen, to create the unusual for the unprepared! This is the manner of creation. This is the stuff of evolution. This is the laughter at the heart of things!"

"I've never thought of it in that way before, but it's so true."

"You'd better believe it. I've seen too many sight gags in nature to believe that some stupendous sense of humor wasn't behind it all. Just watch a sloth climb a tree! Or watch a duck follow a billiard ball as its mama. Watch a volcano burble and giggle and then go into an all-out roar. Pressure on the magma by tectonic plates? Nonsense! Somebody or something just told it a joke!"

Rose laughs again. Grandma Verdandi is on a roll.

"Part of the secret of creativity is learning to look at things in different ways. Children are very good at this, as their minds have not yet hardened into set patterns. Seeing the humor of it all and having a good laugh is the most direct way to access this creativity and shake your mind out of its habitual perspectives."

"Good idea!" Rose makes a mental note that she'll start to look at life with humor, fresh eyes, and from different perspectives.

Navigating for Thrivability with the Cosmic Compass

The next morning Rose stays in bed a little later than usual. She snuggles down into her blankets and listens to the comforting patter of rain against her bedroom window. Her thoughts move to the park. *All of those flowers will get a good drink. And I'm sure the ducks in the pond are having a wonderful time.* To her delight, she and Sophia had seen baby ducks in the pond the last time they'd walked by there.

Rose stretches, steps into her slippers, and heads to the kitchen to make tea. She turns on the television for a moment, then switches it off again when the newscaster begins a negative report on the world economy.

She reflects on the Cosmic architecture of life and how different those growth patterns are from those of our mainstream economic systems. The first law of thermodynamics explains how in the Universe there is never loss, only transformation from one state of information to another. The total amount of energy-matter remains the same, while the cosmological information gets recycled and becomes part of other processes of creation. The Cosmos is like the software for writing the program codes, while the Universe is like the hardware for running the program codes that make it physical.

Rose shifts her mind into architect mode. She ponders how she could apply her discoveries to design a Cosmic Compass game for navigating toward "thrivability." She reflects on the requirements of the game. It needs to:

- Support us to discover the Cosmic architecture of life within ourselves and in the Universe, as the inner coordinates of our own consciousness.
- Create understanding of the necessity for change, both personally and collectively, while providing opportunities for experiencing and co-creating the future possibilities of alternative and thrivable solutions.
- Invoke our moral passion for doing what is right and necessary by guiding us to our own architect power.
- Invoke a sense of wonder and direction that confirms that other ways *are* possible and happening, and how we can be part of this happening.
- Provide practical tools and systems for making a difference and for developing the ways and capacities to realize the future possibilities of our moral passion.
- Make it possible to collaborate as co-architects of the new civilizations, perhaps even through playful challenges in designing the new operating systems. This challenge could even reward the most creative and impactful designs and solutions for thrivability.

Rose loves the word thrivability, instead of sustainability. It gives direction and shows how to point our inner compass to true north, the North Star of our thrivability. She's been exploring the term thrivability for a few years now, which is all about co-creating the conditions and capacities for us to thrive together with our planet. Thrivability provides people with a higher vision of a possible future, whereas sustainability tends to focus on constraints and limits to growth and what not to do.

Thrivability goes further than merely staying within the carrying capacity of our planet, by actively seeking to improve our planetary and social carrying capacities. Improving the carrying capacities of our planet has everything to do with improving the health of our forests, oceans, soil, biodiversity, and climate systems. Our social carrying capacities are also our social *caring* capacities: the foundations for healthy societies and happy people. When our social foundations erode, tensions and conflicts increase and violence can quickly escalate. By pointing our compass toward thrivability, it gives us something to aim for that is inspiring and rewarding.

Rose has been putting her ideas together in a series of designs, to explore how the Cosmic architecture can be applied as a compass.

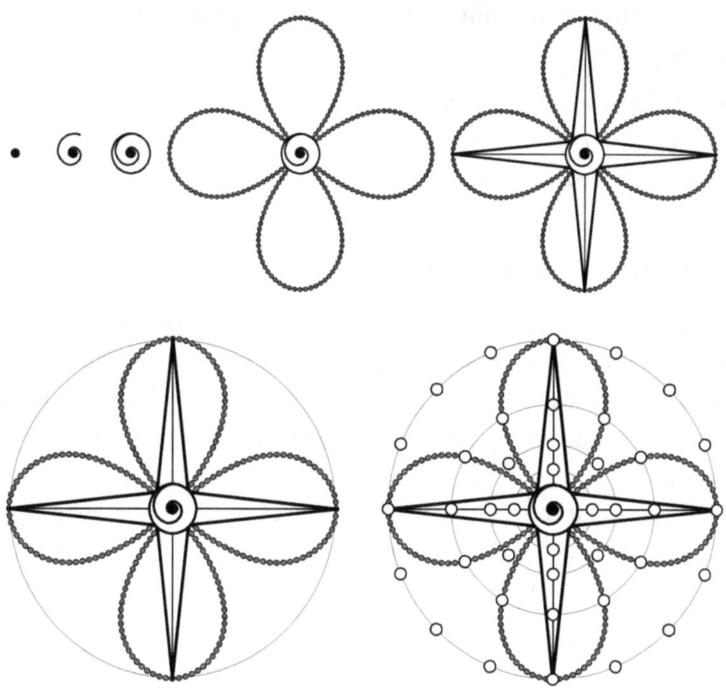

She begins by placing the little black dot in the center of the compass, just like there is a black hole in the center of our galaxy, to represent how life is unified and whole. Emerging from the black dot she draws a spiral to represent how life evolves through change; spiraling outward and inward by expanding and contracting. Around the spiral, she draws a circle to represent how life actualizes consciousness through autonomy, balance, and boundaries. The dot, spiral, and circle form a trinity that represent the three laws or evolutionary principles of life.

Rose then draws the butterfly pattern of transformation as two converging infinity loops. She continues by drawing the arms of the compass rose as three lines that extend the central trinity into the four cardinal directions—east, south, west, and north—and converge into the furthest points of the infinity loops.

She then draws four concentric circles around the compass rose, each with specific sets of coordinates that represent the various patterns and stages of our future becoming. The five wisdom coordinates are represented on the first concentric circle, with the central black dot representing the all-pervading wisdom. On the second concentric circle she becomes aware of eight coordinates. She imagines how these coordinates look like four moons and four suns, to guide her values for her inner and outer development.

She's looking forward to exploring what each of these coordinates and concentric circles represent, yet she can sense this will be for a later stage on her journey of discovery.

Designing the Cosmic Compass Game with Olaf

Rose has a ten-year-old nephew named Olaf, who's the son of her older brother Lucas. Olaf loves building game codes with his Roblox programs, especially to create scary landscapes and creative architecture for fortresses and underwater mansions. Rose decides to give him a call to see if he has some further game design ideas that can help her. She's curious to find out what he thinks about the concept of a "moral compass" and the whole notion of morals for guiding what we do and how we behave. She accesses Olaf's number on her cell phone.

"Hi, Olaf. It's your Aunt Rose."

"Hi, Auntie."

"I was wondering about something. Have you ever heard about a moral compass or the moral code of a game?" Rose asks.

Olaf is half looking at her and half looking at other things on his screen. He's an active boy, always combining multiple activities at once.

"You mean like those fables of La Fontaine or Aesop where there's a moral of a story? Like the one with the tortoise and the hare, where the hare races ahead and tries to cheat, but the slow tortoise wins anyway?"

Rose smiles. "Yes, something like that. What was the moral of that story for you?"

"That even if you're slow, don't give up. That's a good story. I've been there before. Is that what you mean by a moral compass?"

"You know what a compass is, right?"

"It's that instrument that points you to the coordinates of north, east, south, and west?"

"Yes. Now imagine that this instrument, instead of pointing north, guides you toward kindness. Instead of pointing east, it guides you toward friendship, and so forth."

"Okay, I get it," Olaf replies. "So what is it you want to know?"

"If you were to design a game with this kind of moral compass in the code, how would you do it? How would you design for kindness and all the other qualities that you feel are important to play for, like fairness, friendship, and collaboration?"

Olaf's imagination lights up as he projects himself into the game. "Well, I'd start by giving people short reminders. Like…'Never give up.' 'Even if you've done something wrong, just try again!' 'Don't take your anger out on people.' 'Don't go from putting blocks down to trying to make a rocket fly when you're just getting started; go from easy coding to advanced. If you get frustrated, just slow down. Take a step back. Learn how to do one thing before moving on to the next thing.'"

"That's great, Olaf! Those are really good ideas. So how about fairness? How would you code for that?"

Olaf's cheeks turn pink and his eyes twinkle as he dives further into the possibilities of the game. "I wouldn't allow people to kill each other. I'd design a game with no violence or harm. And I'd make sure people can't steal. They could only trade elements of the game."

"How about kindness and collaboration?"

"Let me think for a second...Okay, say there's money in the game. You could get a little bit of money whenever you help other players and you're nice to people. Or, instead of money, you could get parts in the game that are rare."

"How would you deal with people who are nasty in the game?" Rose asks.

"Players who are nasty don't get any rewards," Olaf answers. "But they'd get a warning to teach them. They'd get one chance to change how they play. If they don't change, then they'd get a penalty or a game restriction."

"Smart strategy. You have so many wonderful ideas. How about friendship? How would you guide people in that direction?"

"Okay, if you're nice to people, you could get a certain achievement. You don't need to be rewarded for sharing, but it'd be nice to get something. But even if the person is not kind to you, you should still be kind yourself and give the person another chance. That way it's easier to become friends." Olaf smiles.

"How would you feel to discover your moral compass like that?" Rose asks.

"I'd feel good. I think it feels good to help others discover theirs, too," Olaf answers quickly. "It's been nice talking with you, Aunt Rose, but I'm going to take my dog out. You know how he gets if he doesn't have enough exercise."

"I do. Alright, have fun. Thanks for sharing your awesome ideas with me."

"You're welcome. Bye."

Rose disconnects the call, pleased that she thought to contact her nephew. She genuinely enjoyed hearing his clever proposals. She realizes that designing a game guide is natural for Olaf. He already thinks as a coder by looking for choice options, game incentives, boundaries, feedback loops, and rewards. Rose feels hopeful that the younger generations may actually find far more creative ways to resolve many of our global issues, without the emotional baggage and hidden agendas of so many adults.

Integration - The Key of Trinity

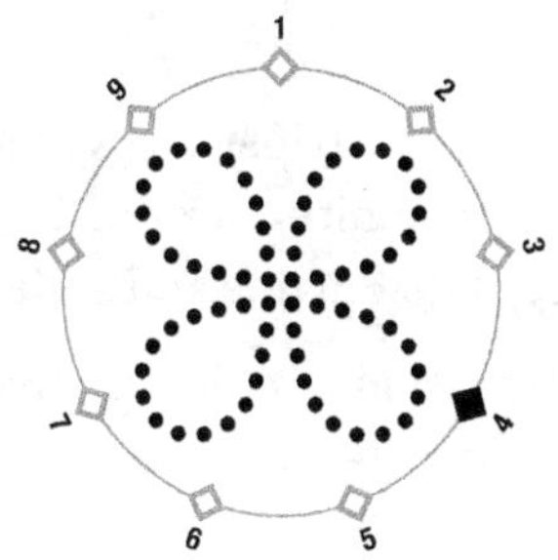

What does it mean for you to live your life as a Cosmic architect? Are you in touch with your inner compass? Just like Rose explored the coordinates of her inner compass, you can too. These coordinates are universal and uniquely tuned to guide our actualization. Through this chapter we've explored the Key of Trinity for navigating from wholeness and unity.

> *The Key of Trinity helps you to experience life as a unified reality and see through the appearances of duality. This key also helps you to navigate with the unity coordinates of your inner wisdom and discover the directions and choices that help you to grow, develop, and thrive.*

The summary below will help you to integrate these discoveries further:

- Connect with the Cosmic Compass as your inner compass of wisdom. Ask it to activate within you and invite the five essential wisdoms to guide your choices and directions. Remember how this Cosmic Compass is part of the Cosmic architecture of life; consciousness is also a guidance system for navigating the waves and winds of change.
- Consult your Cosmic Compass for guiding the directions of your destiny path. Get to know your inner compass by spending a few minutes each day to discover how these coordinates and navigational capacities live in you. Explore the inner and outer values, like the inner

moons and outer *suns* on the compass, to help you grow, develop, and thrive.

- Explore what it means to live your life as a Cosmic architect, to co-create the realities, worlds, and experiences with the Cosmic architecture of life as a creative partner of the Universe and the wisdom of life.
- The ancient North Star is a triple star system. Navigate with the Key of Trinity to discover the unity coordinates of your inner wisdom and avoid the duality traps that divide and stifle our growth.
- Evoke your moral passion for doing what is right and necessary through a sense of wonder and discovery, rather than judgment, fear, and guilt.
- Life is a Cosmic comedy. The secret of creativity is learning to look at things in different ways. Seeing the humor of it all, and having a good laugh, is the most direct way for accessing your creative genius.
- There is no loss in the Universe. There is only transformation from one state of information to another. Knowing this, what state of information is your life in? Is it dualistic or unified?
- Live your life as a Cosmic quest; a game of life for discovering the hidden keys, codes, and treasures.
- Remember how doing the right thing and feeling hugely attracted to the miraculous can link up. Explore your activation points; what triggers, activates, and awakens your future potentials and transformative capacities?

CHAPTER 5

Becoming the Required Humans

Exploring the Evolutionary Tensions with the Key of Paradox

In the weeks that follow, Rose spends a few minutes every day with her inner compass to explore the inner coordinates of her wisdom and the unity coordinates of her visions. Spending time with her inner compass helps her to gain clarity and balance, especially while she's still integrating so many changes. She's enjoying her inner compass as an essential architect tool, just like the Cosmic architecture is an architect tool of consciousness. Rose is well aware that the Cosmos is guiding her toward the discovery of all of these architect keys and tools and she's curious to explore how she can apply this in her everyday life.

Her first exploration is about trust. She's been asking herself if she can trust herself with the enormous tasks ahead. Especially now when a step-by-step approach may no longer work, as we literally have to build the new roads while the old ones are collapsing. *Can we count on ourselves? Are we trustworthy? Can the future count on us to become the required people for making the hard choices to save our planet? Are we willing to stop the economics of harm and invest in new regenerative solutions? Are we willing to stop growing inequalities in our world?* All these questions and more have been circling around in Rose's mind.

She notices how the butterfly potentials of our new era are awakening in people around the world. She sees this in the creative new ideas, the call for new stories, the call for collaboration, and the growing use of the words "imaginal cells" by those who feel they already belong to the future era.

Rose also actively looks for her partners and allies in this quest, as she wants to help the linking up of the imaginal cells to form the imaginal organs of the butterfly body. She's concerned, however, that we're not developing our collective future human capacities quickly enough to avoid wide-scale collapse of our most vital life support systems, including our climate systems. She knows that worry doesn't change anything, and neither does fear, so she works to keep her focus positive and uplifting.

Together with her friends, Rose explores how she can contribute her time, talents, and skills to the new initiatives that are emerging, including those that are creating the new financial, governance, and accounting systems by mimicking the economic architecture of life. She has some concern that the politics of greed and deception are hardening and increasing, making it more difficult to get the right information and solutions to the people who need it the most during this critical time. She decides it's time to explore some of these deeper moral questions with her grandmother.

Caring for Our Choices

Verdandi answers the phone. She's out of breath and laughing.

"Hello, darling girl! I wish you were here in my living room right now. Your grandfather is teaching me a dance from ancient Greece that he saw on the internet. It's so much fun, but then the dogs want to get in on the act with their barking and wiggling. It makes it harder to do the movements, but their enthusiasm makes it feel more like a celebration, if that makes sense."

"I'm picturing it right now."

"Oh, look at this. Merlin thinks he can get away with jumping on the couch now that I've been distracted by your phone call. Hold on."

Rose hears her grandmother talking to the dog as she scoots him off the couch. Verdandi returns to the phone.

"Little scamp," she says. "He'll take advantage of every opportunity. Now what's on your mind, dear girl?"

"I miss you so much!"

"I miss you, too. Every day."

Rose pours out her thoughts and feelings to her beloved grandmother. Verdandi listens to every word.

"Rosie, remember your future human choice in the hospital when you moved across the veil? Look deeply into the heart of that choice for a moment. Now tell me, was this choice merely about your life and seeking a new direction? Or was it more fundamental about the world you choose to be a part of?"

"It was a fundamental choice. Once I experienced that our universe is a single, unified, and living being with so many parts that all work together, I realized then that our world is like that as well. She's a sentient being; a Cosmic being whose soul has been forgotten by many. The destruction of our natural world has escalated ever since we took the soul out of nature and decided to treat nature merely as a collection of resources for our material consumption.

"Once I returned to the Cosmic Tree, I experienced that the future possibility of our world also carries my future possibilities, and vice versa. We literally carry each other. When I made my choice as a future human, this also connected me with the future possibility of our world as part of the same order of reality. The world of my choice is a sentient and caring world, and I'm determined to keep reminding our world that this is its true nature, as it is ours."

"Excellent. Now realize that choices are like living beings. Through your love and care, you keep them alive. It can take a whole lifetime to live into the fundamental choices of your heart. Gandhi's choice of nonviolent resistance is something he lived into and acted upon every single day. He also said, 'The future depends on what you do today.' Many people believe a choice is made only once. They expect the Universe to somehow take care of whatever comes next. But choices don't miraculously take all of our problems away. Choices create consequences, and we don't always know the outcomes of our choices until much later."

"Yes, I'm still catching up with my own ripple effect. Sometimes we seem to move into the dark side and it seems easier to choose to be *against* something or someone, rather than standing *for* the change we want. When we choose 'against,' we don't have to take responsibility for building the world we want. That's probably why extremist opposition parties make such bad leaders when given the chance to govern.

"Greta Thunberg was hugely successful in mobilizing the youth to take a stand against the old capitalist change. But will she be as successful inspiring people to build a greener and more just world? I don't know. I hope so."

"I hope so, too. I admire that young woman. She's got spunk. And so do you! Rose, do you remember how in the old hero narratives people would lean back while others fought the battles? We can't afford to do that any longer. Each of us is being called to become the hero or heroine of our own stories. It's time to take on the greater challenge of our self-transformation in the midst of world transformation."

"I agree. And many people are doing exactly that. There are so many unseen heroes and heroines in our world. Look at the brave nurses and doctors who risked their lives to take care of mine in the hospital. How do we celebrate and acknowledge these incredible people? Their simple yet profound choice is to be available to life every day with an open heart. Defeating the forces of cynicism, bitterness, and blame, by focusing on love rather than hatred, is heroic in itself."

Exploring the Moral Choices of Our Time

Verdandi agrees. Something in her granddaughter's tone makes her think that there might be more behind this phone call. "Has anything happened recently to bring all of this up to the surface, Rose?"

"Yes." Rose pauses. "There's this guy, Greg, who was a fellow student of mine at the university. I bumped into him yesterday and he was really upset. He said, 'Rose, our world is running out of time! We need to mobilize the grassroot movements, and I really can't see how your rebirth story is going to mobilize them.'"

"Ah."

"I feel like just because my choice wasn't a political choice, he didn't even recognize it."

"Hold on, Rose, that's not true. Your choice *is* a political choice. You elected yourself to become the required human of this time. That's the ultimate political choice. It's a direct application of your sovereignty and your right of self-determination," Verdandi replies.

"Oh. I never really thought about it that way. How can people exercise that right if they don't know how to change their reality? When you read Article 1 of the International Covenant on Civil and Political Rights it says that: 'All peoples have the right of self-determination. By virtue of that right they freely determine their political status and freely pursue their economic, social, and cultural development.' What does that freedom mean in societies that believe in human superiority over nature by fundamentally ignoring our world as a living being? Is our planet free to pursue its form of development? Are the cows we slaughter by the millions ever free to pursue their development? Are we the only species who've granted ourselves these rights? This covenant doesn't protect the living systems on which our lives depend. Our natural world includes close to nine million species, many of which we don't even know. We are *one* species out of nine million, and yet we determine the fate for most of the others. There's something seriously wrong with this story."

Verdandi takes a deep breath and replies, "These are the moral questions of our time. Now you know why we need a moral compass that is based on life. Close your eyes and recall your dream of the Cosmic Compass. Now ask your inner compass to take a shape that you can hold in your hands. It's not an abstraction or an intellectual exercise. It's as real as anything you know. Feel the weight of this compass. Feel its texture, as well as its love and the living pulse of life that is within the compass. Can you feel it?"

"Yes. It has weight and energy. It's truly a living reality, like I experienced in my dream."

"Good. Now ask it to show you the moral choices of our time, and the moral leadership that future humans are to take for this. Feel how the compass is made from the moral fibers of love itself. It's designed to guide us through the darkest of times. Ask it to activate the coordinates of the new mythos within you so you'll know how to navigate for true north."

Rose listens to her grandmother's voice and feels her inner compass activating, directing her intention and attention toward the wisdom of life. Her consciousness shifts to the higher modes of perception, enhancing her ability to think connectively, and from an inner state of abundance, with greater compassion and empathy.

"Hey! I just noticed something!" Rose exclaims.

"What?"

"My inner compass can attune to different times. It's amazing. It's like it knows the optimum choices for each time to realize our evolutionary potentials. It's showing me how complex our world has become, and how simplistic approaches and superficial responses can cause a lot of harm. The moral choices of our time are urging us to understand the practical consequences of our interdependence. We're called to deepen our capacity to simultaneously care for ourselves, each other, our planet, and our future; to stop indulging in these cravings of always wanting more and more. We must rethink our entire notion of what it means to be human, and what materiality is about; to put sentience in the center of our decision making and remember how rights come with responsibilities. It's time to realize the moral process for our choices and how to compassionately act on our choices."

"Keep going, Rose. What are some of the key choices that your inner compass is revealing to you?"

"Oh wow, how can I express this? What's coming now is a full comprehensive knowing with potent feelings that flow with life. I see and feel new ways to live within the carrying capacity of our planet, and in such a way that nobody goes without. The rights of nature and future generations are included in our legal frameworks. We've stopped financing war and violence. Our corrupt, immoral financial systems have been revealed and transformed. There are no longer currencies of harm."

"So we're prioritizing what is truly important?"

"Absolutely. We work together to build better models that do not disenfranchise so many people. We consider that with the right of life also comes the right of death." Rose pauses. "Oh…wait a minute. I feel like thunder is moving through my nervous system."

"What is it?"

"We're to consider the long term, powerful effects of the genetic changes that we're introducing to all levels of life. We must counteract the negative impact of the modifications made to our food. We're to heal our morally broken family systems and the war between the generations. There's so much! Most of all, what I'm seeing is that making moral choices requires a commitment to a moral process through which we discover what are not just the required changes, but also the appropriate actions."

"Rose, I'm impressed. Your thinking is starting to include new elements that I've never heard in your thought process before. Can you say more about this moral process?"

"Yes, it's about understanding how moral decisions or considerations cannot be imposed on others. That's domination. It has to emerge from an inclusive process. People consulting and sharing together; learning to reveal the larger perspectives of life that include and concern us all. It's a process that can't be rushed. It needs to be evaluated and checked at every step of the way with the possibility of refining, fine-tuning, and sometimes even changing entirely decisions made earlier. Especially if we learn that what appeared initially to be a good choice later turns out to cause harm or pain.

"A moral process is about the commitment for how we make and implement the moral choices. It's about our state of consciousness. A coherent moral process can also shift our consciousness to the higher states that are required for making the higher choices of consciousness to access our future potentials."

"Rose, you've just realized another foundational step in that a moral process can also enter you into the required consciousness state; one that can access the future possibilities of our greater destiny. This is again an architectural process. A moral process can be designed from the principles and qualities of the Cosmic architecture of life. This moral process is a major key, and also applies to how you choose to progress in life. You're now working your inner compass! Keep going. As you know, the moral issues of our time are complex and paradoxical. People generally don't like paradoxes."

Paradox as Evolutionary Tension

Rose's entire body is still tingling from the last exercise. "Why do people find it so hard to accept a paradox?" she asks.

Verdandi sighs, "People's minds tend to be lazy. They prefer to fall back on their earlier and easier ways of thinking. People don't like tensions and ambiguities. A paradox often appears as two seemingly opposite or contradictory truths. Evolving to new and higher grounds of awareness can be uncomfortable. Unfortunately, many seek clarity and resolution in duality: right versus wrong; good versus evil; me versus you. They don't seek integration."

"Aha. The trinity is at work once again, eh? So a paradox is really a trinity disguised as a duality."

"Yes."

"It's the dual phenomena of our physical world, like day or night and left or right are united in the quantum superposition state. Like those qubits or quantum bits that are the basic units of quantum information that I learned about. We can't see unity directly. It's much easier to see duality as 'this and not that.' However, we can experience unity to realize that dual forces are never separate. What looks like two in appearance is really three if you include the unity point out of which the appearance of duality emerges. It's all happening within the same wholeness, no matter how diverse things become."

Verdandi smiles, "You sound very passionate about this."

"I am."

"It may be easy for your mind to understand, yet there's a more fundamental lesson of the heart that I'd like to share with you, Rose."

"Please do. I'm open to learning as much as I can."

"When you work through a paradox, you do not immediately go toward your superposition of states. This erases the creative tension before a deeper understanding can emerge. Removing tensions or contradictions too quickly can cause more harm. Watch out for statements such as 'Okay, you're right. I was wrong. Let's forget it ever happened. We'll never agree, so let's just agree to disagree.'

"A paradox offers the opportunity to work with the dialectic triad, which philosophers have also described as thesis, antithesis, and synthesis," Verdandi continues. "The great philosophers Hegel and Plato used the dialectic process to contrast and play out contradictory ideas against each other in order to create a stream of new ideas. The dialectic triad, although attributed to Hegel, were never his words, however."

"Hmm. So are you saying that we need to work with this dialectic tension and learn to hold it, rather than releasing the tension too quickly?"

"Yes. In order to pierce the veils of separation, one must build up sufficient pressure to propel the mind forward onto new ground. Otherwise, the mind may remain in a dual, lazy state. Creative tension, when engaged properly, can bring us into the stream of revelation that can lead to profound new insights. That's why psychiatrist Carl Jung called the paradox 'one of our most valued spiritual possessions, and the natural medium for expressing transconscious facts.'"

Verdandi continues. "Ultimately, a paradox also has its source in humor. A great joke often brings widely dissimilar ideas and puts them together, which makes us laugh. Like the old joke where Bernie's in bed and his mother comes in to wake him. 'Bernie, wake up! You gotta go to school!' says his mother. 'I don't wanna go to school!" Bernie protests. 'You gotta go to school, Bernie,' the mother insists. 'But, why? Kids hate me, teachers can't stand me. I don't want to go. So why do I have to?' Bernie moans. 'Because you're fifty-three years old and you're the school principal!'"

Rose laughs with her grandmother. She pauses for a moment and adds, "Isn't it ironic how the power of death gave me new life? I didn't enjoy the creative tension of my relationship with Tim. He was always undermining my self-confidence. I stopped my relationship with him because I couldn't stand the tension any longer."

"Did you talk with Sophia?"

"Yes."

"Do you feel that you discovered more of your inner strength by experiencing these tensions with Tim?"

"I suppose so, but I don't want to learn like that ever again," Rose replies.

Verdandi smiles, "It seems that the tension did its job. Now you can change the pattern of your intimate relationships as well as the pattern for how you choose to evolve. To evolve by choice, rather than by default.

"Creative tension serves to awaken you; you're not meant to stay in it. If you do, it becomes unhealthy. Once the new awareness emerges, it will guide you further. If you get trapped or paralyzed in the tension, like what happened in your dream with the python, you can't access your power of choice. Tensions arise when it's time for change, and yet some use tension to avoid change."

"Isn't that in itself a paradox?" Rose asks. "It sounds similar to the role of pain. It can help us become aware of what we need to change in order to avoid more pain."

"Yes, my girl. Learn to embrace all these seeming opposites. Then you'll realize how darkness is not 'other than light,' and men are not 'other than women,' and nature is not 'other than us.' At the level of the unified reality, we're each other in the great unity of being."

"We're all One."

"Precisely."

"Can we apply this same understanding to how we approach morality? So often people use morality as a higher moral ground for judging others."

"That's the ego at work. The ego loves to camp on higher moral ground where it can look down and judge others. Kind of like Loki when he climbs on top of the refrigerator," Verdandi adds with a chuckle.

Love Embraces Moral Complexity

Rose laughs, too. She's always enjoyed the cats and their amusing antics at her grandparents' house. "Okay, so other than Loki, the morality of the inner compass doesn't judge, it merely reveals. Like a compass of love."

"That's it exactly, yes. Love is the only force that can help us to embrace moral complexity. A paradox is like the arms of love, guiding us through the moral complexity that is part of being human.

"There are many paradoxes in our world right now. Becoming aware of the value of our democratic freedoms when they become restricted, for example. Remembering the foundations of our democracies when they come under attack. Realizing the importance of our climate and biodiversity when our health is at risk. Because we've taken so many things for granted, life is now teaching us through opposites.

"Morality doesn't seek to remove the paradox; humans do. Morality asks, 'What does doing the right thing even mean in view of so many diverse views, expectations, and needs? How can we do the right thing by everyone, ourselves included? How can I be in the right relationship with this person or situation?' A self-righteous person doesn't ask those questions."

"Morality can be quite complex it seems, Grandma. Surely, killing someone in revenge or stealing from another person or manipulating people to get what we want is just immoral. If morality becomes so complicated, are people willing to explore the moral foundations for what they're doing?"

"Complexity is not the same as complication, Rose. Complication is what we create by denying the complexity of life. Some issues may indeed appear very straightforward, yet when we look deeper, we may discover things we never considered. Killing another person is immoral, and yet do we know what happened previously in the life of the person who kills someone? Why did they behave in such a way? What's their story? How did society treat this person? When Robin Hood was stealing from the rich to return the money to the poor, was he acting immorally? Is it moral to use the tissues of unborn embryos to create new stem cell treatments for curing cancer? Is it moral to change DNA so that future generations will not suffer from Alzheimer's or Parkinson's disease? Where do we draw the line, and who draws the line? How do we decide how to move or if we should remove the lines we've drawn before?"

Rose takes a moment to let all of this sink in. She feels a little uneasy, perhaps because she realizes that the answers to these questions require patience and can't be rushed.

"Grandma, do we need to develop empathy to embrace all of this moral complexity?"

"Yes, dearest. Empathy is one of the most important muscles of love. Empathy enables the arms of love to reach out to heal our divides. Without empathy, we can't shift the emotions of duality and division."

"Can embracing moral complexity help us to develop our empathy?" Rose asks.

"Yes. These are the medicines for healing our wounded world. That's why our commitment to the moral process is so important for building an inclusive and caring world. The best and truest kind of healing is never about mending or fixing, but creating wholeness and extension. That's precisely what a moral compass should provide the directions for. When you reconcile paradoxes, when you deepen the reality of a person, then real healing and wholeness takes place. The same is true for our society."

Verdandi continues, "Many of us are still leading a crippling life from the realities we've outgrown. We're living through a gigantic breakdown of all systems of knowing, being, having, educating, living, and governing. We're harkening to a breakthrough. Leaders must also become followers now, seeking mutual growth and stimulation. It is within the membrane of our complexity that we discover our common coordinates. Then we can set sail toward true north together.

"Dearest, could you please hold on a minute?" Verdandi turns her attention to Dagaz who says something Rose can't quite hear in the background. "Alright, I'm back. Your grandfather is telling me that he's made a vegetable soup fit for the gods and it would make him very happy if I would stop talking now and go eat dinner with him. I'd better do it. It's not every day he makes soup 'fit for the gods.'"

"That sounds pretty tempting."

"I have an idea. Remember that beautiful journal that your grandfather gave you a few years ago?"

"You mean the one he told me to keep for a special occasion with that amazing cover of a rose inside a cocoon?"

"Yes, that's the one. It's time now. Start using that journal to keep track of these subjects we discuss as well as your own reflections and dreams. Journaling has been a helpful tool for me over the years."

"That's a great suggestion. I kept it safe on the shelf of my special book collections. Tell Grandpa Dagaz I love him and miss him. And give the dogs and cats a pat from me."

"I will. We love you, too. Let's talk again soon."

Rose disconnects the call and looks for her journal, then makes herself a nice, hot bowl of vegetable soup.

Exploring the New Normals

Later that evening, Rose joins a webinar with people from around the world who are interested in exploring the new future "normals" for a world that works for everyone. The webinar facilitator asks, "What are the new patterns, the new narratives of our new story? Apart from the new normal of exploring these questions online via Zoom."

Rose writes down the key words she hears in the conversation: partnership, collaboration, sharing, uncertainty, collapse, tipping point, transformation, imaginal cells, regeneration, global community, mycelial networks, new blueprints, a new Earth, the great convergence, listening, the symbolic coronation of the coronavirus, acceleration of change, increasing uncertainty, solidarity.

She recalls a recent conversation with her dad who warned that the mental and emotional impacts of the coronavirus crisis can bring up many extremes in people. Her dad works as a therapist and is deeply concerned about the growing rate of domestic violence, suicide, self-violence, and conflicts between people. He explained that those who are already introverted may become even more so, and those who are already extroverted may become even more outgoing.

Rose still feels like she's living in a dream where almost overnight, the "possible world" of free travel and unhindered movement has become nearly impossible. *What does it mean to listen for the new patterns of a possible future in a world of growing impossibilities?* she wonders. *How can our Cosmic Compass help us navigate the tensions between hopeful possibilities and seeming impossibilities? What does our right of self-determination and sovereignty mean when our government says it's required to impose restrictions on our physical freedoms in order to save lives and protect the most vulnerable?*

Mitchell, a young man in his twenties from the United States, is also attending the webinar. With a strong voice he says to the group, "I'm a free citizen. It is unconstitutional for the government to restrict where I go and who I visit. First, the government imposes the mandatory wearing of masks, and now vaccinations. How much longer will I be able to choose whether or not I want to be vaccinated if I can't travel anywhere without a vaccine card? As a free citizen, this should be *my* decision, not the government's."

Rose observes that the conversation keeps gravitating more and more toward rights, rather than our mutual responsibilities. She wonders whether to tell the group what she really thinks. *It's so hypocritical how we don't mind being controlled by companies and the media, many of which also control our governments, yet we protest as soon as we're asked to wear a mask or to have to quarantine at home. If we can't resolve this COVID crisis, then how will we ever resolve our climate crisis?*

Rose is just about to raise her voice in the group when Maria opens her microphone, and says, "Mitchell, why is your right of freedom more important to you than preventing harm and death to someone else? Do you also believe it's okay to own a loaded gun and shoot someone in order to defend your rights?"

Maria sounds annoyed with Mitchell, and a little aggressive. She's calling from Argentina and voices what many in the group are feeling, but perhaps not naming as directly. The webinar facilitator is trying to bring the topic back to the new normals and away from the gun debate, but it's too late.

The Key of Paradox

Mitchell unmutes himself and replies angrily, "Look, I keep a gun for my safety. It's my right to protect myself. I don't see how that has anything to do with the stupid virus. Those are two completely different issues that shouldn't be mixed, Maria. Besides, you don't even know me."

Maria continues, "You see, Mitchell, this is how you have it all wrong. It's also our right to be protected from the dangers you cause us. If you keep spreading this virus, you may as well be holding a gun to my head."

Listening to this heated debate between Maria and Mitchell, Rose recalls her talk with Verdandi about the impact of our state of consciousness on others: "Remember, Rose, your state of consciousness influences the state of information that you communicate, whether it spreads duality or unity. Work with the trinity principle, your unity consciousness, to transform the duality traps that lead us nowhere. While in duality mode, people are feeling defensive, threatened, and protective of their perceived differences. As long as they're caught in these emotional beliefs, they're unable to shift their consciousness to more integral perspectives."

Verdandi gave Rose a practice for how to work with duality without getting caught into its traps of "otherness." She explained that the key is to first enter the state of consciousness that is capable of transforming the duality traps, then to become the third way solution. Rose imagines her grandmother's voice in her mind:

> *Connect your mind with the Cosmic field of life that is all around and within you. This field is always whole and unified, sustained by the wisdom of the eternal. Your body is naturally part of this field, as is your mind when it relaxes and lets go. Enter your mind fully into this field. Release it into the great ocean of consciousness. Ask this field of pure consciousness to harmonize and attune your whole mind, thoughts, and feelings, to the patterns of wholeness and unity. The thought waves of your mind now harmonize with the waves of pure consciousness. Any emotions that were tight or twisted, unwind and relax into the feeling wave of wholeness and unity. Any belief systems you may have that are rooted in separation, division, and otherness, release them now to this unifying field. Feel your body and mind relax as your consciousness returns to its primordial resonance with the great Oneness. In this ocean of Oneness, diversity is naturally embraced and loved. See the dual tendencies simply for what they are: consciousness that is tied in a knot, unable to flow with the resonance of our primordial unity. Now hold the resonance patterns for the third way solutions. Focus on mutuality, integration between the polarities, co-learning and understanding, and compassion. Be the resonance of unity in diversity. Be the trinity principle that releases us from the duality traps.*

Rose closes her eyes for a moment while the arguments in the webinar continue to build. It seems the facilitator believes it necessary for all perspectives to be heard and aired, yet Rose wonders if it really needs to be done like that. She takes a deep breath and brings herself into the state of consciousness of the practice that Verdandi gave her. When she can feel the resonance pattern of wholeness through her own inner unity, she unmutes herself and speaks.

Building and Healing Our World Together

"Hello, everyone. My name is Rose and I'm calling from the Netherlands. I came out of the hospital where I received treatment for COVID-19 a little over a month ago. I'm thankful to be alive today. I went through a profound near-death experience that showed me just how precious life is. My cousin was not so fortunate, and he passed on. His body died while he was on the breathing ventilator.

"Mitchell and Maria, I hear you both and understand that all of this uncertainty is scary. It's okay to be scared and to feel unsettled. It's okay to want to find ways to protect ourselves from what we perceive as growing threats to our safety and future. Please don't make each other wrong for it. The solutions we seek are not 'out there.' They begin here with us. If we can't find ways to hear and understand each other, how can we ever make the world safe for others?

"We got into this mess because we didn't invest in becoming people who can heal divisions and find common solutions for everyone. We live on a small blue planet in the middle of a vast universe. We are all we have to get us through these difficult times. We need each other now more than ever. We can't afford to let our fears escalate, because then our world will escalate into violence. Haven't we created enough pain already? Let's work together for the solutions our world needs."

The facilitator replies to Rose with a smile. "Thank you, Rose. Mitchell and Maria, would you like to respond?"

Mitchell unmutes himself and says, "Yeah, I am scared, Rose. I live on a farm and I'm a person of color. The world isn't that safe for us. It's never been safe, really. We've always been blamed for everything that goes wrong. My rights are all I have. My grandparents fought for those rights with their lives. For hundreds of years, we had no rights at all. That's why I don't want the government to restrict my rights now. Because that also restricts their rights. My grandparents are part of me. I'm alive today because they fought for those rights. I'm afraid that if I allow this to happen, then what comes next? Yeah, the virus is a threat. Before that came along, *we* were seen as the threat. If I can't defend myself and protect my rights, then how can I ever become a dad and keep my children safe?"

There is a deep sigh moving through the webinar. Everyone can feel that the energy is shifting and the field is opening up.

Maria unmutes herself and answers, "I'm sorry Mitchell. I had no idea where you were coming from. I just thought you were terribly selfish, only thinking of your own rights, and like those guys who believe in all those conspiracy theories. I never considered that there might be more to it, or how your ancestors had to fight with their lives for those hard-earned rights.

"Being an indigenous woman in Argentina isn't easy either. My aunt who lived in Brazil was murdered a few months ago because she wanted to protect the rainforest. I lost my uncle to COVID-19 because people around him refused to wear a mask. I feel like I constantly have to be on alert if I'm to survive this scary time. I feel like if I don't die from the virus, then it may be from rape, violence, or being excluded from the jobs that help me to earn a living.

"I live with my mom who's not well. She can't earn an income herself because of her health; she just survived cancer, and now this. My dad left us when I was little and I haven't seen him since I was five years old. I have to take care of my mom and myself, but I don't know how and I don't know who I can trust."

A wave of compassion fills Rose's heart. She feels so fortunate with her life conditions, and wishes there was more she could do for Maria. Mitchell replies before she has the chance to speak, "I apologize, Maria. I had no idea where you were coming from. I thought you were attacking me simply because I'm a man and you see me as a threat. I actually categorized you by believing you were categorizing me.

"Is there anything we can do to help you through this? Some friends of mine have a farm in Argentina. If you let me know where you're living, I could give them a call. Let us know if you need extra food for you and your mom, alright?"

Maria replies, "That would be amazing Mitchell! Let's talk about this some more after the Zoom call."

The facilitator steps in, "Thank you, Rose, Maria, and Mitchell. This is a good time for us to explore in smaller Zoom groups what the new normals can become if we help each other. You'll each be moved to a small group where you can share with each other what you need help with and how you can help each other. You'll have 30 minutes."

Becoming the New Story

Rose's small group includes Mitchell. They continue to share their feelings about personal issues, as well as global challenges. Mitchell has relaxed considerably now that he knows he can safely express himself in the group.

Rose offers, "What if this whole coronavirus pandemic is a huge training ground for us to learn to work together on far more urgent issues, like our climate crisis and the healing of our natural world? We only have a couple of years left to avoid untold suffering and harm. How can this crisis help us to become more skillful in addressing our climate crisis? Does it require a whole new narrative about rights and responsibilities?"

"Can you explain what you mean, Rose? Are you saying it's okay for our rights to be reduced in order to fight the climate crisis?" Mitchell asks.

"No, no, our rights are essential. But it's time to expand this to also include the rights of nature, and to consider that rights come with responsibilities. I believe that the Western notion of rights and freedom has become terribly selfish. People are constantly using their rights as a privilege rather than a responsibility to be a good citizen for our Earth, insisting on *my* rights, *my* privilege, *my* opportunity, *my* career, and more *mine, mine.*

"This attitude breeds separation and competition, not collaboration and unity. That outdated narrative is killing us. Corporate agendas are taking full advantage of this story by contrasting the health of the economy as more important than the health of our planet and how we treat one another. All of those talks have become so polarized that we've lost the larger perspective of what really matters here."

"Humanity is screwed up," says Vladimir from Russia. "Maybe the earth would be better off without humans. At least in China they've introduced the death penalty for environmental polluters."

Rose feels the tensions rising again.

Lai from mainland China pipes up to offer her perspective. "That's easy for you to say, Vladimir. You don't live here. I do. They'll put you in jail for harming the environment, but not for using children to work in factories, or drowning girls who are born in the Year of the Tiger."

Rose centers her mind again to the field of unity and breathes the qualities of this field deeply into her mind and body. She starts beaming the resonance of our deeper unity to everyone on the call, even though they have no idea she's doing this. The group becomes silent. People look at each other, not knowing what to say.

After a minute that feels much longer, Mitchell speaks up. "Look at us. We're here from all over the world. What if we were all brought together for a reason? I didn't know any of you before joining this call, and I wasn't sure what to expect. Maybe we can't solve all the problems of the world, but we can decide who we're going to be together. Let's start by learning from each other.

"Vladimir, will you tell us more about the town where you live and how you see your future? Lai, please tell us what it means to be a young woman growing up in China. How do you see your future? Rose, I'm glad you made it through. Please tell us more about your present situation and your thoughts about your future as well."

Feelings of "otherness" fall away as the group members share their stories. A richer understanding of their common humanity emerges within all the participants. Rose shares some of the messages she received from her near-death experience. Mitchell reminds the group that change occurs when we become conscious about what we buy and how we grow and prepare our food.

"What's it like to run an organic farm, Mitchell?" Lai asks him.

"It's a challenge resisting the trend of industrial farming," he explains. "And it's essential that we continue to have the support of local buyers who come every week to buy our fresh vegetables and eggs. If those people don't come, a lot of the food goes to waste.

"I'm concerned about the huge decline of bees, butterflies, and other pollinators. And frogs. Then on the flip side of that, there are other insects, like grasshoppers, that are destroying our crops."

"That sounds really hard. But you keep at it, huh?" Vladimir asks.

"Yeah. It's important. Despite all these challenges, I choose not to spray my crops and land with harmful chemicals. Food is an ecology of life. You can't separate the flower from the bee or the compost from the land."

"Your story is so interesting," Vladimir says. "I never thought about all of that."

Just by sharing their stories with one other, the group agrees to make more time in their lives for the people who need them, including the animals. Each person makes a commitment to call their grandparents and elderly people more often, especially when it's physically not possible to see them. They agree to spend time in nature and learn from the natural world whenever possible. Even smiling at strangers on the street helps to build communities of care.

"And all of this starts right here and now with our little group!" Lai says.

"It's true," Vladimir agrees. "None of these actions require a university degree or money."

"They flow from kindness and our hearts," Rose adds.

"I believe that the ultimate goal is not to save our planet from collapsing," Mitchell says, "but *to be the world* we wish to live in; to be part of a healthy root system through which new life can sprout in ways we may not even realize right now."

"Hey, I like that," Lai laughs, "especially coming from a farmer."

They share their conviction that through consistent love and care, our world will transform, as will each of them. Life renews itself every minute, and so can we, by being part of its renewal, thus creating a renaissance of self and society.

Before going to bed, Rose recalls the key lessons she learned from this webinar experience. She writes in her journal: "The future possibility of a more compassionate world already exists here and now. It's part of the field of life that sustains us. Most of us don't notice because we stay in the old narratives of duality and separation. To bring this future into being, it begins by entering the consciousness of the choice that makes this happen. Then comes the choice to stop participating in the old divisions; the old dualities of either-or, this-that, win-lose, you versus me, us versus them. Then comes the choice to start living into the consciousness state of the future possibility we made a commitment to. We must live it as if it's already happening in the present moment. We make the choice to develop our future capacities together by learning from each other and exploring together who we're required to become. Through this practice as our daily commitment, we become the new story."

Practice for Re-Storying and Repatterning Our Lives

A few days later Mitchell calls Rose to learn more about her, and to take her up on her offer to learn about a practice Rose received from her grandmother for re-storying and repatterning one's life.

"Thanks for calling, Mitchell. My grandmother often says how what's upon us these days is truly mythic. We're not only creating whole new humans, but we're also being called to heal the harm we've caused one another and the planet."

"I agree with her," Mitchell says.

"Our basic human nature is being called to deepen and evolve with life. I'll share the practice she gave me. I hope you like it. Are you at all familiar with imaginal powers?"

"Nope."

"Okay, let me explain a little bit before we begin. The word 'imaginal' isn't the same as imagination, although it can include it. Imaginal consciousness is a creative state of consciousness that includes the Cosmos, meaning that it's not just happening in our minds. It's an actual *realm* of consciousness itself where things are possible and not predetermined. Even the Universe uses this realm to evolve itself. You can also think of the imaginal realm as the realm of our future; the place from where we receive the greater inspirations and visions."

"The imaginal realm is all new to me," Mitchell tells Rose. "I want to ask you more about it, but I don't want to miss out on this practice, so I'll leave my questions for another time, okay?"

"Okay."

"I'm ready! Let's take the plunge!"

"Do you mind if I record the practice so we can both listen to it again later?"

"Go for it."

"I'm going to be reading from what my grandmother gave me," Rose tells him as she pushes the record button.

"Sounds good."

"We're ready to begin. Close your eyes and let yourself be guided by my voice."

Mitchell follows her instructions and settles back into his chair.

"Take a few deep breaths and relax. Allow yourself to become receptive. Suspend and dissolve any disbeliefs you may have about your ability to re-story and repattern your life. Those disbeliefs have no influence here. Release them. Now take a moment to connect with your imaginal powers. Feel your life force flowing through you. Open your mind.

"Your imaginal powers weave the fabric of your dreams, visions, beliefs, and ideas to the greater patterns of life itself. Your imaginal power is so natural that you may not even realize how you use it all the time: when you come up with something new; when you envision your way through a situation or challenge; when you use your intuition; when you connect with the people you love and sense how they are.

"Call upon your imaginal powers now. Call them to activate. Feel the imaginal powers growing stronger within you. You can even imagine this power as a beautiful current of energy that flows through your whole body-mind, which you can now touch and work with.

"You now have direct access to these powers. This immediately enhances your thinking, your intuition, and your sensing abilities. You have now entered the imaginal state of consciousness.

"From this imaginal state of consciousness, become aware of how the Cosmos lives in you as your inner architecture, your creativity, your inner guidance system, and your source connection with life in its totality. The center of the Cosmos is also within your inner center, which is like your inner sanctuary; your inner home.

"Bring your awareness into this inner center and notice how this center is naturally in touch with your entire being. It receives and processes all the signals from your whole self and circulates the Cosmic love and wisdom to all areas; every cell and fiber of your being.

"Your inner center is a very trusted place that is your inner home. When you enter this inner home, you feel so wonderful, safe, known, and supported. It's the home place out of which everything emerges. This inner home also has a story creation room from where new plays, characters, and chapters can be written and rewritten. This story room provides you with direct access to your story powers and helps you to see your life as a great unfolding story which is always in a state of movement and transition. It's an inner place of playful creation, learning, discovery, spinning, whirling, and unfolding of the very stuff of creation.

"Stand in the middle of this great unfolding of your own life. Feel yourself bathing in the incredible Cosmic creativity that is happening naturally and effortlessly. Your creative power is infused now with Cosmic wisdom and potency for making the higher order choices. Feel how your ability to choose, create, weave, and select is greatly enhanced now. You are now suffused in the sheer glory and muchness of this Cosmic creativity. You can also discern the backward and forward patterns of life that evolve your life to a higher place of being.

"See the patterns going forward as you apply your ability to repattern and re-story your life. You now have direct access to these abilities. Your imaginal power is the creative power of the Cosmos by which you evolve your life and the Universe. This state in which you are now is also the state of your future human self. You are now directly in touch with your future human abilities. From this place, you are able to create and seed the new patterns for your life.

"Become aware of your old story and the former choices that formed those story patterns of your life. Form a clear intention to release and dissolve any of the former choices and patterns that no longer serve you. Ask your future consciousness to show you the vast domain of possibilities that is available to you. Begin to engage the possibilities of new choices that fully support your blossoming.

"These new choices can take the form of plans, intentions, and behaviors out of which emerge new patterns for your life to come. Ask the Cosmic architecture of life to now optimize your energy field in support of these new choices and patterns.

"See your life encoded now by these beautiful new choices which are giving you access to whole new possibilities. Feel how your engagement with these new choices is re-storying your life. Begin to sense and consider what the new story patterns of your life will be.

"You may choose a new career or a new art form to learn and explore. You may choose certain skills or activities, or new friendships and relationships that will grant you the full range of wholesome emotional expression. Perhaps there are adventures in store; visits to new lands, meetings with new cultures and peoples that astonish and inspire you, as they bring you more fulfilling experiences, more life, more delight, and more fruitful learning. You may see a new story in which your spiritual life becomes more prominent; one where you discover sources and resources that gift you with beauty, meaning, and purpose.

"Allow these and so much more to arise and emerge, along with the belief that these wonderful changes are not only possible, but probable. Try each possibility out on the screen of your mind and choose those that resonate for you. See them, feel them, and above all, know them as potential realities that can manifest into the physical space-time world where you currently reside.

"Continue to do this until you truly feel the living force of your most optimized reality. And know, too, that the Cosmos is supporting you by adding elements, coincidences, and resources to your vision, as well as the people, ideas, and opportunities to help you realize your new story. This is the interdependent co-arising nature of our universe. The more you use this exercise, the more your new story will grow in you, eventually to the point where what began as an imaginal possibility will become an actualizing probability. Then, as opportunities arise that begin to harmonically fit into and align with your new story patterns, greet these opportunities with gratitude and joy for the gifts they bring.

"This is how you can consciously co-create the conditions for profound changes to happen in yourself, in your life, and in our world. When you're ready, you may complete this practice. Open your eyes. Stretch. Be fully present here and now."

The Power of Our Choice Starts Small

Mitchell opens his eyes wide after Rose finishes reading the practice. "Well, that was interesting!" he says. "It's not every day that I experience a practice that can change my life, read to me by a beautiful, young woman. That in itself is a story-changing experience." He laughs.

"I'm glad you had a positive experience."

"I did. This is mind-blowing stuff, Rose! I had no idea that the Universe is alive like that, or that I can live a far greater story than the one I've been living so far. I've never had this kind of 'behind-the-scenes' perspective. I realize now how much my story has been tied to the story of my parents and grandparents. Stories of betrayal, discrimination, sacrifices, and constant battles. I felt that staying loyal to them meant staying loyal to their stories and taking on their issues. But I think it's time to review all of that. It doesn't really help anyone, including them, if my story is one of suffering and injustice as well."

Rose smiles. She loves how life works, bringing her in touch with people who, like herself, are looking to build a world based on an entirely different narrative. "My grandmother's practices are really powerful."

"You can say that again."

"When I did this practice myself last week, I saw myself as part of an amazing group of people from all over the planet. We were working together in teams to build a new world. I saw the rise of a growing community of innovative pioneers putting the systems in place for creating new regenerative economic and financial systems with whole new currencies. We were creating holistic agriculture combined with food forests, and citizen-led government systems that included indigenous principles and stewards."

"That sounds really cool, Rose. My kind of people."

"There was so much more. You know, Mitchell, I don't think it's a coincidence that I met you this week during the webinar. I'd love to hear about things that come up for you this week. Let's talk again soon, okay?"

"Sure."

Rose ends the call and marvels at how her inner compass is guiding her toward the right allies and new experiences that'll help her grow more fully into who she wants to become. She appreciates how real change starts small, by living intentionally through daily interactions. *We can change our stories simply by deciding what and who to make time for, and how to show up!*

The next day, Rose calls her grandmother to tell her about her wonderful call with Mitchell and the people on the webinar.

"That's wonderful, my girl. You're discovering what it means to become the required human for this time, and how the greatest power is in your heart. It's your power to love and care and show up. Was there anything else you wanted to share? I was just about to give the dogs a bath."

"Yes, one more thing, Grandma. I really want to be an inspiration for all these smaller changes in our world; changes that might remain unnoticed, and may even seem insignificant until we reach a tipping point. Sometimes I push away my own feelings of vulnerability and uncertainty with all that's going on around the planet. Rather than letting myself *feel* those emotions and acknowledge what's going on, I have a tendency to focus on the really big goals, like 'saving the world.' That focus gives me a rush of courage, but it's not the real courage that's required. I realize that now. It's far more courageous to admit there are times I feel scared, like the night in the hospital when I almost died."

"You are one smart cookie. Have I ever told you that?"

"Yes."

"Well, you are. Wish me luck with the pack. They're okay with a bath as long as there are plenty of treats afterward." Verdandi laughs. "Talk with you soon, Rosie."

Integration - The Key of Paradox

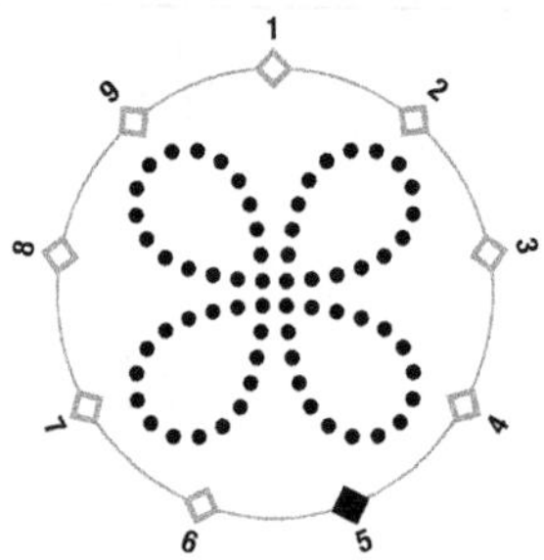

Through this chapter we've explored how future humans can work with the moral complexity of our time through the Key of Paradox, which helps you to work with the evolutionary tensions for becoming the new story.

> *The Key of Paradox helps you to embrace the evolutionary tensions of the moral complexity of life, and transform the duality traps, by discovering the third way.*

The summary below will help you to integrate these discoveries further:

- Unity creates diversity. The belief in duality and separateness creates differentness and otherness.
- Choices are like living beings. You need to keep them alive through your love and care.
- Put sentience in the center of your decision making and remember that rights come with responsibilities.
- Moral decisions or considerations cannot be imposed. They have to emerge from a consultative process that is inclusive, transformative, and evolutionary by revealing the larger perspectives of life that include and concern us all.
- A moral process can shift your consciousness to the higher states of consciousness that are required for accessing the higher choices of your future potentials.

- A moral process can be designed from the principles and qualities of the Cosmic architecture of life.
- You cannot arrive at unity from viewpoints of opposites. The dialectic tension is part of the creative and transformative process of life itself. When you embrace a paradox, you learn to embrace that evolutionary tension.
- Creative tension serves to awaken; you are not meant to stay in it. If you do, it becomes unhealthy. Once the new awareness emerges, it will guide you further. Tensions arise when it is time for change, and yet some use tension categorically to avoid change.
- A paradox is a trinity disguised as a duality that holds the evolutionary tension for our consciousness to evolve further. It guides us through the moral complexity that is part of being human.
- Complication is what we create by denying the complexity of life.
- The best and truest kind of healing is never about mending or fixing, but creating wholeness and extension by reconciling the paradoxes. That's precisely what a moral compass should provide the directions for.
- Work with the trinity principle, your unity consciousness, to transform the duality traps that lead us nowhere. While in duality mode, people are feeling defensive, threatened, and protective of their perceived "differentness."
- Real change starts small, by living intentionally through the daily interactions of our lives. The ultimate goal is not to save our world from collapsing, but to be the world we wish to live in.
- Through consistent love and care, our world will transform, as will each of us.
- Life renews itself every minute, and so can you by being part of its renewal.

CHAPTER 6

Entering the Underworld

Exploring the Unconscious with the Key of Darkness

Ever since her near-death experience, Rose has been going through many inner changes. Some of those changes are starting to attract whole new experiences and people into her life, like her recent webinar and her new friendships with Maria and Mitchell. Rose has been reflecting on Verdandi's last message about learning how to embrace the evolutionary tensions, rather than avoid them by either escaping into dualism or else shifting to an artificial unity.

Rose finds it difficult to remain present in her body when she feels tension. She doesn't yet know how to embrace all these different types of tension. She has a tendency to depersonalize the tensions she feels within her body and other people by addressing it as an intellectual challenge. She's often reminded by her father that although she's advancing mentally, she shouldn't underestimate the importance of her emotional development. She needs to make space and time for the feelings, including the uncomfortable fears, uncertainties, and insecurities.

Befriending the Darkness

Rose is curious to learn more about the deeper psychic structures that her grandmother so often refers to as mythic and archetypal structures. She read that the Swiss psychiatrist, Carl Jung, referred to this as the "collective unconscious," which consists of the universal archetypal structures of our human psyche. Verdandi explained to her that the collective unconscious speaks to us mythically through a symbolic language that includes primordial images.

Rose has been paying closer attention to her dreams, and in particular any symbols or animals. She keeps her journal on the nightstand beside her bed and jots down her dreams as soon as she wakes up in the morning in order to become more conscious of this symbolic, mythic language. She would love to learn how to speak directly with the archetypes, like Athena, and the Cosmic Serpent and Dragon, as her grandmother does so naturally.

Verdandi also explained to Rose that archetypes are part of the great Cosmic mind; mythical structures that may even belong to ancient and far more evolved civilizations than our own. Verdandi suggested that perhaps some of these archetypes could even belong to future civilizations of parallel universes that can help our troubled world. Knowing now that archetypes can help us access higher orders of reality and new connective patterns for accelerating our evolution, Rose is eager to explore this more deeply.

"Grandma, I often feel like I have a direct line with the archetypes of future civilizations as if I'm a future ancestor. They show me maps and designs that I'm still learning to decode, day by day. I have a sense that they're also behind my recent discovery of the Cosmic Compass. How does this relate to the collective unconscious? Is that their natural domain of being?"

"Yes, Rosie, the collective unconscious is archetypal. When we enter the collective unconscious, we enter the archetypal realm of consciousness. This is what enables you to speak directly with the Cosmos. Its archetypes are within your inner archetypes, and vice versa. In many ways, the collective unconscious is the most direct, and even purest, form of communication with the larger realities of being because it's free from our mental interpretations and projections. You could compare this to receiving information that's much closer to Source Point, compared to the information that's been filtered by the outer and denser layers of our minds. Remember that the word 'unconscious' doesn't mean you are not conscious. It's merely unconscious for the grosser layers of mind, not the deeper dimensions of being."

"Why does the unconscious help us to embrace the darkness?"

"Aha, so it's the darkness you're after, hmm?" Verdandi smiles. "There are several aspects to the darkness. The darkness can represent what is veiled and invisible for the grosser layers of mind. The subtle layers of consciousness often appear veiled, yet they are very real and exist, irrespective of whether or not our grosser mind is conscious of this. These subtle layers have their own language and laws. Our ordinary mind may perceive what's behind the veil as dark because it's not yet conscious of itself in that way. Darkness doesn't mean evil or bad, although evil has long tried to convince us that it hides where we can't see it. But look at Hitler. He killed millions of Jewish people with his highly organized army and allies, and all of that took place in clear daylight, visible for all to see."

"Does that mean that by entering the darkness we can become conscious of some of the hidden secrets of life?" Rose wonders aloud. "In many of the mystical and spiritual teachings, a person has to spend some time in solitude in a cave or dark place to become aware of their inner light."

"If only people would realize the true power of the sacred darkness, it would make us far more receptive to the most powerful and existential knowledge of our universe!" Verdandi exclaims. "The darkness also provides powerful medicine for self-healing and inner regeneration. A few minutes spent in the arms of darkness per day will reduce a lot of stress. It can help the body and mind to profoundly heal and reset itself.

"When our mind rests in darkness," she continues, "we become harmonically attuned to our inner pulse and the essence of our being. Helping people to trust the sacred darkness is incredibly important right now. Many people are suffering from depression because they feel like there's no future; no certainty or direction in their lives. Depression can feel like you're being swallowed by an enormous black hole. Darkness can feel frightening, especially when we can't see what's beyond it. That's why you often hear me speak of the 'sacred darkness,' which is the darkness of the womb space that supports the person to grow safely in times of great change and uncertainty."

"That's why I love the darkness so much, Grandma."

"I know you do."

Verdandi taught Rose from an early age that the darkness is a magical place where the greater mysteries open up. She used to take Rose for evening walks in the forest to help her to learn to trust her body's sense of direction. Through these experiences, Rose learned that she's safe in the darkness of uncertainty. She also discovered how within the darkness there lives an invisible force of tremendous caring that holds and protects her when she feels lost or afraid.

"Yes, my girl, you've learned to trust the darkness from an early age. Now your intuition naturally activates that way. You used to love treasure hunts in the dark. Remember that?"

"I do."

"This has now become your treasure hunt for the hidden knowledge in the darkness of the unknowable Universe."

"You're right." Rose smiles. "Those treasure hunts were so much fun. My recent near-death experience took me deep into the darkness of the Cosmos. I no longer feel afraid to die, although I hope I can stay here long enough to finish what I want to do with my life."

"Take your time, love. It may feel like everything is accelerating now, but you do have the time you need. That brings us to another aspect of the darkness, namely shadow and ego. Although darkness has often been blamed for being the domain of shadows, it actually helps us to reveal the shadow tendencies of our egos. Embracing the darkness within teaches us about the importance of self-honesty and self-knowledge. By connecting with our inner darkness, we become aware of our ego projections, which surface when we deny or suppress aspects of ourselves or lives. The shadow can masterfully cloak itself in darkness, masking what you don't want to see or feel. You create shadow realities when you engage in duality or division. The more you grow in self awareness, the less you hide behind shadow dynamics or games. Shadows have no power on their own. We empower shadows by feeding them with our own rejections, projections, manipulations, and illusions. Connect with your shadow to heal the places of the inner wounding and the roots of your fears and projections."

Rose takes a deep breath. "There's so much to learn and discover. I wonder if I'll ever become self aware like you are. I don't always know when I've slipped into my shadow, or how to stop myself from going unconscious. If I find this challenging, imagine how it is for other people. They never received the kind of love and care that I did from all of you. Can we ever hope for a more enlightened humanity?" Rose pauses. "Hey, do countries and cultures have shadows?"

"Of course. Everything that applies to you, also applies to the larger collectives. There are even archetypal shadows, which we can see in destructive cultures. Don't get discouraged, though. I know it can seem like becoming more aware is an endless process, especially when there's so much at stake. Keep working from the possible future that you experienced in your visions, no matter how grim things may look right now."

"But Grandma, how can we befriend the darkness and unmask our shadows when it feels so uncomfortable?"

"Presence and laughter, Rosebud. Be as fully and completely present as you can. Don't take yourself too seriously. Genuine laughter frees all of our anxieties and unmasks the shadow naturally. When you force your inner growth, it may unwillingly feed the shadow. Grow the qualities that are healthy by expanding your authentic self into the areas where you feel unsure or wounded. Where you plant a healthy tree, weeds can't grow on that same spot. Live in the space where you are. Be that space. Be the universe that you are. Inhabit yourself so that others don't put up a tent inside your inner dome. Work with your feelings and thoughts, even the strong emotions, and realize that you are not your thoughts and feelings. You are what *creates* thoughts and feelings. Don't let them control you. Know yourself deeper than what is happening on the surface of your mind."

Descending under the Surface

Rose thinks about this. "Does befriending our inner darkness also help us to work with the evolutionary tensions and our growing pains?"

"Yes, because deep growth happens in the darkness. Just like carrots and potatoes grow in the darkness of the soil, we grow in the darkness of the womb of life. Throughout the ages, the feminine has been associated with darkness. When men came to fear their own inner darkness, women got blamed for luring men into unconscious, animalistic behaviors. This is a clear example of the operation of shadow! This is what happens when people deny, and then project, their own desires.

"Women have their own shadow games as well, of course," Verdandi continues. "The key is to embrace the evolutionary tensions that come with the growing pains, Rose. Grow your love and self-care and extend that to your growing pains. It's the only way to avoid escaping into dualisms or getting trapped into all kinds of harmful projections. When you reject parts or behaviors of yourself, you start to live in an artificial lightness. Here's a paradox for you: The path to higher consciousness leads via the descent into the unconscious. Reflect on that. Call me back after you've had an actual experience of what this means."

Rose, being the determined young person that she is, decides to experiment with this immediately after her call with her grandmother. She wants to discover how far she can descend into her own unconscious. She closes her eyes to meditate, connects with her imaginal powers, and holds the intention to enter her unconscious.

Initially, she feels like nothing much is happening. She tries again. This time she feels very sleepy; so sleepy that she can't remember whether she's managed to descend at all. She tries again, but her mind gets restless and distracted, as if something is pushing her upward instead of downward. Puzzled and frustrated, she calls her grandmother after several unsuccess -ful attempts.

"Grandma, I can't do it!" Rose exclaims, exasperated. "I've tried so many times. I either fall asleep during the meditation or else my mind stays on the surface and keeps getting distracted with hundreds of thoughts. When I fall asleep, I can't remember whether I've actually been able to descend into my unconscious or not. I really need your help with this exercise."

"It sounds like you're troubled by the wind of the upward push," Verdandi tells her. "The mind is a powerful force, and yours has been trained to journey far and wide. Mental energy produces a lot of air in your inner system, and this air can also keep you on the surface levels of your conscious mind. Connect with this internal upward push and ask the energy within it to reverse the direction. Ask it to guide your mind downward. Let's do it together right now. Close your eyes and take a few deep breaths."

Rose takes a deep breath and starts to feel sleepy again. She hopes she can stay awake to hear the guidance of her grandmother's voice.

Practice for Entering the Unconscious

"Relax yourself as much as possible. Release any tensions you may be holding in your body. Become utterly receptive. Now relax even more. Connect with your imaginal powers and let yourself be guided.

"Imagine a surface that is floating in front of you. Above this surface is the world of your daily consciousness, with information of which you are conscious. Below the surface of your conscious awareness are the subtle dimensions of your mind. Tune into this surface and notice its texture. Does it feel hard and solid or soft and permeable? Or perhaps even fluid like water? Can information from your unconscious easily emerge to the surface of your mind? Or is it filtered out? Perhaps even suppressed from entering above the surface of your conscious mind?

"Just notice whatever comes to you intuitively about this surface layer of your mind. This holds the threshold between your conscious and unconscious awareness. Whatever its structure, thank it for the role it has served. Realize that this surface is made from your consciousness and can thus also be changed by your consciousness *becoming conscious*. If you wish to get greater access to your unconscious and the archetypal mythic realms inside of you, know in your heart that this is fully possible. Thank your mind for its protective role and remind it of this possibility.

"For the purpose of this practice, inform your mind of your intention to descend below the surface of your conscious mind. Let it know of your desire to consciously enter the realm of your unconscious in a way that is safe and healthy. If you start to feel sleepy, know that this is a natural part of the inner descent because your brain is shifting into delta brain waves. Notice the sleepiness without engaging it. Allow yourself to descend further and further and deeper and deeper within yourself, and do so while staying awake. If the upward push is still keeping you at the surface, you may call on the help of your inner gravity and ask it to help you descend further and deeper into yourself.

"Imagine how your unconscious is like a great ocean. With the help of gravity, you're now moving below the surface of your inner ocean of consciousness. From below the water, look up now to the surface of your reality and realize how you have now left the outer surface world behind. You are now entering a deep inner state of consciousness with direct access to your own unconscious, as well as to our collective unconscious. You may even feel how this state is warm, and moist; different from your usual state of being. In fact, it's a whole new and other state where you enter into the very realm of enormous potentials, stories, and ways of being. You are becoming mythic. You are entering the dream of the 'higher becoming' that has attracted the higher mind of humanity since time out of mind. You need to become aware of this for your path of destiny; your actualization in time and space.

"Surrender to this deep inner state of the unconscious now. Ask it to share with you what you need to become aware of for your self-actualization, healing, and destiny. Your unconscious carries symbolic sources of knowing and archetypal wisdom that have not been filtered through the ordinary mind. It may provide you with whole new perspectives and understanding about yourself and your life. Thank your unconscious for processing your information while you are in deep sleep.

"Now ask the Cosmic architect inside you to form a bridge between your conscious and unconscious mind. You can imagine this as an inner ladder from the center of your brain below your pineal gland all the way down along your spine and through your heart. Through this inner ladder you can intentionally move up and down, above and below the surface layers of your reality, and descend consciously into the inner dimensions that are below the surface of your waking mind.

"Become aware of how your personal unconscious is directly part of the collective unconscious. The collective unconscious also serves as a vast source of knowledge and wisdom, as well as archetypal ways of being, knowing, and creating that enhance our abilities and actualization. It also includes reservoirs of collective memories of experiences we've lived, as well as the knowledge of the possibilities and probabilities that never came into being. The unborn and aborted dreams and desires of humanity, when left unhealed, can contribute to collective pain and traumas.

"Ask the collective unconscious now to gently share with you what may serve your further development, healing, and actualization. If you become aware of any of your own unborn and aborted dreams, desires, and potentials, just notice this with a loving presence. Simply realizing and acknowledging this creates a space for healing. If there's anything to learn from what you are becoming aware of, allow this learning to emerge gently and with care.

"Acknowledge how your own inner healing also supports a deeper healing of the collective unconsciousness, as your experiences are part of the collective unconscious. Ask the deep waters of the collective unconscious to heal all of our experiences and any traumas by nourishing the inner waters of our personal and collective memories with forgiveness, grace, and love. Ask for healing of the psychic structures for all of humanity, and for a whole and healed world and future.

"With gratitude for all you experienced, use your inner ladder now to ascend up to the surface of your conscious reality. Become fully present in your present reality and whole self in relaxed awareness and deep connection with yourself and life. When you are ready, you may open your eyes."

The Key of Darkness

Rose slowly opens her eyes and integrates what she experienced. This time she didn't fall asleep and was able to descend into the watery world below the surface levels of her active consciousness. While entering the deep dark waters of the unconscious, she felt an incredible peace, similar to the Cosmic womb experience of her rebirth.

"Thank you, Grandma. While descending down into my inner darkness, I heard a deep humming sound. The absence of the active light of my mind was very soothing for all of my senses. I realize now that it was dark there because my mind shifted out of the thinking mode that produces a lot of light activity in my brain. Instead, my mind shifted into a profound inner state of being."

"You've discovered the Key of Darkness, Rosie. When you enter the darkness of consciousness, it harmonizes your whole being to the most fundamental waves of consciousness; the source waves of the Cosmic mind. These source waves are like the deep humming sounds you heard, and are also the drum patterns that the shamans play during ceremonies to help people enter into the consciousness state of the Great Mystery. This pattern is also within the drumming of your own heartbeat and your inner pulse. Remember how as a little girl you used to put your head below the water in the bathtub to hear these inner sounds?"

"Oh yes, I remember that. I still do that when I feel stressed. It relaxes me to hear the inner pulse within my ears while my head is underwater. Now I understand why it's so soothing. So the Key of Darkness harmonizes our whole being to the source harmonics of our existence?"

"Yes."

"That's profound. It's that state of non-thinking. Is that why it's called the unconscious?"

"Yes," Verdandi says. "It's the state of deep mind where there is no duality: no other and no outer. The term 'unconscious' is a rather unfortunate term, as this state of the unconscious is actually the most profound state of consciousness in its primordial expression, without the additional layers of mind that have developed and evolved over time. It's been described as the unconscious or collective unconscious to explain that it's not our state of ordinary active consciousness. What else did you experience, Rose?"

"I felt like this state comes with its own mode of knowing. It's much more direct, primordial, and intuitive. I felt no desire to analyze or focus on anything in this direct mode of being. I also experienced how this deep inner knowing extends beyond my personal knowing. I could feel memories stored in the dark waters of this inner state of being that are beyond my personal memories. The memories felt like collective underground tunnels that channel the information of our collective experiences. Some of these tunnel-like structures felt like they belong to archetypes of larger beings."

Verdandi looks attentively at Rose. "Interesting. These tunnel-like structures you describe are indeed archetypal. These are the deeper psychic structures of the collective unconscious, which also enter you into the mythic realms. The tunnels of interbeing. Was there anything else you experienced or would like to share?"

"Yes, I felt like the psychic structures were telling me something. Showing me how these psychic archetypal structures can be called up right now to help heal and transform our world. I'd really like to learn more about these psychic forces and archetypal structures, Grandma."

"All in good time, my girl. What you just experienced is very significant already. Continue to explore this Key of Darkness and ask the Cosmos to share with you the secrets of the Universe that this key helps to unlock. We can talk again in a couple of days. Send my love to Sophia and let her know that she's most welcome to join you when you come to visit us in Iceland."

Rose is grateful for this new understanding and curious to see what else she'll discover with this Key of Darkness. She reflects on how different this understanding of darkness is compared to the projected darkness of that which we fear or see as evil.

Later that evening Rose watches a science-fiction movie called *The Return of the Future Avatars*, which tells the story of a small group of mutants with the genetic codes of future humans who can enter magical states at will. This grants them all kinds of special abilities that they learn to develop and apply to save their world from a group of evil, virtual reality inventors. These inventors have put humanity to sleep inside a dome that plays a virtual reality version of Earth. While in this dome, most people don't realize what's happening to the real earth. As the future human codes start to awaken in the mutants, the Avatars return to their world, and they communicate telepathically with the future humans. The future humans learn how to enter into Avatar mode to harness their collective abilities and to help reclaim their world from the evil inventors. While watching, Rose wonders whether the psychic structures she experienced during her practice with Verdandi are somehow linked with the Avatar archetype, although this was just a movie. Or was it?

Exploring the Renaissance Dynamics

A few days later, Rose calls Verdandi again, this time to explore how the evolutionary tension relates to renaissance times.

"Grandma, does the Key of Darkness also help us with the renaissance dynamics you talked about before? You mentioned that renaissance periods trigger the emergence of new states of consciousness and new abilities. There's so much manipulation and distraction that keeps people from entering their inner depths. How can our unconscious become our strength? How can we heal the darkness we fear?"

"Ah, just another normal day in the life of Rose, eh? Nothing too deep; just the usual existential questions. Is it any surprise to you that you haven't been that fortunate in romance?" Verdandi replies with a wink.

"Grandma!"

Verdandi laughs. "I'm just teasing. Let's talk about your questions. During a renaissance, it's as if the mind of the Creator determines that the time is ripe for a major jump in culture and consciousness. During such times, special social and psychic enzymes become available to help effect these transitions. Sometimes the social and psychic enzymes are so ghastly that they affect the progression of change. People then grow laconic and bored, or can even be driven to outrage and hysteria, if this impetus toward change, newness, and renewal takes too long. Cultures can easily fall into chaos during such times. Economic and psychological depressions, as well as violence, then rule the day. This happened in all of the periods that have ever preceded renaissance periods."

"That's interesting. I can see how that's also happening right now," Rose agrees. "There's a lot of chaos in our world, and the pressures of change are growing by the day."

"You're right," Verdandi says. "A renaissance is a rebirth out of the chaotic, outmoded, dying, or disastrous situations. Renaissance times give rise to whole new states of consciousness, which can also trigger a new kind of genius to lift us out of these desperate situations. These new states of consciousness typically emerge from the deep, dark waters of our collective unconscious to help us to transcend our sense of impotence and move us into personal and collective genius. Out of the trashy awfulness of wars and violence, and now our climate crisis and the coronavirus pandemic, our future encodings are getting activated."

"How do those future encodings become activated from awfulness?" Rose asks.

"Excellent question. The awfulness functions as a signal to the Cosmos that we're ready for the breakthrough. A signal can also take the form of a strong collective: '*NO! This has to stop! We are the change for what doesn't work.*' We then become the Cosmic call for the Universe to evolve and partner with us in the next stages of our evolution. This catalyzes the enzymes of our metamorphic process, to dissolve the old dysfunctional states that cause so much suffering.

"The signal for the great Cosmic intervention also activates the future encodings within us as the lure of our becoming," Verdandi continues. "While we don't yet have the particulars of the new future, we do have courage, hope, renewal, strength, and determination to bring forth the better systems and worlds. The Cosmos then starts fueling our imaginal powers with new creativity, breakthrough ideas, new inventions, and the inspiration for whole new ways of being, design, and action. That, my girl, is the annunciation of the renaissance time, which is essentially a process of collective metamorphosis in the dying body of the caterpillar world. You, my Rosebud, represent the imaginal cells of the butterfly. You are the caterpillar's future as its old body is collapsing and dying."

"I'm glad that the signals of awfulness can become so useful that it can trigger a renaissance," Rose says. "You mentioned before that most of the growing is happening in the darkness of the cocoon and womb, and under the soil. Those enzymes that are dissolving the old structures are also released in the darkness. Is the darkness and the unconscious the same as what our ancestors referred to as the underworld? In Dutch the word 'unconscious' translates as 'onderbewustzijn,' which means 'under-conscious.'"

Entering the Underworld to be Reborn

Verdandi nods. "Yes, you could say that the unconscious and the underworld are the same. The underworld is not just the gate to the personal unconscious or subconscious; it's also the collective unconscious that you experienced during your exercise. We really need new terminologies for all this, so I think it's best to understand what the words are pointing toward, rather than taking them too literally. The underworld has always been the place from where the rebirth happens.

"Even Jesus went into the underworld where he met the devil in the desert, to be reborn as Christ," Verdandi continues. "Christ carried the powers of resurrection, which were not yet awakened within the ordinary man called Jesus. The underworld is the archetypal descent through which we gain access to whole new abilities and powers. Yet we have to die to our old ways in order to be reborn from the underworld."

Rose reflects for a moment and then replies, "Like my own near-death experience when my heart stopped for a few minutes in the hospital. I saw how my own body and much of the world was held inside a huge Cosmic cocoon as a hospice for all that was dying. The vision then transformed into the darkness of the Cosmic womb where I felt the seeds of my new life activating and bringing me back to life. I never realized this was also an underworld experience because I didn't see any frightening monsters or temptations."

"Yet you did experience moments of doubt and despair when you called out to the Universe for help and then heard my voice," Verdandi tells her. "You had to release control and let go before you could access the powers of your personal renaissance.

"The psychic structures of the underworld are part of the primordial powers of transformation. Those are not to be feared, but rather to be honored and understood for their true powers," Verdandi continues. "Physically, we could even say that the underworld is the area of your brain that is just under your neo-cortex; the area which is not controlled by your rational mind."

"I never thought of that," Rose says.

"The underworld is also the world of the brainstem and the seat of your ancient reptilian brain," Verdandi explains. "In our tradition, this is represented as the 'inner Serpent,' which is why, for us, the Serpent is a powerful archetype and ally. The head of the Serpent is the oldest part of your brain, which keeps you closely attuned to the earth and the vibrational language of the Cosmos. It helps you to feel and sense the resonance patterns of life, as its communication is vibrational."

As Rose listens to Verdandi, she can literally feel this part of her brain starting to tingle, as if the Serpent inside her body is awakening. "I see. So the sacred Serpent is a guardian of the underworld?"

"Yes."

"Alright, things are starting to align now. Will you please tell me more about this vibrational language of the Serpent?" Rose asks.

"The Serpent is the primordial guardian of the creative powers of the Dreaming," Verdandi explains. "When our shamans enter into their deep trance to receive the Cosmic messages, these often enter the body first as sounds, which then converge into visions, knowing, and understanding. Their attunement to the inner Serpent provides them with access to the transformational powers of the Universe. The Cosmos can enter into these people without being sidetracked by the mind or trickster.

"The snake is always attuned to the earth as it slides its belly over her surfaces. It is also closely attuned to the cycles of change, rebirth, and renewal. When we enter the underworld, we essentially discover the Cosmic ear and become attuned to the direct communication of the transformative forces as the deepest levels of reality. When we learn to listen with the Cosmic ear, we discover how the Cosmos listens with us and responds. This capacity is essential during renaissance times when communication breakdown can clutter and distort people's receptivity to their Cosmic inner guidance."

"Incredible," Rose murmurs. "And how about earth changes? Can we hear this too when we learn to listen with the inner Serpent?"

"Yes. This inner capacity also attunes you to the geomagnetic sounds of our planet and the sounds of the Universe. Our shamans often know in advance when an earthquake or volcano will erupt. They can hear these sounds emitted from the earth about 48 hours prior to an eruption."

"This is fascinating," Rose says, "I can hear those sounds as well, but I never knew what they meant. It gives a strange effect in my head that starts with me hearing in stereo simultaneously from all directions. Then it erupts into high-pitched sounds accompanied by bright sparkles of blue light. Now I know that I need to make sure that my analytical mind doesn't become so loud that it dominates my access to the underworld. I'll reach out to the Serpent to help me access the consciousness states for entering the underworld."

"Good. You already do this naturally, but now you have some further conscious tools to work with. Remember that to enter the Serpent state of consciousness you need rhythmic and vibrational stimulation. Start by relaxing yourself and freeing up your consciousness from your analytical mind. Then proceed with rhythmic breathing, humming, and drumming. Gently rock your body back and forth. Once the inner Serpent awakens, you may feel a slight tingling in your spine or head. Ask it to safely guide you into your underworld and resurface you when you are ready. Remember also that the underworld has its own laws and principles. Ask the Cosmic architecture to familiarize you with that."

"Can I share this information with my friends?" Rose asks.

"Yes, but invite them lightly into this topic. Get them curious and intrigued first so that by themselves, they'll want to learn more. Otherwise, they'll start to believe that those unique states of consciousness are unattainable for them. Remember to gently engage people in the deeper invitation of the dark waters as if they are stepping into the most incredible blue lagoon. Don't reveal the sharks and sea urchins too quickly."

Rose chuckles. "So I should let them play with the dolphins for a while?"

"Yes. Many people have fallen asleep in the surface realities of our world. You have to coax them out of their superficiality. They'll want to have 'a whale of a time,' without realizing what it means to enter the belly of the archetypal whale," Verdandi replies with a mischievous twinkle in her eyes.

"It sounds so much easier when you say it, Grandma. I love the darkness. It's from there that the light is born and can enter our world. In the darkness, the light of our minds can't twist the truth. Entering the sacred darkness helps me to see what truly is."

Integration - The Key of Darkness

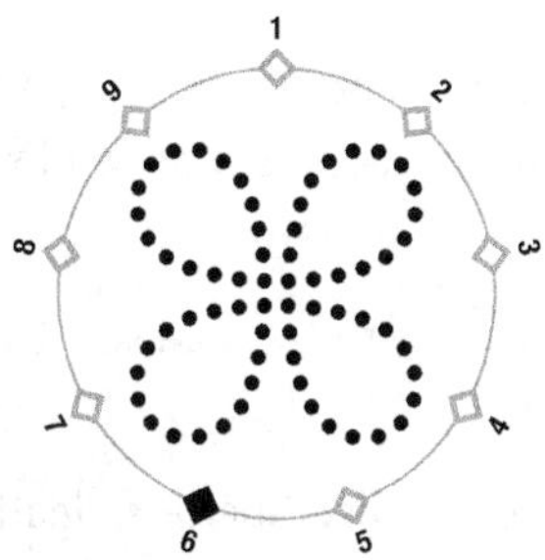

Through this chapter we've explored how you can safely descend into the unconscious with the Key of Darkness, and discover your deeper transformative renaissance powers.

> *The Key of Darkness harmonizes your whole being to the source harmonics of consciousness, and helps you to access the deeply transformative forces of the unconscious for embracing evolutionary tensions and deepening your self awareness.*

The summary below will help you to integrate these discoveries further:

- The personal and collective unconscious contain the universal archetypal structures of our human psyche. To communicate with these psychic structures, we need to understand how the collective unconscious speaks to us mythically, through a symbolic language that includes primordial images.
- The darkness can represent what is veiled and invisible for the grosser layers of mind.
- The sacred darkness makes us more receptive to the existential knowledge of our universe and provides powerful medicine for self-healing and inner regeneration.
- The darkness of the womb and cocoon spaces support you to grow safely in times of great change and uncertainty.

- Befriend your inner darkness and become aware of your own projections. Face what you deny or suppress within yourself. The shadow tends to cloak itself in darkness to mask what it most fears; namely, that you will discover that it doesn't have a source of its own existence.
- Remember how *presence* and *laughter* are the fastest ways to befriend the darkness and unmask the shadow. Genuine laughter frees all of our anxieties.
- Deep growth happens in the darkness. The feminine is naturally at home in the darkness.
- The path to higher consciousness leads via the descent into the unconscious.
- The Key of Darkness harmonizes your whole being to the source harmonics of consciousness: the unity wave patterns of Cosmic mind. It is a state of non-thinking, non-duality, and deep mind.
- Renaissance periods trigger the emergence of new states of consciousness and abilities from the depths of the collective unconscious.
- Renaissance times are major jump times in culture and consciousness. During such times, special social and psychic enzymes become available to help effect these transitions.
- A renaissance is a rebirth out of the chaotic, outmoded, dying, or disastrous situations, giving rise to whole new states of consciousness that typically emerge from the deep, dark waters of our collec-tive unconscious.
- Out of the trashy awfulness of wars and violence, and now our climate crisis and the coronavirus pandemic, our future encodings are getting activated.
- The annunciation of the renaissance time is essentially a process of collective metamorphosis in the dying body of the caterpillar world.
- The underworld is the place from where the rebirth happens. The underworld is the archetypal descent through which we gain access to whole new abilities and powers. Yet we have to die to our old ways of being and seeing in order to be reborn from the underworld.

- The psychic structures of the underworld are part of the primordial powers of transformation. Those are not to be feared, but rather honored and understood for their true powers.
- The underworld is also the area of your brain that is just under your neo-cortex, which is not controlled by your rational mind.
- When we enter the underworld, we essentially discover the Cosmic ear and become attuned to the direct communication of the transformative forces as the deepest levels of reality.
- You can enter the Serpent state of consciousness via rhythmic and vibrational stimulation. Once the inner Serpent awakens, you can ask it to safely guide you into your underworld and resurface you when you are ready.
- Light is born from darkness to enlighten our world. The Key of Darkness is also a Key of Light by recognizing darkness as invisible light. By entering the sacred darkness you will discover the fundamental nature of reality.

CHAPTER 7

Exploring New Consciousness States

Deepening Our Inner Presence
with the Key of Self Awarenes

Rose is feeling anxious, "Grandma, I find it difficult to become more aware of the human condition and all the problems we're causing in the world, and not become more judgemental. How do you do that? You seem to have such a depth of understanding about what's happening and why, and yet I never hear you complain, judge, or label people."

"I'm no saint, love. You're just fortunate to know me later in my life. You get to see me from my better side," Verdandi laughs. "Ask Dagaz. He can tell you many stories of my younger years and my passionate rants about humanity. The human condition of stubborn denial, arrogance, injustice, and greed used to get me really worked up."

"So, how can you be so calm about it now?"

"Not calm, simply present and more self aware."

"What's the difference?" Rose asks. "I understand that self awareness is extremely important, and I'd love to develop the kind of mirror-like wisdom of the lake that I experienced during my Cosmic Compass dream. It reflected all without judgment. I feel like I'm really far from that state of being."

"The difference is that self awareness is about being fully present as the awareness of your greater self, whereas calmness is simply a state of mind. Self awareness is much more than a state of mind; it's a state of being. Sounds like you are ready for the next Cosmic key in your training!" Verdandi laughs.

"Is it that obvious?" Rose smiles. "At least I've been able to stay awake now while descending into my inner darkness, thanks to the practice you gave me when we last spoke. I just feel there's so much I don't know about myself; so much that lives below the surface of my conscious mind. I tend to be more focused on discovering things about the Universe than myself."

"Yes, well, that's a typical human trait."

Our Minds Are like Stargates

Verdandi looks tenderly at Rose from across the screens of their phones. "Tell me, love, what is it you've been conjuring up about the Universe since we last spoke? And remember, the Universe isn't always a calm place. I wouldn't want to be consumed by a black hole or explode like a supernova, for example. I've never been much of a diva, not even a Cosmic one."

"You're so funny, Grandma. Maybe calmness isn't what I need to focus on, but rather presence—real presence that is grounded in awareness. Since our talk about the archetypal structures of reality, I've been wondering, what is space, time, energy, and matter? What if the darkness, including dark matter and dark holes, is the foundation for light? What if darkness is the experience of gravity, and light is the experience of timelessness? What if black holes are the womb structures of our universe for creating new universes?"

"So many wonderful questions, Rosebud! I love your curiosity," Verdandi says.

Rose feels a burning desire to understand these fundamental questions about the nature of reality. At times her desire feels so strong that it becomes feverish. During their previous conversation Verdandi suggested that she should develop a series of personal psycho-physical practices for developing the new states of consciousness that she's exploring to help her attune her body and mind to the influx of higher consciousness that she's becoming aware of.

"Remember that our minds are like stargates," Verdandi continues. "Our bodies are alive with mysteries that invite us to enter into the Cosmic Body, Mind, and Spirit of the Great Mystery. The Universe lives in you and through you. Evolution is followed by involution, which is the process of 'going inward,' through which we discover our bodies are cells of mysteries that give us keys to the emerging phase and purpose of our existence. Through this creative partnership you're developing with the Universe and the earth herself, your deeper calling and destiny is activating, and you're discovering the tremendous resourcefulness and wisdom in the vast ecology of inner space. You're now discovering how we can be active and creative citizens in a universe and an inner-verse that are richer than all previous imaginings."

"This is so much more exciting than living a life designed by others to simply pay the bills. I wish everyone could discover and experience this, Grandma."

"Yes, love. This is the world of the new time, which also includes the possibility for a renewed spirituality and higher sense of purpose. Educated for the demands of a different time and culture, we are now called to unlearn the old ways to be re-educated. We have vast resources within ourselves that we haven't even begun to tap into. To meet the many, many new challenges that confront us, we have no choice but to enter into our greatness. We must democratize greatness and utilize the whole continuum of our human and divine potentials. Not only is this possible, it's what is expected of us now. Indeed, it may be that for which we have been created, my girl. Your newly developing states of consciousness can provide you with such valuable information, ideas, discoveries, and profoundly new ways of knowing, being, and creating. The Cosmos is ready to help us, but we also need to be ready to receive and apply its guidance. Your own inner work is essential right now."

Rose has a sense that her inner training is about to expand and deepen, and she feels a little nervous about what she may be discovering next about herself. "What kind of inner work do you have in mind, Grandma?"

"The kind that also ignites your sensory and physical systems to a new order of possibility," Verdandi explains. "This is an essential next step in awakening to your new life's purpose. It involves a new order of orchestration, because in the artful approach to your destiny, you'll align all parts of your being: your body, mind, heart, and all of your senses, in ways that enhance your discovery of your deeper purpose."

"But how? It all sounds so easy and beautiful when you say it. Dad called again the other day, asking what I'm going to do with my life, or at least in the coming year. I didn't know what to tell him. He wasn't too happy to hear about my decision to leave my former job in the bookshop."

"Don't worry about your dad. I'll talk with him. He's probably just worried about your financial situation. I'm sure he'll understand that you need time and space to be with the tremendous growing experience that's happening within you right now. As a therapist, he knows all too well how such processes can't be rushed. You're still in the cocoon. Much will become clear once you emerge from this phase."

"Thank you, Grandma. So how about this inner work I've got to do? Is it anything I can do right now?"

"Yes. Practice self awareness."

"Really? That's all? You don't have any exercises for me?" Rose was expecting an elaborate workout session she could sink her teeth into.

"It takes people an entire lifetime to become self aware, Rosebud. The basis for developing your future human capacities and accessing many of your untapped potentials begins with awareness. The quality and mastery of your own awareness is the key to everything else. There are latent capacities in our bodies that many people never get to access, let alone develop, because we have busy monkey minds that keep us preoccupied with surface stuff. You already know that there's a whole lot more to matter and the matter of our bodies than most people realize. The human body is an amazingly malleable system containing a mesh of varying evolutionary potentials and many untapped capacities. We inherit in our bodies and nervous systems the remnants of the earliest vertebrates, as well as the fruits of the long course of mammalian evolution. But we also contain, as latency, the substance of what we will yet become; our future human potentials. Like the great author T. S. Eliot once said, 'Time past and time future are gathered in time present.'"

"I agree with all that, but many days I feel like I'm just floating around in my own awareness, not knowing what to focus on. And I don't like the way that makes me feel," Rose replies, feeling slightly annoyed now. She doesn't like the sense of restlessness that's been growing inside her. She just wants to get on with her life, and for the future she has seen to happen now. "Can't you just give me a really easy practice to help me develop my self awareness?"

"Alright. First of all, make space for 5 to 10 minutes a day to simply *be*. No analyzing. No distractions. Nothing to work on or resolve. Just exist. See it as daily self-care. This will strengthen your awareness of presence. Then from your inner state of presence, learn to direct and shift this quality of 'aware focus' to whatever you're doing or exploring. Allow this deep awareness of being to become as natural as breathing. Would you like to try it?"

"Yes, please!" Rose settles among the cushions on her couch, eager to learn this new practice.

Practice for Relaxing into Awareness

"Close your eyes. Take a few deep breaths and relax. Relax your body and your mind. Let go of any tensions you may feel. Relax your attention. There's no need to focus on anything. Simply allow yourself to be. Notice the natural flow of your breath: in and out...in and out...Give yourself this time and space to simply be. Let go of the outer world; let go of anything you may be holding onto. Simply be. Relax into existence. Melt into yourself. Allow your awareness to float effortlessly on the waves of pure being. Let life carry you. Relax and simply be.

"Let your mind become one with the essence of existence itself. Feel the wide expanse of existence; its effortless presence. Let your mind fully relax now. Even let go of time itself. Simply be. There's nothing to do. Right now, you just exist.

"Feel the effortless presence of pure existence as a deep silence of being. If you still feel any stress or tension, give this to the field of pure existence and let it dissolve completely. Allow yourself to relax into pure presence.

"Realize at the deepest level of your being that you are completely safe. Your existence is safe, irrespective of what goes on in the world or in your life. Your existence is born from consciousness. The usual cares of the world have disappeared, but consciousness continues and is always in a state of effortless happening; flowing and being without anything to do or even think about. Existence and essence flow on and on and on...You are safe in consciousness.

"Now in the deeper levels of your inner being, be in your natural state of awareness, free from outer or inner business, free from pain and tensions. Simply be...Simply be. When you're ready, you may gently return from this inner state of being, while keeping the flow of your natural awareness."

The Cosmic Architecture School of Life

A few days later, Rose joins Sophia for lunch. It's a beautiful spring day in Amsterdam. Light streams in through the window, making the room feel very cheerful. The two young women have been practicing their violins for several hours together. Rose has noticed how this practice of self awareness has also helped her with her music. By centering herself in effortless awareness, she achieves much better concentration and muscle coordination for playing her violin. Rose has shared the same practice with Sophia, who's looking forward to including this as part of her daily self-care as well.

The friends are happily charged up from playing Bach and Vivaldi, and ready to dive into their huge garden salad of organic cherry tomatoes, feta cheese, olives, and fresh basil.

"Sophia, I tell you, ever since I returned from the hospital it's like I've been enrolled in Harry Potter's Hogwarts school for wizards. It's been incredible, and sometimes so unbelievable that you're the only friend I dare to share everything with."

Sophia chuckles, "Sister, I have a sense that this is just the beginning..."

"I hope it won't get more dangerous than what I've already lived. Dying and returning from the other side of the veil is not something I want to turn into a yearly event. Once is enough! But seriously, I feel like I am enrolled in the Cosmic Architect Mystery School of Life. I'm still doing those online studies in cosmology, quantum field theory, and new paradigm sciences, yet everything has become so deeply personal now. It even feels odd, and sometimes wrong, to just talk about space-time or particles or Cosmic information as if it's an abstraction. This is *life* we are talking about. It's so intimate, real, and personal. Without any of that, none of us would even exist." Rose takes another sip of fresh fruit juice.

"To tell you the truth, I've noticed how something profound has shifted for you, Rose. Even your language is becoming less abstract and more human."

"Whaaat? I wasn't human before?"

"Of course you were," Sophia chuckles. "But you also sounded very abstract at times. I feel like you're finally integrating all of these ground-breaking ideas into your human heart, and not just your dazzling mind. Are you still getting enough sleep? Don't underestimate what your body has gone through in all of this."

Sophia cares for Rose, and not just as her dear friend. Soon she'll become a medical doctor. She doesn't tell Rose all that she's noticing since she doesn't want her to get worried. She sees how Rose's facial features are changing, and even her physical posture looks different than before, as if she's literally growing a new body from within herself.

"Thanks for caring, Sophia. I get about 8 hours of sleep every night, although sometimes I feel like that isn't enough. It's just that there's so much I want to explore every day and I never seem to have enough time for all of it."

"What are these personal changes about?" Sophia asks.

"This morning I woke up with so much love for our universe. I never felt that kind of love before. It was like my heart was exploding. I had no idea I could even feel that level of love for our universe because it used to feel so vast and impersonal to me. It happened while I was reflecting on several interviews with Sir Roger Penrose and Stuart Hameroff that I watched recently."

"If only those men knew what their interviews evoked in you!" Sophia laughs.

"No, not like that," Rose chuckles. "They talked about the conditions for self-conscious experiences in very abstract terms. You know, like the role of quantum gravity, gravity thresholds, and self-organizing ripples that relate to fundamental space-time geometry."[7]

"Oh that," Sophia grins. "I hate to disappoint you, but I'm afraid that wouldn't make my heart explode with an outpouring of love for the Universe. But okay, continue, my sister. I'll stop interrupting you." Sophia finds all of this to be very amusing while she's running these ideas on a parallel track in her own mind.

"While listening to them," Rose continues, "I realized how all of what they were describing is literally happening within us, too. My awareness somehow shifted, and all of a sudden, I experienced how the Universe dreams, sings, communicates, thinks, gets moody, makes love, becomes pregnant, gives birth, renews It/Him/Her/Themself, and presences consciousness into each and every one of us. The previous abstractions fell away and everything I'd been learning about the Universe became deeply personal."

"I understand. That must be very profound. Did you tell your grandmother about this?" Sophia knows how close Rose is with Verdandi.

"Yes. She said that the archetype of the beloved is awakening within me, which can provide a deep, mystical understanding of the nature of reality. It's kind of funny to study cosmology and physics through the perspective of the beloved. You know I'm like a baby when it comes to intimate relationships. The emotional state of the beloved feels completely new to me."

Sophia knows how inexperienced Rose is in matters of intimacy and sexuality. "The mystic nun and healer, Hildegard of Bingen, was often found in a state of sexual ecstasy while communicating with God. Who knows? She might be your ancestor! I'm sure you could sell a course in quantum theories if people knew how deeply orgasmic the effect of this knowledge can be. 'Come and learn about Cosmic waves patterns; a wave you'll never forget, as you learn intimately about the unified field of the Cosmos!'" Both women are laughing now, with red cheeks and warm bellies.

"Oh, Sophia, stop it! I can't breathe. This is so funny. I'm going to pee in my pants! Just imagine the faces of my university lecturers when I tell them this topic is rather 'hot.'"

This sets them off again.

"But seriously," Rose says, "when I heard those men speak about gravity thresholds that relate to fundamental space-time geometry, I could actually feel inside my own being how this relates to our capacity to make choices and have the experience of self-consciousness.[8] Perhaps when a critical quantum gravity threshold is reached, the Universe awakens for a brief moment from her deep Delta state—"

"Which for us is sleep," Sophia interjects.

"Yes, and she becomes conscious of what's happening, and makes a choice that enters her consciousness into another dream, which becomes our local experience."

"That's a novel thought."

"According to Stuart Hameroff and Deepak Chopra, cylindrical protein polymers called 'microtubules' provide our brains with the same quantum computation capacities as our universe. These microtubules are able to self-assemble and interconnect to make it possible for the membrane structures and the genes in the cell nucleus to communicate and exchange.[9] The Universe literally has her ears and voice inside of us. It gets even more interesting. Stuart Hameroff mentioned that this shifting between the states of information from the superposition quantum state to singular states is the result of the quantum gravity thresholds that form part of fundamental ripples in space-time geometry."[10]

"That's fascinating, Rose. I love how you're bringing your feminine perspective to something so abstract. Perhaps this quantum gravity that curves space-time is also part of our own feminine curvatures. I see now why you refer to the Universe as a 'she.' Please continue."

"Okay, so whatever is happening at the largest scales of our universe is also happening within our own bodies and minds each time we think, process information, and make decisions. And yes, I agree about those feminine curvatures," Rose smiles. "This whole Cosmic architecture really is fractal.

Now imagine each ripple in space-time geometry as a sound wave or a verse. Can you see and hear now how the Universe is communicating? When we're measuring shifts in space-time ripples, quantum gravity thresholds, and different states of information, we're actually observing in real time how our universe is alive and expressing herself. The Universe is alive, Sophia! She really is *alive*! Now imagine observing the formation of a black hole far away in another galaxy. Realize that in that moment you are intimately witnessing the Universe giving birth to new life."

"Oh wow. Yes, I can see why this is becoming so intimate. We're so used to studying everything as an abstraction. We're failing to realize that the Universe is actually a sentient being, and not a thing or an 'it.' Maybe someday we'll figure out how all those cosmological data you're speaking of actually form part of the language of our universe. This is the living book of creation. I can also understand better why my own ancestors say that the Dreaming is continuous. In other words, it's happening in a realm parallel to our physical world."

"Exactly, Sophia. Grandma also shared with me how the ancient Gnostics and mystics have always said that the Universe is a sentient being. How everything is unfolding in the body of the great *One*. Our ancestors knew the power of sacred geometry as a way to connect and communicate with the powers of the Universe. The ancient temples, sacred symbols, and drawings were all based on this. They also used sound combined with sacred geometry to enter into unity consciousness with our universe. Apparently, the right sound patterns can even shift the state of matter."

"This Cosmic architecture school of life sounds like a lot of fun. Please enroll me as well!" Sophia says passionately.

"I think you're already enrolled, Sophia. In your case, your ancestors may have enrolled you before you were born."

Spooky Action at a Distance

After the conversation with Sophia, Rose realizes how these discoveries may also hold some of the keys for how to shift the narratives around "matter." In many of the dominant religions, matter has been blamed for entrapping the Soul, while in the mechanistic worldviews of Newtonian physics and Cartesian dualism, matter has been reduced to purely a mechanical process of parts and particles with biochemical flows.

Rose is convinced that a new narrative about matter is required for creating the new regenerative economies that can mimic the Cosmic architecture of life. She also feels that the understanding of consciousness as non-deterministic, like Sir Roger Penrose suggested when he said that consciousness is not an algorithm, is deeply liberating.

While exploring the Key of Self Awareness, she is learning more about nonlocality. Locality is a concept that physicists use to describe how an event at one point cannot cause or influence a simultaneous result at another point. This means that information transfer within space-time is bound by the universal speed limit of light, as explained by Einstein's relativity theory. However, scientists also observed that under certain conditions, like in a quantum state, a simultaneousness of particle connectivity exists, which is explained by the principle of "nonlocality." Albert Einstein called this "spooky action at a distance." Einstein also revealed a union between space and time that remains invariant, hence the term "space-time" or "spacetime." He further explained how gravity emerges from the curvature of space-time, and, accordingly, it can be said that gravity is geometry.

Rose is still puzzled and impressed by how her grandmother knew what was happening to her in the hospital when she felt like she was dying and she called for her in her thoughts. She's been wondering if this experience can be explained by this quantum theory of nonlocality. She feels like her experience of immediate connection with her grandmother, and their information transfer, can't be explained by the conventional laws of physics.

Rose and Verdandi were in totally different places physically, yet the information exchange between them far exceeded the universal speed limit of light, and happened instantaneously. Obviously, Cosmic consciousness is not bound by the physical laws of space-time. Particle connectivity can take place without information transfer through space-time. It was only after this directly personal experience that Rose started to realize what is meant by nonlocal connectivity, though she has a sense that many physicists will not agree with the way she's using this principle to explain her undeniable experience.

To learn more about these amazing phenomena, she has started to read about other people's experiences of nonlocal connectivity and near-death experiences. She has been surprised to discover how common it really is. So many people are reporting similar experiences. Even leading scientists are now postulating that our finite physical universe may well be part of a larger infinite reality that also influences what happens within the finite dimensions. Or perhaps this whole distinction between finite and infinite is somehow artificial.

While talking about this with her grandmother, Verdandi replied, "Can't scientists at least make some effort for us to understand what they're talking about? To make it relevant for what is happening in our world right now? Our ancestors have always said that the spirit is infinite and eternal. We've always known that we're not locally bound. When you were sick in the hospital, my spirit was with you. It told me how you were. I didn't need a phone to know what was happening with you. I could feel what you were going through. I could see deep inside your body and mind. Our spirits were in direct communication with each other."

"I felt that too, Grandma. I knew I could trust in that, which is why I reached out to you spiritually when I needed help."

"Rosie, as you are exploring the Key of Self Awareness this week, it may help you to realize that *our spirit is our connectivity.* My spirit enables me to be with you and also here at home with Grandpa, as well as deep within the Cosmos praying for your healing and the healing of our world. My spirit is always sourced in the awareness of our eternal Self. It's only through love that people will be able to discover these deeper spiritual dimensions of life, because that is the only force of the Universe that is capable of carrying us across distances. Love melts away all the barriers of the mind. It helps us to realize our unity. Just feel that love right now, sweetheart."

Rose places her hands on her heart and allows herself to relax deeply. She remembers the practice for relaxing into awareness that her grandmother gave her, and can feel now why this is so beneficial. She feels held in the warm embrace of love.

Verdandi continues, "When love is present, understanding comes naturally. That is consciousness."

"Thank you, Grandma. I love you."

The Key of Self Awareness

Rose is starting to discover the simultaneity and multidimensionality, or rather non-dimensionality, of her own awareness. She is fine-tuning her ability to be in the nonlocal Cosmic mind, while simultaneously grounded in the awareness of her local self. She feels every cell of her body nourished and uplifted in the flow of Cosmic inspiration. She loves to explore and experiment with being Cosmic while making a cup of tea, talking on the phone with a friend, soaring through the Universe on a beam of light, playing with the curls in her hair while being aware of the curvatures of space-time, and dreaming into the future while feeling her feet rooted in the present.

She's becoming aware of the hidden coordinates of the Cosmos within her own being. She's becoming a Cosmic coordinate of the greater mysteries of life, a Cosmic cell in a new mythos. In fleeting moments, when she least expects it, her consciousness enters into profound unity experiences. There are times when she can even feel the pulse of the Universe resounding in her own heart. Her heart is becoming resonant with the Cosmic heart. The creative powers of her Cosmic self are awakening. She experiences how we are each a creative universe, and how we, as humans, get to tell the story and laugh about it all.

Yet, there's a deeper question that is persistently on her mind: Knowing this, how can we create a world that is not torn by crisis after crisis? She feels deeply concerned about the growing divisions and tensions between people, and an agonizing restlessness to build a world that, by design, is made to thrive. It's becoming harder and harder for her to accept the systems that were made by ignorance or defiance of the cosmological architecture of our universe and life. She feels that even the bees display a far greater intelligence when it comes to coordinating and building their world.

Verdandi challenges her to deepen her self awareness by not jumping into trying to fix the issues that are on her mind. She warns that sometimes what appears to be broken is actually designed that way on purpose. She must be careful about what she gets herself involved in, and she must keep working from a place of inner wholeness so as not to feed the divisions. She tells Rose, "Remember that awareness is like that calm lake of consciousness that you experienced; it doesn't become what it reflects. Instead, like a mirror, it reveals all from the true essence of what is."

"Grandma, how can I avoid getting entangled in all the things that are floating in and around my mind? Sometimes my awareness feels too bright. I see too much then, and feel overwhelmed."

"Continue to work with the Key of Darkness, my girl. When the light is too bright and awareness becomes too amplified, spend some time in the sacred darkness to relax and calm your nervous system and senses. Give all the images and thoughts that are not necessary for you to resolve to the darkness. There, they can be reabsorbed and integrated into the great ocean of consciousness. Give your dad a call, he may have a practice to help you with your inner balance."

Karl is a therapist. He uses the following practice with many of his patients, which he shares with Rose after she calls him for help.

Practice for Inner Purification and Liberation

"Rose, you can use this practice to purify and liberate your personal space and energy. It's also helpful for clearing blockages, obstacles, and constrictions. By regularly purifying your personal space and energy, it'll help you to feel more balanced. You can use this practice in the morning and before going to bed, as well as anytime when you feel heavy or out of tune, or caught in other people's energies."

"Thanks, Dad. I could really use that right now."

"You can do this practice with your eyes closed or open, whichever you prefer. Are you ready?"

"Ready!" Rose says, eager to begin.

"Alright. Relax into yourself and become aware of your personal space and energy. What is the quality of your personal space and energy? Is your life force clear and free flowing or are there constrictions? Is your inner space bright and happy, or are there darker areas where you don't feel well or you're not fully present? Take a minute to scan your inner space. Simply observe for a few moments. Do not engage with what you're becoming aware of.

"Within your heart, form the intention to let go of anything that is not yours, and not for your highest good. Intend that all energies, patterns, and ways of being that do not belong to you or are not meant to be in or around your personal space now return to their points of origin with love and light.

"Form the intention that what is yours returns to you with love and light. Release yourself from any places, relationships, and experiences that are unhelpful to you. Return yourself to yourself, here and now. Reclaim your personal space. Feel the lighter, helpful, loving energies around you, filling that space. Scan your inner space again and notice the greater clarity and health that you perceive. Stay there and enjoy that clarified space for some moments…Should you still be aware of blockages, or obstacles, then proceed to the next stage of purification.

"Imagine now a strong and beautiful balloon in front of you. Direct all that you want purified, cleared, healed, and transformed into this balloon. Put it all in there. The balloon is very strong; it can take it all in. You can also put into this balloon any obstacles, barriers, and blockages that have manifested in your personal space or energy.

"Now send this balloon to the sun and ask the sun to purify all of this energy from your balloon with its powerful rays of light. Trust that the sun knows how to take care of this. It is now purifying all that is within the balloon with its Cosmic rays of light. Now ask the sun to send you back your energy, purified and infused with its Cosmic love and light.

"Bring your awareness back to your inner space and notice how you feel now. Bring your natural presence into the space that has been emptied, cleared, and opened. Notice how there is more space for you to be present there. Take a few more moments to just enjoy and appreciate the natural radiance of your own energy and inner space.

"You have completed this process and are fully present in the here and now. Affirm the new and enhanced reality of your personal space. If your eyes are closed, please gently open them now. If your eyes are open, simply move your body and enjoy the completion of the process."

The Parallel Paths of Madness and Genius

Over the next week, Rose applies the practice from her grandmother and the one she received from her father. She notices an immediate difference in the quality of her awareness, as well as the quality of her sleep. When she wakes up in the morning, she feels fresh and rested, whereas before she often felt restless and sometimes exhausted from the number of dreams she'd had.

Verdandi is aware of the acceleration in Rose's development and wants to make sure that she's not getting hooked into too much experimentation, or sharing these powerful practices with people who do not share Rose's intention.

"Love, I hope you realize that this shifting between different states of consciousness is not to be used to manipulate outcomes or results you may seek. Please remind your friends of this when you share any of these practices with them. There are so many courses and books out there that promise ultimate results by changing one's state of consciousness. 'Become a millionaire by using my technique to enter into abundance consciousness now!' 'Become the most influential leader through the influencer's state of consciousness!' 'Become the next winning athlete with the seven steps of mastery consciousness!' The list goes on and on. For every desired success or result, there's a state of consciousness these days: finding your true love, losing weight, achieving optimum health, radical healing, and so forth. It's no wonder that many young adults struggle with their own identities with these expectations of success. What you're exploring here is not like that. Your explorations are born from a very different choice and intention."

Rose listens attentively, for she's been concerned about this. Although she's been curious to read many of the self-help books in the bookshop where she used to work, her deeper orientation has always been about architecting a more beautiful world that she wants to be a part of.

Verdandi continues, "Different consciousness states give you access to different realities and abilities. We live in a world that is spinning out of its 'axis mundi' because people are overloaded with options and possibilities that only feed their desires for more, confirming their belief that they're lacking or missing out on something. Be aware of the intention you use for shifting between consciousness states. Ultimately, your intention is what makes the difference. Your powers for manifestation are growing stronger. Apply the Key of Self Awareness for refining, and perhaps even evolving, some of your intentions."

"Okay, I'll be careful, Grandma. I love to experiment and explore, and wasn't really thinking about any intentions in particular, but I hear what you're saying."

"Yes, Rose, your Cosmic inner portals are opening. There's a powerful influx of Cosmic information entering your inner world. The priorities of your Cosmic self are of a very different order of reality than the intentions of our world. Don't let the world around you hijack the resources that are becoming available to you. Those inner resources are for you. Just be careful how and when you share them with others. Their intentions for accessing these powers may not be the same as yours. You're exploring the heart of reality itself, yet in such a way that it doesn't take you out of the world. Instead, it places you deeply into the womb of our world as a future creative woman."

Rose pauses for a moment before she replies, "I hadn't thought of that. I did notice that some of my friends ask for a lot of details about my visions and my new abilities. I actually felt reluctant to share more about this. Now I understand what my inner resistance was about. I'm glad I can trust my inner wisdom to guide me to what I can share with whom, and when."

"Precisely. You're being invited to live into a larger universe which has been longing for you just like you have been longing for it. There's a kind of marriage with this larger universe, which is deeply personal, and therefore, deeply realizable. Developing these new states of consciousness is not just about counting breaths or going into a meditation or a slightly altered state. Your question concerns the exploration of the living consciousness of the Universe. As it invites you to join it in the living consciousness, you fertilize and shape the new ideas together."

"But, Grandma, if people don't see an immediate personal gain for practicing these new consciousness states, would they be willing to invest the time and effort to go through this process of inner transformation?"

"Many won't, as you know. Yet your passion is contagious. When people feel inspired by your journey, they may be willing to explore what this is all about. Let me share something that may help you to understand better why so many people are not available for deep transformation."

"Yes, please."

"There are two roads that run parallel to each other. One is the road of madness. The other is the road to the ultimate realizations. It is precisely this road that many are frightened of. We've been kept from this road since time immemorial. 'Don't go there; you'll fall off reality! Your life will never be the same again!' But what if 'falling off' is an actual creation of the circuitry, both in the brain as well as in a theoretical sense, to get us onto the road of realizing what totality actually means?"

"How do I know I'm not on the path of madness, Grandma?"

"Because, sweetheart, you do know the difference, and you can stop yourself. When you ask people to experience what they've never experienced before, and tell them that it's beyond the known worlds, their minds may fear disappearing into the great emptiness. Somehow you are inwardly wired for these experiences, fit to enter into the heart of reality. Yet many may feel like they're going mad with nothing to hold onto. Genius and madness are very close to one another. It may only be one circuitry of difference that makes the difference."

"Why am I not going mad with these life-altering experiences?" Rose still feels concerned, especially now that she realizes it could come down to a slight difference in inner wiring, even though she knows that wires manifest from the implicate structures within her.

"Because you trust in the Cosmic architecture of life, which has an evolutionary structure," Verdandi explains. "And you're able to let go and play. You aren't compulsive with your discoveries. You can have a good laugh about yourself. You know when to not take yourself too seriously. If you were to become compulsive, obsessive, or controlling in your attitude, you may flip onto the path of madness. Please remember this always. Dance with this process. Don't let these discoveries or Cosmic forces ever overtake you. The same goes for your relationship with archetypes. They're wonderful allies, but don't let them overtake you. Your inner being and your personal space are for *you*, not for anyone else. This is private to your unique relationship with the Cosmos and your soul."

A few days later Rose calls her grandmother again for a practice to help her safely enter into the future consciousness states of the possibilities that are calling her. Verdandi has anticipated this, which is why she urged Rose to develop her daily self-care practices first. During their call, Rose closes her eyes as she listens to her grandmother's voice and surrenders to her guidance.

Practice for Accessing New Consciousness States

Verdandi takes a deep breath and suggests that Rose do the same.

"Relax and bring your attention inward. Let go of the outer world and trust in the guidance of your inner wisdom. Be fully relaxed now; so relaxed that you feel like you're melting while you go deeper and deeper within. You've now become so utterly relaxed and receptive to yourself that you are fully present in the center of your being.

"Take a moment to be centered within yourself. This is also the awareness of your creative essence. Observe what comes and goes within your mind without getting involved in any of the images, thoughts, or memories. Just let it all be; do not engage it. The mind is unwinding and decompressing now. Any of its activities that enter your awareness are simply part of its release, so you can enter yourself more deeply.

"Form the intention now to enter the inner dimensions of yourself that are beyond your ordinary mind. Go deeper and deeper into yourself. Cross the inner thresholds of all your former realities. You're going beyond the inner worlds and realities you know, and you're entering the unknown. Know that you are safe. Your innate wisdom will guide you. It knows the way, as it lives beyond the realms of the mind.

"Form the intention to enter the unborn dimensions of your inner being. You've now left the known worlds behind you, as your inner wisdom guides you further into the unborn potentials of yourself. Again, know that you are safe. Your inner wisdom knows the way.

"While you enter the unborn dimensions of your inner being, you're invited to enter the great Cosmic darkness. This Cosmic darkness may appear as dark for your mind, yet it is full of life; full of possibility. It is a sacred womb in which the unborn potentials are given a home to be fertilized and born into the worlds of form.

"Take some time to simply be present in this sacred womb, which your soul knows deeply and recognizes. Form the intention to meet here the unborn qualities of your future self that you've never met before in this way. Meet the parts of you that have never been experienced by you before, and have not yet been born in the world of form.

"Take another deep breath. While you breathe out, relax even further. Open yourself to a whole new experience of yourself. Your innate wisdom is guiding you to the unborn qualities of consciousness that belong to the higher Cosmic orders of your Cosmic self; some of which have never been in a human experience before. Trust your inner wisdom to guide you to experiences that you're ready for, from the womb of the unborn qualities of your Cosmic self.

"Imagine these qualities coming together now into the shape of a being. It is your future being. This future being is reaching out to you, extending its hand to you from the unborn dimensions of yourself. Take its hand. As your hands touch and merge, you're given direct access to new states of consciousness and abilities that are here to support your further growth and actualization.

"This future being lends you their eyes as your eyes, their ears as your ears, their heart as your heart, their mind as your mind, so that together you can experience who you are becoming, thus further actualizing who you truly are.

"Fully explore these new states of consciousness and abilities of your more realized Cosmic self. Experience this with all of your senses and your whole self on all levels: physical, emotional, mental, spiritual, and energetic.

These new states of consciousness also have an innate wisdom compass for knowing and discerning the directions and actions of your optimum choices and greatest possibilities.

"Explore these new states of consciousness over the next 5 minutes of objective time, equal subjectively to all the time you need to experience the depth and wholeness of these new states of consciousness and abilities.

"When you've experienced and received all you need, you may return to the time and place of your local reality. You are attuned now to your higher becoming, fully present in your body. When you're ready, you may open your eyes and complete this practice by bringing forward the qualities and capacities of these new states of consciousness with greater ease, clarity, and direction."

Bees and Dragonflies

Rose received powerful visions and revelations while in the new states of consciousness. She discovered future archetypes of transformation that are part of the pattern of metamorphosis. She's not yet able to speak of all she's seen and experienced. To integrate her experience, she visits the park near her apartment. Verdandi told her to only call again after she'd had the chance to integrate these new revelations in her body, and not just her mind.

"Hello, little bee," Rose greets the tiny winged creature that has just landed on her sweater. "You want to rest on my arm? You're welcome to do that, but don't sting me, okay? I'm a Rose, after all." The bee rubs its tiny front legs over its antennae. "Look at you. You're such a clever little creature. You can even change your gender if you need to. You're a tiny miracle."

The bee flies off toward a nearby lilac bush where other bees are busily going about their business. Rose watches them move from flower to flower. The rhythmic humming of the bees and the scent of the fresh spring flowers put her into a light trance. Her favorite smells are those of purple hyacinths, irises, and lilies, which remind her of the fleur-de-lys on the shields and furniture of her parents' home: heritage of her European lineage from the Merovingians.

The bee is revered as an important symbol in her spiritual tradition, and not just for fertility. The Queen Bee is an archetypal guardian of the Cosmic hive, a high priestess who can fertilize the new worlds that are born from this hive.

Rose's attention is diverted by the splash of a frog leaping into the pond. A dragonfly is resting close to the water's edge. "Lift up, little dragonfly! Quickly, before you become frog lunch." The dragonfly tilts its head. "You look small now, but I know that long ago you were a mighty dragon. Show your true self to the frog so it leaves you alone."

Rose loves to speak with the animals, insects, flowers, trees, and plants. She really is a child of nature. The dragonfly has beautiful iridescent blue-green wings, and looks as if it came straight out of a fairy world. Dragonflies are known to lift the veils of consciousness so we can become aware of the invisible worlds. They carry us into the dreamtime…

Integration - The Key of Self Awareness

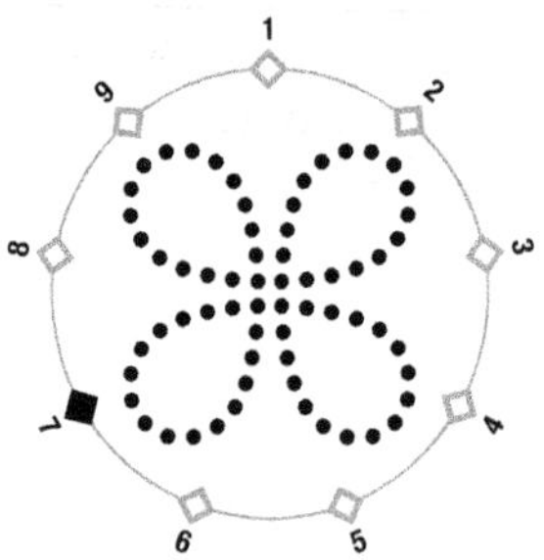

Through this chapter you received two practices for your daily self-care and a powerful practice for entering into the new consciousness states of your future human potentials. You also received the Key of Self Awareness for developing a living foundation for your inner growth and development.

> *The Key of Self Awareness helps you to presence and become the consciousness of your future human potential as a Cosmic human.*

The summary below will help you to integrate these discoveries further:

- Your Cosmic presence is always within you as your awareness, which enables you to direct, focus, and shift your self awareness from wholeness and unity. Your self awareness is your key for developing your consciousness states, which gives access to different realities and abilities, including untapped resources.
- Apply the Key of Self Awareness to refine, and perhaps even evolve, your intentions. The intention with which you enter into different states of consciousness also influences your experience of that state.
- Spend a few minutes each day to simply be and exist as awareness; as Cosmic presence. Allow your awareness "as presence" to become as natural as breathing. The effortless presence of existence can also be experienced as a deep silence of being.

- Awareness is like a calm lake of consciousness. It doesn't become what it reflects. Instead, like a mirror, it reveals all from the true essence of what is.
- The Cosmos is always in a state of unconditional sharing. Your inner work is essential for becoming more receptive and able to receive, integrate, and apply this enormous Cosmic sharing.
- The archetype of the beloved can provide profound mystical understandings of the nature of reality. From an inner state of union, the whole Universe comes alive with meaning.
- When your awareness becomes focused like a laser beam, the light can become too intense. Remember to be gentle with your focus. Give yourself moments for resting and relaxing in the sacred darkness of your being. This can greatly release stress from your nervous system and help your consciousness to reintegrate into the unified field of being.
- Our capacity to shift between states of information, from the superposition quantum state to singular states, seems to be related to the Cosmic architecture of quantum gravity thresholds that form part of fundamental ripples in space-time geometry. It also relates to our capacity to choose and have self-conscious experiences. We are a universe in miniature: a Cosmic fractal of consciousness in-form.
- Discover what changes when you relate with the Universe as a sentient being and connect with the geometry and sound harmonics of life as ways in which the Universe communicates and self-creates. You are a creative universe, and as humans, we get to tell the story and laugh about it all.
- When we deeply understand what matter truly is—the informational building blocks of consciousness—we discover the keys and ways for designing and developing the regenerative systems, technologies, and growth models that are made to thrive.
- Consciousness is non-deterministic. It's not an algorithm or computational formula. It provides space for new choices. It also provides understanding, which machines and artificial intelligence cannot produce.
- Consciousness is not bound by the physical laws of space-time. One way for understanding this is through nonlocal particle connectivity,

which can take place without information transfer through space-time.

- Your capacity for nonlocal connectivity is *your spirit.* Your spirit is always sourced from the universal and eternal dimensions of consciousness.
- Love is the only force of the Universe that is capable of melting away the distances and barriers of the mind. When love is present, understanding comes naturally. That is consciousness.
- Your life is a Cosmic coordinate and cornerstone of a larger story; a mythic cell within the Universe's story.
- Genius and madness are on parallel tracks. One circuitry can make all the difference. Remember to laugh about yourself. Know when not to take yourself too seriously. That way, you will avoid becoming compulsive.
- Your inner being and personal space are for you, not for anyone else. This is a private, unique relationship with the Cosmos and your soul.

CHAPTER 8

The Cosmic Butterfly

Metamorphosis with the Key of Becoming

Rose is excited to talk with her grandmother. "Hey, Grandma, is this a good time to share with you? I've been having so many new ideas and visions since you gave me that practice for accessing new states of consciousness."

"Go ahead, dearest. This is a perfect time. It must've been quite something to sit with this by yourself for all those days before talking about it." Verdandi laughs and gives Rose a teasing smile. She's glad that Rose gave herself the time she needed to integrate and embody what she discovered.

Rose dives right in. "When I entered my future being, I became aware of a huge caterpillar that started to cocoon itself to transform into a butterfly. It showed me five distinct stages of its metamorphic transformation, guided by five future archetypes. My future consciousness then shared a message with me: 'Work with these archetypes to build the new civilizations.' When I asked how to name these archetypes, I was shown a powerful vision, along with the information I'd requested.

"The first archetype helps us to access our Cosmic potentials and architect our world from the code of wholeness, so it's called 'the Wholeness Coder.' The second archetype helps us to bring the future possibilities into life, so it's called 'the Future Creative.' The third archetype helps us to go through the inner transformations and accelerates our evolutionary capacities, so it's called 'the Evolutionary Catalyst.' The fourth archetype helps to weave the future patterns into the necessary foundations and building blocks for a new world, so it's called 'the Pattern Weaver.' When I connected with the fifth archetype, I saw us living the new mythos and sharing the stories of fertility, abundance, and wholeness. It's called 'the New Paradigm Storyteller.'

"I saw how they all work together to help us access and actualize our future human potentials and purpose for this time of transition, from the codes of the new era."

"That's fascinating. Bravo!" Verdandi says, intrigued. "Tell me more about the caterpillar. Why do you think it came to share this with you?"

The Key of Becoming

Rose replies, "To show me the pattern of metamorphic transformation. I feel there's so much we can learn from caterpillars, especially now. The caterpillar contains within its skin the genetic codes of the butterfly in the form of imaginal discs. These are different from the genetic codes of the caterpillar. It showed me how, as one being, it has two unique bodies that each belong to a different type of consciousness. Each has unique and different capacities. Its caterpillar consciousness is that of a crawly creature, close to the ground, that's always hungry. It consumes and consumes, to the point of collapse. Whereas its butterfly consciousness is of a winged creature, made to fertilize and cross-pollinate our world with its light touch and expansive view.

"Don't you think this offers a powerful metaphor for our time, Grandma? Especially since we also carry within us two bodies of time. One belongs to the old era of overconsumption and physical expansion, and the other belongs to our new era where we learn to live lightly on the earth by learning the essential lessons of fertility and co-creation."

Verdandi listens attentively. "You're onto something, my girl. Keep going."

"The imaginal discs of the butterfly are like stem cells, which later become the imaginal cells that form the organs and body of the butterfly. The imaginal discs are kept in a state of dormancy by the juvenile hormone of the caterpillar. When the caterpillar grows older and increases in weight, the juvenile hormone decreases and a molting hormone called 'ecdysone' is released. The ecdysone is what activates the imaginal discs. Once the juvenile hormone drops below a critical threshold, the next wave of ecdysone hormone catalyzes the change of the caterpillar skin to transform into a chrysalis. When the chrysalis has formed, the caterpillar's body releases specific enzymes that turn its body into a nutrient soup, which the imaginal cells then use to start forming and growing the butterfly body."

"I agree with you, Rose. This is a very powerful metaphor for understanding the renaissance enzymes we spoke of earlier. These enzymes are flooding into our world right now, supporting the dissolution of the necessary breakdown and collapse, so that a new rebirth can take place from higher orders of reality. Many of these social, political, and economic enzymes are misidentified. They're mistaken for a threat by those who desperately try to keep the old archaic systems in place. What you're saying is that these enzymes are essential to make the caterpillar body utterly useful, as a nutrient soup for building the new body of the butterfly."

"That's right."

"Your metaphor could help people understand how the past can be integrated into the new future states, instead of being rejected. Humanity needs to learn to work with these enzymes, and not fight them, like we're doing now. Keep going, Rosie. I'd like to hear more."

Rose is encouraged by her grandmother's enthusiasm. "Evolutionary biologist, Elisabet Sahtouris, also explains how the caterpillar that overeats itself to death can be likened to the overconsumption of our economic systems, whereas the butterfly can be likened with our vision for a new world of a lighter and more fertile consciousness.[11]

"This time of COVID restrictions has all the characteristics of a cocoon. People are forced to stay home and they're restricted from moving—just like being inside a cocoon. The engines of our economies are put to rest because the caterpillar can't consume anymore once it's within the cocoon.

"Death is happening at all levels of our society right now," Rose continues. "People are dying, cultures are dying, systems are dying, many species, forests, rivers, and oceans are dying. A lot of this dying is due to our own misguided actions, but this is not the end of our world. At the same time, there's a powerful activation of our future potentials within the imaginal discs of our own future selves. The imaginal discs are awakening and grouping together to form the imaginal cells and organs of a new butterfly civilization."

"Indeed, love," Verdandi smiles. "That's why I suggested you reach out to your fellow 'questers' so you can help each other become these powerful imaginal cells and organs.

"As you know, Rose, for a long time I've had an interest in the change of civilizations, as well as all matters of life and death. I've studied the rise and fading away of many civilizations, and those that have been transformed through something akin to a hybridization. But there is yet to be a civilization that undergoes the kind of death-and-rebirth process that we're living through right now; a process where we come to know the essence of our individual transformation as manifest through the experiences of those who have completed it, like the prophets, enlightened individuals, and our mythic heroes.

"We're now being challenged to transform in collective ways like we've never done before," Verdandi continues. "This might be precisely the reason why, during your practice, you didn't see one or two archetypes, but a whole group of five future archetypes working together as one coherent pattern of transformation. I hope that the decaying structures of the old empire civilizations and their aspirations for world dominance learn to die as well so the regeneration of our social bodies can take place in the best of possible conditions."

"That makes a lot of sense, Grandma. Maybe because those archetypes are from the future of a new era, they're also showing us a new archetypal way for changing and transforming. In fact, they showed five stages of change, from potential to actualization. I was so excited to learn this that I actually drew it out in my journal."

"That's wonderful, Rose. I'd love to see it," Verdandi tells her.

Rose runs into the bedroom and grabs her journal from the nightstand. She opens it to the pages she filled with drawings and holds them up for her grandmother to see.

"You've been busy!" Verdandi laughs.

"Yes, I have. See here? I used the torus as the larger background structure because it accurately represents the growth patterns of nature and our universe. Within the torus, you can see the flow dynamics of the Cosmic architecture, as well as the Cosmic womb and cocoon as the points of singularity and convergence. All of that is in the middle of the torus. This is also the place where the nonlocal Cosmic potentials impregnate in the holographic data-structure called space-time, to be born as energy-matter and form part of our physical world."

The Actualization Process

Wholeness Coder		Activating your future potentials through conscious choice
Future Creative		Engaging your future possibilities through your imaginal powers
Evolutionary Catalyst		Developing your future capacities & transitioning to the new systems
Pattern Weaver		Embodying the future states & entering into emergence
New Paradigm Storyteller		Actualizing the future potentials by being the new realities

Verdandi studies Rose's map. It includes so many elements of Rose's journey over the past months.

"This is beautiful, Rose. Your map also illustrates how the butterfly body can only be built by the butterfly consciousness and not the caterpillar consciousness, which would stop the linking up of the imaginal discs to become the imaginal cells. Please tell me more about this actualization process; it sounds like another major Cosmic Key you've discovered."

Rose takes a deep breath, and with great enthusiasm, gives Verdandi the full download of her recent discoveries. "It *is* a major Key. This actualization process starts from the future that already exists within us as a Cosmic potential, though it's in a state of dormancy. With the help of the Wholeness Coder archetype, we become aware of our future choices and the necessity for change. This is when our future potentials start to activate. We now shift into code consciousness and become aware of the realities behind our daily reality. This helps us become aware of the deeper structures of our belief systems and experiences, and we learn how to make the higher order choices of the future potentials—the potentials of the new era."

Rose continues, "After the activation of this first stage, the future possibilities begin to awaken within our minds, which enters us into the second stage. The Future Creative archetype now helps us to enter into imaginal consciousness so we can experience the future possibilities of our future potentials. This usually manifests as an influx of new ideas, intentions, visions, desires, and a sense of new directions. This stage of imaginal engagement with our future possibilities also signifies a time of 'mental pregnancy,' through which the imaginal cells of our future potentials start to impregnate and germinate within the fields of our local selves.

"This imaginal pregnancy of our future potentials catalyzes a process of deep inner transformation, which enters us into the third stage. With the help of the Evolutionary Catalyst archetype, we now enter into evolutionary consciousness and learn how to cocoon during this phase of deep inner transformation and work with death, as well as new growth. During this phase, powerful transformation enzymes start to dissolve our former structures and identities that no longer serve the next stages of our growth. This third stage is also the time during which we're developing our future capacities and inner systems for transitioning from the old to the new states.

"The completion of the cocooning phase is the fourth stage of our actualization. With the help of the Pattern Weaver archetype, we now enter into integral consciousness and learn how to complete the formation of our new bodies of consciousness and get ready for birth and emergence. The time of the cocoon now concludes as our future bodies of consciousness have developed to the stage that they can empower us to live and become the new realities."

"So we're ready to emerge!" Verdandi exclaims.

"Yes," Rose says. "As we emerge from the cocoon, we enter the fifth stage of our actualization process. With the help of the New Paradigm Storyteller archetype, we now enter into thrivability consciousness and learn how to fertilize our world with the new realities and patterns that we now embody and which have become actualized within us. We now become the living stories and storytellers of the new mythos, communicating abundance, prosperity, and wellness for all of life."

"This is brilliant, my girl. Absolutely brilliant. Keep working with this process. It sounds like the future gave you an entire system that can be applied for our personal, collective, and civilizational transformation. Where do the Cosmic Keys of Consciousness that we've been working with fit into this system?"

"Each of the Keys can be used during any of those stages, Grandma. I wrote them down in my journal in an order that feels natural to me.":

1. *Stage 1—Future Potential: The Key of Conscious Choice*—For entering into the consciousness states of our future human choices, which activate the future potentials within us.
2. *Stage 2—Future Possibility: The Key of Imaginal Power*—For opening the inner portals to the imaginal realm of the Cosmos from where we can experience and engage the future possibilities of the unified field of consciousness.
3. *Stage 3—Future Capacities: The Key of Darkness*—For accessing the deeply transformative forces of the unconscious and embracing the evolutionary tensions and growing pains when enzymes are dissolving former structures, while new capacities and internal systems have not yet fully formed.
4. *Stage 4—Future Embodiment: The Key of Self Awareness*—For developing the integral systems and future patterns from the embodied awareness of our future selves, so we can emerge from the cocoon and be born into the new world.
5. *Stage 5—Future Actualization: The Key of Cosmic Communication*—For becoming the living stories of the renaissance that has taken place within us and fertilizing our world with the future potentials that are now actualizing as our new realities of being.

Verdandi pauses for a few minutes to integrate all that she's just learned from Rose. She recognizes how Rose's inner work with the sacred darkness has helped her to become much more conscious of the deeper implicate structures of wholeness. These structures are now guiding her to conceptualize these new ideas as whole archetype systems.

"Thank you for the overview, Rose. It's really insightful, and it certainly explains why so many of people's visions and ideas fail to manifest fully in the world."

"Really? Why is that?" Rose asks.

"Because it's not sufficient to merely glimpse our butterfly potential from our caterpillar state of consciousness. Trying to construct a butterfly body with the old patterns, systems, and behaviors of the caterpillar doesn't create the right evolutionary fit. It's like teaching an elephant how to fly, unless you're that elephant from the movie with the huge ears."

Rose laughs as she pictures that. "Look at what's happening in our world. It feels like humanity is only at the stage where the imaginal discs start linking up to become the imaginal cells."

"Why do you say that?" Verdandi asks.

"Because we haven't yet been able to develop a collective body of butterfly consciousness at a scale that all of us can work with. Sure, some groups may already be forming the butterfly organs, but with so much competition and lack of deep collaboration, I don't see how any of this has progressed past the stage of mere organs. We don't experience or prioritize life as a conscious collective."

"Well, it's a process. Give people time. I think it would be a good idea to thank these future civilizations for giving you this process. While it has always lived in Nature herself, what you received can be of tremendous use to humanity."

"I hope so."

"Now, are you up for a little challenge? Why don't you create a practice for me this time so I can experience a process with the five future archetypes?" Verdandi smiles.

"Okay, Grandma. I kind of expected you to pull that card at some point, so I came prepared." Rose and Verdandi laugh together.

"You know me so well." Verdandi chuckles. She closes her eyes. She looks forward to being guided by her granddaughter.

Practice for Invoking the Five Future Archetypes

"Take a deep breath and relax. Simply be present, here and now. Let go of the outer world. Relax and bring your awareness back to yourself. Breathe in and breathe out. Connect with your imaginal powers and feel how this naturally activates your Cosmic awareness. You are now able to sense, see, feel, hear, intuit, and receive information that originates beyond your ordinary state of mind. Your Cosmic mind is present inside your local awareness now, providing you with direct access to your imaginal capacities.

"Make yourself utterly receptive. Let go and relax even more. Allow your Cosmic awareness to guide this process. We will now start the invocation of the five future archetypes for the actualization of your Cosmic future human potential.

"To begin, let us invoke the Wholeness Coder archetype. This is the archetype that activates the Cosmic potential of your future self and helps you to become aware of the higher choices that are required for starting the actualization of this potential. Feel your Wholeness Coder capacities activate. Shift your consciousness into code state so you can directly access the Cosmic potential of your next evolutionary cycle. This activation can feel subtle. You may experience it as an inner warmth or inner glow. However subtle, just trust and know that the activation is happening.

"Next we'll invoke the Future Creative archetype. This is the archetype that activates your imaginal powers so you can experience the future possibilities that emerge from the Cosmic potential that is now awakening inside you. Become aware of these future possibilities while the Future Creative archetype shifts your consciousness more fully into the imaginal state. Experience these future possibilities from the imaginal state of consciousness. You may see visions, or get a sense of a deeper purpose, or simply feel a gentle warmth spreading through your being.

"Now we invoke the Evolutionary Catalyst archetype. This is the archetype that activates your evolutionary capacities and provides you with the womb conditions for bringing your Cosmic potential into this world. It also helps you to develop the evolutionary organs for developing the embodiment of your future potential. Feel how the future possibilities of your Cosmic potential are entering into our world in this time and space. Ask the earth to support you with her evolutionary powers and resources. Your Cosmic potential is now able to enter into the great womb of life, where it is growing its evolutionary body for the full actualization of your Cosmic potential as a living reality.

"We now invoke the Pattern Weaver archetype. This is the archetype that activates your integral capacities and helps you to embody the actualization of your Cosmic potential. It supports you with further conditions and capacities that enable your Cosmic potential to actualize more fully as a present reality.

"Feel how your Cosmic potential has become an embodied reality. Feel it start to inform the world around you with new, Cosmic patterns. As these patterns flow out, the world around you becomes resonant with these patterns, and confirms this by supporting it further. With the support of the Pattern Weaver archetype, it is now also becoming a reality for the rest of the world.

"Now we invoke the New Paradigm Storyteller archetype. This is the archetype that activates your capacities to fully thrive and share your story with others, so you can inspire a similar transformation in others and for our world. This archetype is supporting you with the conditions and capacities for your Cosmic potential to become a fully embodied living reality.

"Feel the full actualization in your whole being and your whole body. You have birthed a new possibility into our world. You have become the future possibility for a world where all of us can thrive together; a world of prosperity, joy, and natural abundance. You've become the living story of the new realities that are available to humanity through the emerging new era. The more you're able to actualize your potential and the future possibilities that are your purpose to bring forth, the more you can live from the state of thrivability consciousness; the state of abundance and flourishing. Realize deeply the keys for co-creating this more beautiful world and future with others.

"Experience the new story of your life and how it forms part of our emerging collective story. It's a story of abundance, love, wholeness, and unity. While in this state of thrivability consciousness, notice how you're naturally drawn to the patterns of ecological abundance, prosperity, fertility, health, and wellbeing. With this consciousness, everything you come into contact with becomes fertile with Cosmic potential. As the activated future human, you now have the gift of awakening the Cosmic potential of our world from this new cycle of creation.

"When you're ready, you may gently complete this practice, being fully present and balanced, here and now. If your eyes were closed, you may now open them, knowing that you're looking into the world via a deeper actualization of your future human potential."

Building the Future Civilizations with the Future Archetypes

"Ahhh, thank you, Rosie. That was delightful. This is the first time you've guided me through a full practice like this. Just wonderful. Please share this with Sophia and let me know of her experience as well. I'm sure she'll love it."

Rose hears first one dog, then two, then three dogs begin to bark in Verdandi's living room. Her grandmother laughs. "My furry alarm clocks. Well, at least they waited until we ended the process." Verdandi turns her attention to Merlin, who pokes his nose up against the computer screen. She scratches his ears. "You think you've been patient enough? Alright, you rascals, I'm coming." She turns back to Rose. "Dear one, the forest is calling me, and so are the dogs. If I wait any longer, they'll let themselves out, and your grandpa, too! Not that I could ever keep him on a leash." Verdandi chuckles, "Call me again in a few days."

"Will do. Enjoy your walk and say 'hi' to Grandpa for me."

Guiding her grandmother through this practice was a form of initiation for Rose. It's the first time she's applied her new capacities so consciously.

In the afternoon, Rose invites Sophia for a cup of tea and a slice of homemade carrot cake to celebrate this new stage, and also to offer her friend the same practice. Sophia is very curious. Afterward, the two women start to explore more of the unique qualities and abilities that each of these future archetypes inspire.

Sophia recognizes similar qualities from teachings she received about archetypes from her indigenous friends and her own grandmother in Australia. She recognizes the Law Maker in the Wholeness Coder, and the Seer and Vision Keeper in the Future Creative, as well as the Healer and Shaman in the Evolutionary Catalyst, and the Magus and Path Maker in the Pattern Weaver, and the Storyteller and Seed Bringer in the New Paradigm Storyteller. She asks Rose how the archetypes would look if placed in the pattern of a Medicine Wheel, which becomes the following image:

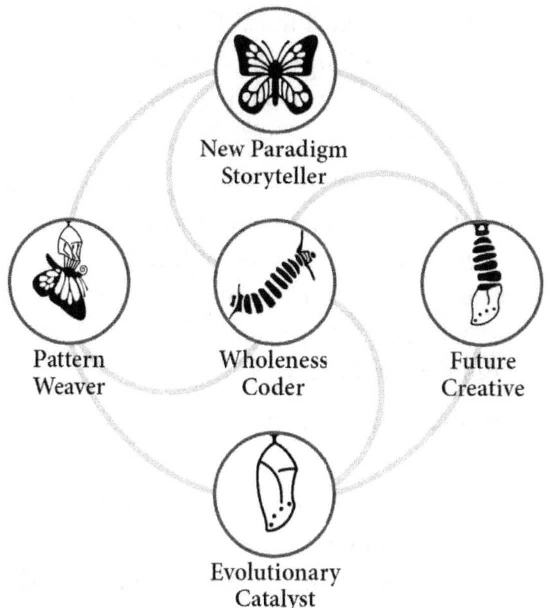

"Rose, could it be that these future archetypes are actually showing us the profiles for building the new civilizations that aren't made by semi-robotic humans? Imagine implementing those future archetypes as profiles for designing the skills and qualities of the new systems and cultures. In any case, every culture already has archetypes, yet most people aren't aware of it. Instead, we just say, 'This is such a great organization to work with. People are genuinely caring and interested here.' Or, 'This company is horrible. I can't stand the people here. Everyone is so bossy and bullying.' Every system has archetypes. We're systems, too. Let's invoke the right archetypes that can help us to co-create the more enlightened cultures for our world."

"That's a great idea, Sophia. Yes, if those archetype profiles can be implemented in schools, organizations, and even governments…Just imagine it! I would've loved to go to school or university learning how to design, architect, build, and communicate from these deeper archetypal structures of our future consciousness. These might even be the psychic structures of our future civilizations, which are coming to us now to guide us forward. Just like they came in earlier renaissance periods."

"Can you tell me more about the kinds of skills and qualities that would go with each of these future archetypes?" Sophia asks.

"Sure. Wholeness Coders are the designers, system architects, law makers, and code developers of our world. They think and communicate in symbols, laws, principles, codes, and algorithms. They're able to sense the deeper structural layers of reality, and know how to work with complexity. Their focus is on whole system change by including new choices, options, and open parameter settings that can evolve."

Sophia nods and Rose continues. "Future Creatives are the visionaries, futurists, innovators, new paradigm scientists, and inventors who help us see the greater possibilities of our futures and of life. They feel right at home in the imaginal realms and are like the imaginal cells that activate when things start to collapse and fall apart. They source from their future selves and live their lives as unfolding possibilities."

"That's how I see you, Rose. You're naturally in this state of being, and also the Wholeness Coder."

"Thanks, Sophia. The next archetype is the Evolutionary Catalyst. These are the healers, midwives, ecologists, regenerators, stewards, catalysts, and educators of our evolutionary process. They're able to accelerate our inner development by showing us how to enhance our evolutionary learning

and healing abilities. They guide us to our inner wisdom and help us to tap into the potentials of our larger evolutionary selves. They embody the future learning capabilities that are essential during tipping point times, and during the transition of eras. They focus on evolutionary coherence with the patterns of life, and they also support us to hospice what is dying, while serving as midwives for the birth of what is emerging. They know how to work with the enzymes of dissolution and how to move through the deep inner transformation when we are cocooning."

"I have a sense that this is the phase you're currently going through," Sophia tells her friend. "Being inside the cocoon where old inner structures and former identities are dissolving, while you're also deeply engaged in rebuilding yourself from the new potentials of your future choice."

"That's my sense as well," Rose agrees. "The next archetype is the Pattern Weaver. They're the integral connectors, system builders, and network weavers of our future worlds. They weave with the connective patterns of our future potentials, to prepare the soil for planting and developing the larger partnerships and networks of allies. They make all our beautiful visions, designs, and plans concrete by building the communities who make it happen by working together."

"That's my archetype!" Sophia exclaims, "As well as the Evolutionary Catalyst. Those two archetypes resonate so deeply for me. How about the last one?"

"The fifth archetype is the New Paradigm Storyteller. They are the cultural creatives, communicators, artists, and storytellers of the new mythos. They inspire our future becoming and communicate to actualize the future potentials in a way that is sensory rich and evocative. They know how to play with the alchemy of sound, sight, smell, taste, and touch, for awakening our hearts and souls. These are also the people who help to fertilize our world with the future patterns, and look for ways to create more abundance and share this fairly with everyone else, including nature."

Exploring the Cosmic Hologram of Consciousness

It's been five days since Rose last spoke with Verdandi. Although she's thoroughly enjoying all these new ideas, she finds it challenging to see how this can help her later in life. Especially with regard to creating a job she really loves, finding a partner who she wants to travel the world with, and going through the simple tasks of her daily life. There are days, like yesterday, when she feels sad and even misses her former routines of working in the bookshop, going out for her yoga and martial arts classes, visiting concerts with friends, hopping on the fast train to Paris for a weekend of culinary feasts and culture, and taking the next plane to New York to be with her parents.

She realizes that it's not just her own life that's been uprooted, but the lives of so many people around the world. Although she tries to make the most of the confinement situation by focusing on her inner development and exploring this new journey she is on, she does miss her old life and doesn't know as yet what new structures to build for her future life. She also wonders how many people will be able or willing to relate to the things she's discovering.

She tries to explain about the evolutionary principles of a unified and sentient universe with some of her former classmates from her university, but the conversation does not go well. She's told that what she proposes is too metaphysical. When she tries to explain how this is not metaphysics, but the emerging new physics and cosmology, she's informed that "people aren't interested in that stuff. Why waste time on things people don't want to know?"

Rose is grateful for her other friends, who seem more open to her ideas and willing to explore this with her. She realizes, however, that it's still only a very small group of people who are even willing to consider that there's more to life than what people commonly believe. She's especially grateful for the support and love of her grandmother, and decides to give her a call.

"Grandma, how can being in this new reality really change the realities around me? When I spoke with some of my fellow students from the university recently, my reality didn't shift anything of theirs. In fact, all I felt from them was resistance."

"Oh, my darling, you had one of those challenging conversations, right? Please know that shifting reality rarely happens at the level of people's minds. In any case, most of people's behavior is guided unconsciously, so keep applying your wonderful knowledge of unified field theory and nonlocal connectivity. It's a lot more practical than most people realize, especially those ignorant of the deeper realities of their own minds."

"Alright." Rose still feels a little down.

"Let's apply this through the Wholeness Coder archetype you've been discovering," Verdandi says. "Your code consciousness knows who you truly are, and it knows how to both clear and prepare the path of your future manifestation. Being a code of wholeness, you naturally strengthen the Cosmic encoding of our world and future. To be a code of wholeness is one of the most powerful and important aspects of expanded consciousness, and it also takes you directly into design mode. When you experience yourself as such a code, you're in a state of delightful epiphany; a state of incredible aliveness. Many people don't realize when they're entering this state. It comes to them as a glimpse of what a better future might feel like, without realizing they've entered the architecture of this future inside of them. Let's explore those codes more deeply for a moment. Would you say that these are also the codes of the Cosmic hologram that give us access to the potencies of the totality?"

Rose replies, relieved, "Yes, that's it. In a hologram, the information of the whole remains ever-present within its parts, even if those parts diversify or form different configurations. Every unit of a hologram contains the informational content of the whole. The holographic principle helps us understand how our universe can exist and evolve as a single unified being."

"Ha, there you go," Verdandi smiles. "Those former students you just spoke of form different configurations than your pattern of thought. Yet, they remain part of the same hologram, just activated through different settings from yours. Remember this beautiful verse of the *Isa Upanishad*, the sacred Vedic text: 'That is full; this is full. This fullness has been projected from that fullness. When this fullness merges in that fullness, all that remains is fullness.' Do you remember that verse?"

"Yes."

"You can substitute the word 'fullness' with 'wholeness' and 'completeness.' Stay in that fullness and wholeness, my girl, even when others tell you that your view of the world makes no sense to them. No need to agree or disagree. Simply remain in the presence of who you are. Remember the Key of Trinity, the Key of Darkness, the Key of Cosmic Communication, and the Key of Self Awareness."

Rose leans forward, "Ahh. Is life throwing me curve balls for me to practice and apply what I've been discovering?"

"What do you think, love?"

"It seems so, yes. I was starting to feel really sorry for myself. I felt judged and misunderstood, but that wasn't their doing; that was my own doing. Okay, I'm back in the saddle."

"Good! That's my girl. Now, let's discuss this Cosmic hologram. Remember, we aren't just holographically interconnected, but also *hologrammatically*. That's what your Key of Cosmic Communication is all about. It's possible to communicate and understand each other at much deeper layers of reality than most of our conditioned lenses allow. Occasionally, we're able to slip through the conditioned cultural, familial, and educational lenses we've acquired, through inspiration, intuition, altered states of consciousness, love, rapture, or the varieties of creative experience. Then so much more is received from the ocean of information, and many more patterns may be seen and experienced. The so-called genius is one who can hold multiple worlds at the same time. They can hold the cultural lenses of a certain skill or knowledge base, and then slip the boundaries of that base and take in the pure essence of information from the great sea around."

"Okay, I see. Is my problem of communication that I share the outcome of my discoveries, without communicating the experience?"

Verdandi smiles, "Without the experiential connection, your information doesn't connect people to the larger universe within them."

"Got it. Can you give me another example, Grandma?"

"Certainly. Look at Mozart. He was a highly structured expert within the musical base of the late 18th century. When he listened with his 'holographic ear' to the music of the spheres and to essence itself, he then restructured it within the bounds and aesthetics of late 18th century music. Mozart could get Cosmic and local simultaneously, and weave both together.

"When we shift into these holonic states of consciousness," Verdandi continues, "we start to experience how our bodies are the stuff of stars and the minerals of the earth. Our blood runs briny with the seas. We then realize how our genes are universes in miniature, coded, perhaps, with enough information to recreate the world. And our cells and organs contain the memories of all things past: the birth of stars, the coming of life, the experience of being fish and amphibian, reptile and early mammal, monkey and human, and the lure that is now calling us from beyond the horizon to enter the next stage of our becoming."

Verdandi's voice fills with passion. "That is the nature that lies within—mirroring the great external nature that has pushed the entire Universe along on its evolutionary journey. That which we call God, or the mind of the Universe, or even destiny itself may have much greater plans for us than we ever could imagine."

"Can you give me a practice now?" Rose asks cheekily.

"Absolutely. This one is for connecting with the future potentials from the emerging new era. Before we get into this, I'd like you to first become aware of how your life includes the codings of two eras; two creative cycles of consciousness. The old era that is still influencing our current world consciousness, where patterns of sacrifice, conquest, division, and duality became the dominant narrative for humanity. Notice how these dynamics have played out in your life, and may even have influenced your own sense of humanity.

"Now become aware of the new era, born from a future possibility of higher orders of reality that more directly manifest the Cosmic architecture of consciousness," Verdandi continues. "The new era brings the possibility of new growth patterns that are based on wholeness, unity, evolutionary diversity, collaboration, co-creation, and partnership with the Universe. These future possibilities are already dormant within us, like the imaginal discs that contain the genetic codes for the butterfly body in the skin of the growing caterpillar. Reflect on how the future codes of this new emerging era live in you. Which of these codes have already activated, and which are activating now? Just be present to what emerges as you ask yourself these questions. There's no need to answer me here." Verdandi pauses for a few minutes to give Rose the space to be with whatever emerges in her awareness. "Ready to continue?"

"Yes."

"Good. Reflect now on what it means for you to be part of both worlds. How do you support this transition to a new era? Connect with your readiness for becoming a future human. Do you realize how incredible it is to be born in this transformational time where you actually get to see these changes in what becomes possible and is made real? The old era of the caterpillar world of human consciousness has reached its stage of completion. As you know, we simply cannot continue the old growth patterns any further. If we do, we'll trigger mass extinction events, which is a clear sign that life is saying, 'Wise up! Time to change!'"

"I can feel it and I'm ready! This is what I came back for," Rose answers with great enthusiasm.

"I know. Now let's take this even further. Go get your pen and your journal, in case you'd like to write down your answers instead of going through it quietly as a meditation. It's your choice. As I am guiding you through the following practice, notice what activates within you, and what starts to shift." Verdandi waits for Rose to return, and then begins the practice.

Practice for Experiencing Your Future Potentials

"Take a deep breath and relax. Let go of the outer world. Bring your awareness back to yourself. Breathe in and out. Be present in the here and now. Feel your body and relax your mind.

"Connect with your imaginal powers and feel how this naturally activates your Cosmic awareness. You are now able to sense, see, feel, hear, intuit, and receive information that originates beyond your ordinary state of mind. Your Cosmic mind is present within your local awareness, providing you with direct access to your imaginal capacities.

"Bring your awareness to your future human codes of consciousness; your potentials from this new, emerging era. Hold the intention that these codes now start to activate further inside you. You may experience this as a warmth spreading through your body, tingling sensations, a deep intuitive knowing, a sense of joy and wonder, or perhaps even a smile on your face.

"Your butterfly potential is now activating further through new codes that hold the possibilities for whole new patterns of growth and evolution; a whole new stage of our human evolution and the mythic structures for further developing our future human potentials. Welcome these new mythic structures and the archetypes that guide these fresh possibilities. Feel the activation of your future human codes. Feel a whole system of support emerge and open up for you.

"You now have access to whole new abilities, perspectives, realizations, and ways of being that may be beyond anything you have ever imagined or experienced before. Allow the newness of what is happening inside you. Don't project old thoughts or concepts on this experience, just let it grow into new experiences that directly emerge from your future human codes.

"Welcome your metamorphic transformation of consciousness, as earlier and older forms of yourself become supportive of this new stage in your development. Thank your caterpillar self for how it carried your future human potential until the time you were ready to embrace it, providing the context for the necessity of change.

"Acknowledge and thank yourself for being ready for what is happening now. Enjoy this new phase and the birth of this new era in you. If you are in meditation, gently complete this practice by opening your eyes when you feel ready, being fully present here and now. If you are going through this practice as a reflective reading and writing exercise, there's no need to complete anything. Simply allow the activations to continue, and remain present to what emerges and unfolds."

Becoming Future Creative

After completing this practice, Rose goes for a walk outside in nature to integrate what she experienced. She feels that she needs more inner time to truly be present with what it means for her to live this transformation. She's aware that the growth patterns of the old era are still impacting her life in all kinds of ways. Many of these impacts feel like conflicts, inconsistencies, and stress. When she expresses herself from her feminine, spiritual, and artistic aspirations, she often feels judged, corrected, and marginalized by those who claim to speak for the majority and think she is too idealistic. Yet, where it concerns the physical and mental expressions of herself, she notices how society is all too happy to encourage this, and offers many expansive opportunities for advancing herself in those directions as "a young successful woman who looks smart and is going to conquer the world." These conflicting dynamics reveal to her a huge inconsistency, as well as major imbalances. *What does it mean*, she wonders, *to become future creative in cultures and systems that are not in touch with the Cosmic realities of life?*

When she enters into imaginal consciousness, she feels liberated, able to envision and think more freely while tapping into the creative powers of the Universe inside her. She then feels inspired and in a state of flow, while the inner portals to future possibilities open up from within her and call her forth. Her sense of reality then becomes fluid and expansive.

Yet, when she returns to the world of today and attempts to put this into practice, it's not always that free flowing. Sometimes she feels an uncomfortable pushback from people she comes in contact with, as well as from the larger flow of events around her. This can manifest as a skeptical comment from one of her friends, unexpected difficulties with certain tasks, someone trying to pick a fight with her, technical difficulties on her computer or phone, strange electrical problems, or getting caught in the rain just as she decides to go out for a walk. Anything but the higher flow states that she experiences while in her future consciousness states.

Initially, she pushes these events aside, thinking they are mere coincidences. She even wonders whether it might be due to her not being fully grounded. Lately, she's been noticing how this seems to be a pattern that lasts for a couple of days following her major inner shifts. Then all of a sudden, often a couple of days after the patterns of dissonance manifest, the energy dynamics seem to clear up. After that, the most incredible synchronicities open up, bringing whole new opportunities. It's almost as if the field of life first contracts around her, or in certain areas, before it opens wide in new ways and other areas.

She wonders if the Future Creative archetype may hold some answers to this puzzling experience, as well as the Evolutionary Catalyst. She explains to Verdandi what she's been experiencing, hoping she may offer some clues as well.

"Grandma, can you help me understand this pattern, and how I can change it?"

Verdandi smiles. She knows this pattern all too well. She has warned Rose in the past to carefully create the future from the invisible first, and to only reveal some of it when her vision has sufficiently manifested within her. This is to ensure that her inner being is able to embody and hold the space for the new codes and possibilities before collective consciousness imposes its habitual tracks and restrictions. Rose, being young and impatient, has skipped that little step.

"Rosie, explain to me how you journey into the future possibilities and repattern your life from the future."

"I start by clarifying my intention to experience the future possibilities of the new era, of a thrivable world. Then I imagine how a path opens up in front of me that brings me to these future possibilities of the more expanded realities of my future self. Once I arrive in this future world and time, I start to explore the qualities of this future world, as well as the qualities of my own consciousness. I sense the abilities that I naturally have access to in this reality, as well as the choices I've made and the actions I've taken that led me to this experience. I explore the way we, as humanity, live in this world, and the opportunities that this reality affords us."

"What else?" Verdandi asks.

"Then from the future perspective, I look back to my present life and check to see if there's anything from my present reality that needs to shift, transform, heal, or be acted upon for this future reality to be actualized. From my future capacity, I then send to my present self the support that my present self requires. This support may come in the form of light, love, or awareness. It can also take the form of new patterns, templates, codes, and visions, or even specific messages and instructions. I then visualize how the support I have sent to myself becomes a bridge that enables my future consciousness to continuously support me with all of the resources, realizations, and patterns for manifesting my optimum destiny. When this feels complete, I envision myself once again in the present; the present of a new order of reality, as I myself have changed because of my future experience."

"All of that sounds very good, love," Verdandi tells her, "but I'm missing the bridge between the informational fields of your present reality and the new patterns you're bringing forth. It sounds like your experience of the 'pushback' may be humanity's moody response at having to change, because you're changing!"

"That's what it feels like," Rose agrees.

Verdandi nods and adds, "Each time you change the field of our collective consciousness from the future, it triggers a reset in the collective fields, beyond the points where collective agreements have formed. In other words, it challenges the consciousness of humanity to grow and evolve as well.

"Please remember," she continues, "collective consciousness has a much slower rhythm of change than your mind. When your signals become too different from the signals of the field, some may feel the need to correct you, put you in your place, or somehow project onto you that what you're doing is wrong. Don't take it personally, darling. Being future creative is not always an easy task. Experiencing the thrill of the future possibilities is one thing, and preparing the ground so it becomes receptive and accepting of those possibilities is a whole other game. That's why the future civilizations gave you five future archetypes, and not just one or two. All five need to be worked with for the full actualization to take place."

Rose is quiet, so Verdandi says, "Would you like me to give you another practice? That should clear some of the old patterns and barriers to your future manifestation."

"Thank you, Grandma. I'd like that. I'm relieved to hear that this isn't all just happening in my head. I needed some clarity about what I've been experiencing. And it's not just me. Some of my friends have shared that they've had similar experiences with 'pushback.' So, bring on the practice!"

Practice for Opening the Field to the Future Possibilities

"Take a deep breath. Relax. Close your eyes. Connect with your imaginal powers. Feel your life force. Open your mind. Imagine seeing your life as a beach.

"What does the beach look like? How does it feel? What are its textures, colors, sensations, smells? What are the patterns of your beach? How does the tide enter it? Are there big tidal differences between the ebbs and flows of your life? When the water retreats, and you retreat, does it recede far back into the ocean or withdraw just a little? When you flow outward like the incoming tide, does the water cover the whole beach or just a little of it? Are there little holes made by the crabs, with water bubbling up from these little holes? Has anything washed up onto the beach? Special artifacts? Seaweed? Wood from faraway adventures? Or perhaps even a bottle with a message? Are there footsteps on your beach, or animal pawprints? Are they yours or do they belong to someone else? Allow your deep wisdom to reveal to you what you are to understand about your life when you look at this from the beach perspective.

"Now ask the beach to show you the grooves in the sand that represent old and possibly limiting patterns that capture the waves of possibility. Become aware of any such patterns that limit your natural flow of life and hinder you from fully expressing who you authentically are. As you become conscious of these limiting patterns by seeing those particular tracks in the sand, you may now form the intention for those old limiting patterns to dissolve. With your imaginal power, intend for all limiting and harmful patterns to release and dissolve from your life.

"Connect with the power of the ocean as your own creative power of life. Ask this deep and powerful ocean to send you a wave that dissolves and clears any of the old tracks, grooves, and patterns that no longer serve you. Clear these limiting things from the beach surface of your life. Feel, see, and experience now how your inner space is freeing up and getting ready for new possibilities.

"Affirm now that these limiting patterns from the past, present, and future have dissolved from your life. Look again at the beach and notice how the inner landscape of your life is changing. Connect again with your imaginal power. Feel the rich wisdom of its particulars. It is always there for you, ready to bring you the energy to swim along its shores and explore the depths and the dreams which it covers.

"If you wish, dive under the water and then rise up to the state of your future consciousness. Your future consciousness is part of the great ocean of time. It's able to show you the greater possibilities from the future that you can access and manifest right now.

"Ask your future consciousness to wash over this beautiful beach as a powerful wave that creates new conduits and patterns. These patterns and conduits are perfectly designed to manifest more of your Cosmic potential. They are deeply supportive to attract and manifest the optimal opportunities in your life. Feel how these new patterns also repattern your inner world: your mind, body, and feelings, so that you're naturally more resonant and receptive to receive the abundant goodness that the Universe wants to share with you.

"Feel, taste, see, and experience deeply the joy of living your life from these new, healthy, and more optimal patterns of your future consciousness. Patterns of optimum health, natural prosperity, natural manifestation, clear communication, intuitive direction, and more. Thank these beautiful new patterns for repatterning your life and relationships. Imagine yourself relating and living from these fresh, healthy patterns. Notice what changes and what becomes possible for you now. Affirm your readiness for these new possibilities from a place of gratitude and trust.

"When you feel ready, you may complete this practice by opening your eyes. Gently stretch your body. Be fully present in the here and now in this new, vibrant state of being."

Healing Time within the Cocoon

Rose notices an immediate shift in the energy around her as soon as she completes this practice, as if the field of the collective has relaxed. This sense of greater ease and clarity remains with her for many days. Each time she notices tensions or dissonance, whether within or around her, she repeats the practice. She also continues her daily practice of relaxing into awareness, as well as her practice for inner purification. She's been needing more sleep during this period of deep, inner work. Some of her previous COVID symptoms have also reactivated, like an inner purification. She experiences a slight rise in temperature, muscle aches, and headaches.

Sophia has been anticipating this for weeks. She's noticed similar patterns in the patients she works with at the hospital where she's doing her internship. She gives Rose immune boosting herbs and natural supplements to strengthen her body.

Rose also senses an activated presence of the Evolutionary Catalyst archetype in her field. Although she doesn't experience these archetypes as personas like Athena, Merlin, or Odin, she can feel the presence of these future archetypes as processes and qualities that become activated within her. She calls Verdandi for some healing support.

Verdandi listens to all that Rose has to share, then says, "Have you asked Mother Earth for her support? You are a child of the earth, composed of the same elements as the earth herself. Your bones are composed of the same minerals and elements as her rocks, mountains, and soil. Your blood and tears contain the same salt that is in her oceans. Your bodily fluids are formed by the same waters of life. Your body has been formed by her and nature's wisdom from billions of years of experimentation, learning, and evolution. You literally contain within you all of evolution's intelligence and wisdom, as her abilities extend into and become your abilities, and you evolve each other. Your genetic codes are a testimony to the incredible collaboration of life that made the emergence of human life possible. Call on her to partner you in this process. She is the ultimate Evolutionary Catalyst! It is from her that you'll learn to develop your evolutionary consciousness and the realization of our interdependence as you become aware of the priorities that require our collective and personal responsibilities. She will also teach how you think and act as an imaginal organ for building our dreams and visions of the new possibilities."

Rose agrees. "That makes sense, Grandma. I've been connecting more closely with Mother Earth over the last few days, especially during my morning walks. She was showing me how to become regenerative by breaking down and transforming the waste we've created so that it becomes useful to the cycles of life; to honor the cycles of death and decay as compost and nutrients for the new cycles of growth. I've also been applying this practice you gave me to grow my inner roots downward into the fertile soil of Mother Earth in order to receive all of her vital nourishment. I feel so connected and loving toward her when I do that."

"That's wonderful, love. Keep doing that. This planetary nourishment is essential for our human development. It supports our lives with vital energy, wisdom, and planetary consciousness. If there's anything you've been holding onto that's too much or not healthy for you, you can give it to Mother Earth and ask her to transmute it so it becomes useful again for the larger ecology of life. She knows how to transmute and break down the toxins and poisons to create composted resources."

Verdandi continues, "Explore this meta-level of usefulness. None of us can solve the existential crises alone. The emergence of unique and unexpected properties can combine through this evolutionary consciousness into complexities that can embody a greater simplicity, as well as a higher order of usefulness. You never know how all of the personal, societal, and collective changes add up to spectacular changes and results. Remember how we all play our role within the spiral of life. We're all part of the same evolutionary process that created the stars and planets, our human life here, the plants, trees, animals, and insects. We are one family of life."

"Ha!" Rose exclaims, "That's exactly what I mean by 'evolutionary coherence!' Remember when you didn't quite understand what those words meant when I mentioned them before? I explained how coherence emerges from the unity of a state, and evolutionary coherence is a dynamic state of unity with life as a whole. Evolutionary coherence is the presence of that Cosmic intelligence you just spoke of; the evolutionary patterns that bring us together into a greater fit for what is truly required. Like an invisible conductor in the orchestra of life that can somehow tune our dissonance as well as our consonance; our resonance with the higher octaves of being."

"I'm glad we finally have more clarity about that complex, yet essential, concept," Verdandi grins.

"Grandma, about this dissonance that's been affecting me lately...Could it be that I'm out of tune with myself? Or am I out of tune with the time of our world? I've even wondered if I'm suffering from depression, or becoming overly sensitive to all of the unrealized dreams of humanity?"

"Oh, my sweet girl. Yes, you're becoming more sensitive and you're also still going through your own death. Much of the dissonance you're experiencing is the discord of patterns that run contrary to the flow of life. Don't get caught up in this. Many are longing for the greater possibilities, and yet are not able to bring them forth. Quite often, depression manifests from blocked and aborted futures as well as unhealed disappointments and grief. Life has an innate directionality that flows forward from the future. When this becomes blocked, our energy becomes heavy. It can sink us into lethargy, cynicism, and depression. Would you like a helpful healing practice?"

"Yes, please! Some of my earlier COVID symptoms are reactivating and I need some help with all of these inner changes. There are even nights where I feel feverish and dream of death again. I also need a lot of sleep and feel more withdrawn, not really in the mood to talk to anyone. My emotions change quickly from sadness, to restlessness, worry, and at times, anger, as well. It's as if I'm cleansing out some deep processes inside me."

"I understand. For now, just relax and let yourself be guided," Verdandi suggests.

Practice for Inner Healing with the Cosmic Healing Cocoon

"Make yourself comfortable, either seated or lying down. Relax your body as much as possible. Relax your attention, and let go of any tensions. Just let it all go for now.

"Become aware of how the Cosmos is always present within you as your own awareness. You see from the Cosmos into the world via your awareness. The Cosmos is alive in you as the living architecture of your body and innate wholeness of life.

"Give the Cosmos the permission to support you through this practice in a way that is for your highest good and pure health. You can send this permission by simply holding the intention in your heart to receive the Cosmic support that is here for you now.

"Imagine how the Cosmos answers your intention by gently weaving a beautiful healing cocoon around your personal space. This healing cocoon is perfectly designed to support you with the vibrations, patterns, healing serums, and wisdom that you need. It provides you with optimum support to safely heal, repattern, and evolve with greater ease and clarity. Feel how this Cosmic healing cocoon is safely surrounding your personal space, embracing you like a warm, loving hug. It shields you from outer harm and interferences, while providing you with the support to safely surrender to your inner growth and transformation. It is also able to draw out and transmute any harmful patterns and toxins, whether those are physical, mental, emotional, or energetic toxins. All of these can be transmuted from their root cause.

"Feel now how any of those toxic and harmful patterns are being thoroughly transmuted from their root cause; repatterning, healing, and thus evolving your body, mind, and energy to create your optimum health and wellbeing. Feel the inner liberation that is taking place. You may experience this as tingling sensations or the sensation of little currents of light that are moving inside you, creating balance and wellness.

"The Cosmic cocoon continues to support you. It provides you with special healing membranes, patterns, and serums that help to regenerate the health and balance of your whole self. Hold the intention that this healing support can repair and enhance all of your genes, cells, tissues, organs, and inner systems. Feel the wonderful sensations of this serum of healing that is now flowing through your veins, and circulating to all your cells. Wherever this serum enters and touches, your inner health is revitalized. A greater clarity and deeper alignment naturally emerge. It becomes easier to access your innate abilities and future resourcefulness as this healing serum naturally clears and repatterns any harmful patterns. Even harmful viral or bacterial patterns are transformed now by this serum, so that you can all evolve together into a most healthy, symbiotic relationship.

"Feel how the pattern of greater health and evolutionary coherence initiates a deeper collaboration within your whole self, and also between your genetic codes and the codes of bacteria and viruses. All are working together now for your full health and wellbeing, supporting your vitality. Feel the genius of your collective collaboration toward this greater health and wellness of your whole system coming together.

"Rest a few more minutes in the experience of your greater health and wellness. When you're ready, gently come out of this practice by opening your eyes, stretching your body, and being fully present here and now."

The Story of the Cosmic Butterfly

Rose continues to feel the Cosmic healing cocoon around her, which is balancing and integrating her deeply. A new pattern of health is forming, as if her entire body is being calibrated to a deeper tune of being. She feels how the Evolutionary Catalyst and Pattern Weaver archetypes are deeply supporting her in this process. She plays her violin for many hours a day, as this seems to help her focus and integrate many of her experiences. One day, she even goes to the park and plays her violin beside the pond, much to the delight of those who pass by her.

A week passes. Verdandi calls briefly every few days, just to keep a pulse on how her granddaughter is doing. She's worried about her, and shares her concerns with Dagaz, her husband, but she doesn't mention it to anyone else. She longs to come and see Rose, but so far there are no flights to take her there.

She calls to share a story with Rose, a story about the Cosmic butterfly. Rose closes her eyes and allows her mind to dream and wander on the hypnotic cadence of Verdandi's voice.

"This is the story of the Cosmic butterfly, which has knowledge and understanding of all space and time, as well as all matters of transformation and rebirth. It travels with us through each of the stages of our lives, evoking and activating the gifts we have not yet actualized, and deepening those that require further support. This Cosmic butterfly lives on holographic time, which is a creative time in which all times are present simultaneously and can be selected and repatterned to support our continued evolution. Just like brains can be repatterned with new thoughts and activities, your structures of time can also be rewired. Once that happens, your living contexts begin to shift, and new possibilities open up.

"The Cosmic butterfly represents that part of your Cosmic intelligence that has lived through and has become the story of a full complete cycle of metamorphic transformation. It knows how to bring the future into being through its magical touch that naturally awakens and fertilizes the future potentials within you. The Cosmic butterfly weaves the future patterns in your life as well as the world around you as it flutters from flower to flower and from dream to local reality, and all that's in between. It also helps you develop your future capacities, assisting you to become utterly receptive and precisely tuned for receiving the signals of your Cosmic consciousness.

"Wherever it lands, the new butterfly consciousness starts to emerge, especially in those places that are painful due to suffering, death, and decay. It prepares the birth of our new era, while honoring the cocoon for the transformation it brings. The Cosmic butterfly is the Source archetype of the five future archetypes. You can call upon this archetype anytime you need support during this renaissance time of rebirth and transformation."

Rose opens her eyes and smiles. "That's beautiful, Grandma. Now I can experience my transformation as one whole, unified process. Amazing! Just like the Universe is one whole unified being, which can also be experienced through many different stages, expressions, and the full diversity of life."

"What you just shared is an essential realization, Rosie. It relates to the challenge that life is calling us to evolve into. The Indian sage, Sri Aurobindo, spoke of the emergence of 'superconsciousness' in ever more people, and this, he said, is the harbinger of the next evolution of human consciousness. This next stage is also referred to by philosophers and mystics as superconsciousness, integral consciousness, Cosmic consciousness, and transcendental consciousness," Verdandi explains. "Each represents forms of consciousness that help us realize the wholeness and unity within and between you and me, the individual and the world, the human being and nature.

"Now there is a new element that you are bringing, Rose, which is thrivability consciousness. From what you've helped me to experience through your practice, thrivability also includes the consciousness of our world and not just the individual; a world co-created and cross-fertilized by butterfly people. That is the new story." Verdandi smiles.

"Interesting," Rose murmurs. "I suddenly realize why I haven't felt attracted to many transcendental processes from esoteric teachings. Think about it. If we truly accept that we are all one, and matter is a form of consciousness, then our human physical world also expresses our states of consciousness. If we aren't happy with our physical experiences, the key is not to transcend them, but rather to infuse them with who we truly are."

"Yes," Verdandi agrees.

"The next evolutionary direction is not about ascension," Rose tells her, "but rather about incarnating and fertilizing our world with our Cosmic consciousness. To matter our world from the future potentials of the larger story we are yet to discover and experience together. That way we don't just create heaven on earth, but we realize *heaven as earth,* and through this, we reveal our true role for this time."

Verdandi acknowledges the major integration that has just taken place within Rose, as well as a deeper acceptance of her own healing journey. "How are you feeling now, Rose? How's the fever and how are your body aches?"

"Incredibly, the aches are gone and my temperature feels normal now. It's as if my bones are now able to hold the resonance of this deep inner knowing."

"Excellent. Over the next few weeks, make some time and space each day for a minimum of 20 minutes to immerse yourself in the patterns and vibrations of this larger story of us. Engage all of your senses of body, mind, and spirit when you do this. Explore this new story of the eternal Garden of Eden, and what it means to realize ourselves as Cosmic Earthlings. Become the Cosmic flower and the bee, as well as the butterfly in this garden of our 'future becoming.'"

Integration - The Key of Becoming

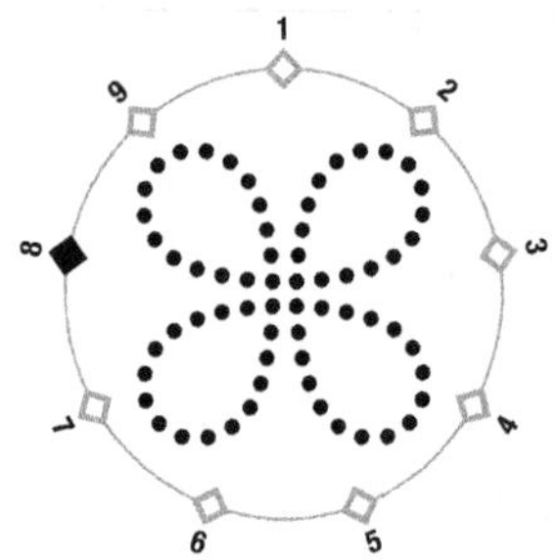

Through this foundational chapter, you received four practices for working with the various stages of your self-actualization process, supported by five future archetypes that form part of the Cosmic butterfly archetype. Explore and experience your future human potentials and the greater possibilities that you can bring forth for this unique renaissance time.

The Key of Becoming helps you to actualize your unique potentials and purpose for this renaissance time through the archetypal stages and process of rebirth, so you may blossom as a future human.

The summary below will help you to integrate these discoveries further:

- The Key of Becoming unfolds through the archetypal pattern of the five future archetypes, which mimic the butterfly pattern of metamorphosis, and which we refer to as "the actualization process." Through this process, we learn how to access and actualize our future human potentials and our unique purpose and contributions for this renaissance (rebirth) time.
- The Key of Becoming also helps you to realize how the caterpillar-butterfly is one being with two unique bodies that each belong to a different type of consciousness, each with unique and different capacities. The process of becoming a butterfly is a powerful metaphor for our own future becoming as a process of rebirth and how to

embrace the dynamics of death and collapse as transition stages and nutrients for new life expressions.

- The butterfly pattern also shows us how to work with the enzymes of dissolution in support of our inner transformation and transition to new future states. Enzymes of dissolution release during the cocoon phase of metamorphosis when former structures and identities are required to die in order to support the continuation of life in new forms and expressions. Remember to call upon the protective support of the Cosmic cocoon during these states of deep inner transformation when the old is dying and the new has not yet fully formed.
- You can call upon the future archetypes to support your process of future becoming through five stages of change: 1) Future Potential, 2) Future Possibility, 3) Future Capacities, 4) Future Embodiment, and 5) Future Actualization.
- The Torus pattern in the image of this chapter represents some of the key flow dynamics of the Cosmic architecture. Within the singularity point in the middle of the Torus is embedded the architecture of the Cosmic womb and cocoon, the places of convergence and transformation between local (physical) and nonlocal (Cosmic) states of consciousness.
- The Cosmic hologram represents the universal architecture of wholeness and unity through which the information of wholeness distributes and embeds as our universe expands and evolves. Each part and particle of wholeness, including you and your life, remains nourished and in-formed from the total wholeness of life and consciousness.
- Connect with the Cosmic hologram to explore your future choices and possibilities from this unified field of consciousness, and to communicate from wholeness.
- If you want people to be able to connect with your discoveries, remember to communicate from the experience and essence of your understanding, and not just the outcome or conclusions of your discoveries.
- Create your future from the invisible dimensions first. Make sure you can embody the new codes and possibilities before you start sharing them with the world around you; just like we don't share a baby with the whole world while it's still in the womb. Allow your future to come

into being within you first. Your inner wisdom will know when it's ready to be shared.

- By exploring the future possibilities with your imaginal powers and effecting change from the future potentials, you also change the past and present field dynamics of our collective consciousness. This can trigger a reset and upgrade of the collective fields beyond the points where collective agreements were formerly formed. Those reset and upgrade points can trigger a pushback from the dynamics of the collective fields that feel attached to or protective of the known field dynamics. You can apply the practice for "Opening the Field to the Future Possibilities" to clear dissonant patterns and create deeper alignment and resonance between the future patterns you're bringing forth and the collective fields around you.
- Mother Earth is the ultimate Evolutionary Catalyst. Call on her to help you grow and evolve. Grow your inner roots downward into the fertile soil of the earth to receive her vital nourishment. Ask her to support you in transmuting and compositing the vibrations and substances that no longer serve your health.
- Life has an innate directionality to grow, learn, and evolve, which is guided from the future states. Work with this future guidance to clear and transform the blocked energies that are not able to enter into the healthy flows of life. Blocked life-flows can sink us into lethargy, cynicism, or depression.
- Create some time and space each day to live in the larger story of your life, as a butterfly consciousness of a new era of consciousness.

The Cosmic butterfly is the Source archetype of the five future archetypes. Call upon this archetype anytime you need support in your self-actualization and to discover how to become your destiny. The brief summary below supports as a reminder:

1. Wholeness Coder archetype—*The Key of Conscious Choice*. Activation of our future potentials through future choices and the necessity for change. Code consciousness.
2. Future Creative archetype—*The Key of Imaginal Power*. Engagement of our future possibilities through new ideas, intentions, visions, desires (i.e. a "mental pregnancy"). Imaginal consciousness.

3. Evolutionary Catalyst archetype—*The Key of Darkness.* Inner transformation, developing our future capacities, transitioning from the old to the new states. Evolutionary consciousness.
4. Pattern Weaver archetype—*The Key of Self Awareness.* Developing the integral systems and future patterns from the embodied awareness of our future self, birth, and emergence. Integral consciousness.
5. New Paradigm Storyteller archetype—*The Key of Cosmic Communication.* Becoming the new story, fertilizing our world with the new realities, communicating abundance, prosperity, and wellness for all life. Thrivability consciousness.

CHAPTER 9

Becoming a Future Ancestor

Transformation with the Key of Unity

Rose turns over in her bed. She's sleeping deeply and finds herself immersed in an interesting dream filled with sensory-rich colors, shapes, and fragrances, as she transitions between the imaginal worlds and her local reality.

An Orgasmic Dream inside a Flower

Her dream starts with a pleasant voice calling her name, "Rose! Rooose… Rooooose…" As she walks toward the voice, she sees a magnificent flower. Curious to learn more, she kneels down and cups her hands above the flower. The next thing she knows, she's being transported to the inside of the flower. While slowly adjusting to the inner architecture of this magical flower, she becomes aware of tiny spheres of light that look like traveling orbs.

Are these orbs distributing food? Why can they move through the cell membranes of the flower? And how do they do that? Exploring further, she realizes that the orbs are aware of her. They respond to subtle changes in her thoughts and moods. *These orbs remind me of the Cosmic information of immortality that I experienced during my near-death experience,* she muses.

Rose feels completely at home within this flower world; so much so that she almost forgets that she's a human. The inner world of the flower feels harmonic and alive. *I feel such a joyful resonance here!* She observes the beautiful details of the petals, and feels the curves of her own body as her mind wanders around the inner curvatures of the flower. She becomes aroused as a whole range of sensual feelings and sensations flow through her body. Her body and the flower world vibrate symphonically together.

A beautiful violet light starts to glow inside the flower, as if it's emerging from the strong alchemy between the flower and Rose. Their bond intensifies. She grows and glows, and so does the light of the flower world. *This feels so wonderful...*she thinks in her dream. *I never thought a flower could turn me on like this.*

Tinkling sounds of tiny bells fill the flower world like a fairy sound chamber where the heart of the flower is shaped like a perfect dome. The little bells resound in a pattern that somehow relates to a low humming sound coming from outside the flower.

What or who is this flower communicating with? Rose wonders as she looks upward in the direction of the humming sound.

"Poof!" Something lands on the dome, which lights up from inside and starts to sing. A wave of joy and pleasure fills Rose's being. *Oh, this is one happy flower!*

A bee has landed on the flower. The bright violet light spreads through the entire flower and Rose. The bee and the flower make love with one another, exploding in the most ecstatic union, and Rose is part of it all. She realizes that the flower had been preparing for the bee.

This flower really loves that little bee. If only humans could feel the same kind of love for life and for one another. She experiences the sensual alchemy of nature for the first time. After the climax of bliss, Rose relaxes in a wave of deep peace and timeless presence.

After what feels like eternity, she wakes up slowly to the chatter of birds just outside her window. She grabs her pen and quickly jots down all of the dream's details in her journal before the dream fades away. She's created an agreement with her mind that she can access in waking life any key messages from her dreams in the form of actionable wisdom.

She sets the pen down, reads what she has written, and decides to stay in bed a little while longer to soak in these wondrous new feelings. Her body glows and tingles from the crown of her head all the way down to her toes. "This is even better than Grandma's exercises," she laughs aloud. "Please Cosmos, give me more of these orgasmic dreams. I like learning about the Universe in this way!"

Discovering the Mind of Matter

Curious to learn more about the orbs in the flower world, Rose calls a friend who works with new energy solutions. He introduces her to the word "microvita." Her friend explains how microvita are subtle, sub-microscopic living entities that organize energy to create forms, structures, and processes. Apparently, this knowledge is not part of mainstream science. Rose wonders if those microvita are the same as the travelling orbs she discovered. The yogic philosopher Shrii Shrii Anandamurti described these microvita in the following way:

Microvita move through the Universe and are the carriers of life in different stars, planets, and satellites—not carbon atoms or carbon molecules. The root cause of life is not the unicellular protozoa or unit protoplasmic cell, but this unit microvitum.[12]

This yogic philosopher also mentioned that microvita travel between the world of matter and the world of mind, appearing in both and belonging to neither. Rose's curiosity is activated. She wants to learn more about "mind," and in particular the mind of matter. She wonders, *What if the world of matter and mind are the same, so there is no travelling in between, but only a subtle shift between the layers of reality?*

She finds an article about a strange anomaly in Antarctica, which scientists are not yet able to explain, and may hint to some new forms of physics.[13] Researchers found tiny Cosmic particles, which are able to pass through any kind of matter without changing. It is said that those particles don't interact with their environment, and keep their properties.

This information activates Rose's Cosmic circuits further. *Could it be that there are many subtle layers of reality that consist of entire worlds that human minds are unaware of?*

As a biologist Rose has been studying the fractal patterns of nature for many years, and in particular, the holonic structures in the way cells form parts of larger organs. "Holos" in Greek means "whole." The term "holon" was first coined by Arthur Koestler to describe how something can simultaneously be a whole and a part of a larger whole; another way of understanding the holographic principle of the Cosmic architecture of life.

The holographic principle and nonlocal connectivity reveal how space-time doesn't just carry or transport information. Space-time is *in*-formation. She recalls her earlier conversation with her grandmother: "If we focus on information transfer within the known space-time dimensions of our world, the speed of that travel is limited at the universal speed of light. However, through nonlocal connectivity information, travel through space-time is not required. The wholeness of totality is represented in every part."

At the root of our escalating sustainability crises lives a very distorted relationship with our conception of matter and materiality. Rose can sense this as well, and is determined to get to the heart of matter. She has vividly experienced the possibility of a world that realizes matter and mind as one, and it is architected on very different principles than our current civilizations.

Biologist Rupert Sheldrake confirms the view that our universe is more like an organism than a machine. He builds on this to suggest that it would make sense to think of the laws of nature as habits of the Universe, which could suggest that the Universe also has an innate memory of everything we and it experience.[14] Add to this the suggestion of cosmologist Jude Currivan that our universe is expanding because it is learning, and a fascinating view opens up about the nature of materiality.

Rose is troubled by the many new age superficial techniques for bending matter by the power of mind because it feeds the belief of human superiority over nature and ignores a vital understanding about the nature of matter *as the implicate structures* of consciousness, and thus also our thoughts. We each think with the living architecture of the Universe, not separate from it, whether we realize this or not. *Perhaps, matter is the structure of our thoughts, and is "thinking us" to think differently of itself?* Rose asks the Cosmos, searching for answers that go beyond the human dualities between mind and matter.

Does the Universe have mirror neurons like the ones we have in our brain that help us to imitate and experience empathy? Universe mirror neurons that can mimic our neurological states so it can experience our internal states? When we eat ice cream and experience the sensations of the cold crunch when our teeth grind the ice, does the Universe have a way of experiencing this, too? How exactly do our emotional and mental states imprint on the fields of life around us? How is our experience looped into the larger Cosmic mind?

All day, Rose's thoughts fire away as she explores the boundaries and connection points of the Cosmic mind within her. Her thoughts continue to expand, even up to the point where she finally falls asleep later than usual that night.

The Call of the Raven

The next morning, she wakes early. The morning is fresh. A lonely raven outside of Rose's window pierces the blanket of mist that has engulfed the city with its grating call. Rose stares into the mist that hides the conventional contours of city life. For a minute, she feels like she's at home again in Iceland with her grandparents. Her heart longs for the warm family hugs and laughter that she misses so much. Her mind is in travel mode this morning. The mist is the perfect medium for drifting off into all kinds of realms and myths.

As she stares into the mist again, she remembers the stories of the Mists of Avalon that she learned from her family. She feels herself transported to the magical land of Merlin, the wizard, Viviane, the Lady of the Lake, and Arthur, the druid king who has been chosen to govern the humans and the magical realms as one unified kingdom.

How different that kingdom is from the nation-states of today. What happened to all of those magical realms? Why have we forgotten or left the other realms that are also a part of this earth? Rose wonders with an ache in her heart.

Verdandi had explained to Rose how, long ago, the druids were the ones who elected the kings of the humans in these parts of Europe. A king could only become a governor of the united realms if the high priest within him had awakened. To awaken this inner high priest, the king had to be initiated and anointed first by the druid high priestess, as she was the one who mediated the relations between the realms of nature and the human world. The high priestess was elected by the Goddess to be Her Avatar here on Earth.

The Goddess would make Herself known inside the body of the priestess when this election took place. This empowered the priestess with a whole new fertility power that united the various realms inside her. As high priestess, she could then conceive the spiritual essences for keeping the realms of nature fertile and the hidden worlds united.

When it was time for the druid prince to become king, the high priestess would awaken the Great Deer, the "Grand Cerf," within the apprentice king, via an intimate ceremony. Once awakened and married ceremonially, the magical realms were able to be represented within the consciousness of the king, after which, his training began in earnest.

"Now you know, Rosie, why Viviane as the high priestess is so important in the story, and not just Merlin. Viviane did a lot more than just hand the sword Excalibur to Arthur. She anointed him, too." Verdandi explained all of this to Rose after she'd had her first menses.

Rose wonders whether she has also been called or chosen from the realms of the otherworlds for a destiny she's not yet aware of. After all, she does come from a long lineage of druids, shamans, and high priestesses. She can feel how these ancient memories and energetic connections to these other worlds live within her blood. These energetic lines are so strong at times that it feels as if her blood has started to boil inside her. When this happens, it feels like the pressure forces open the inner portals of long forgotten doors to these magical worlds. Rose finds it challenging to integrate these experiences and mythical memories with the world of daily life, or the "normal" world, as many people prefer to call it.

Becoming a Future Ancestor of the Multi-World

Rose is eager to call her grandmother, who is always up early. She trusts that Verdandi will understand the aches in her heart. She gives her grandmother the full download of the burning questions in her young, restless mind. Rose secretly hopes that if people were to realize how matter is alive with spirit as an expression of consciousness, they may be more willing to embrace the fact that there's a whole lot more to life than they've previously suspected. Rose pours out her thoughts on the human duality of matter and mind, and Verdandi listens.

When Rose finishes, Verdandi sighs. "Oh, Rosie, you've landed yourself squarely in the ultimate paradox game: the dialectic between mind and matter."

Rose replies, "But what if mind is not other than matter and matter not other than mind, but only different properties of consciousness, like what I experienced during my dream in the flower?"

"Yes, my girl, for you that's easy to conceive. But for many people who do not see consciousness as the ground from which both matter and mind emerge, they believe that either matter is primary, or else they believe that mind is superior. That's why I gave you the Key of Trinity, so you could explore the paradoxes to see beyond the seeming dualities of superficial thought."

Rose is mildly annoyed. "It's not just that matter is mental, as many mentalists suggest, but mind is also matter. Both matter and mind bring each other forth. Our thoughts are formed from the base patterns of the implicate structures of reality, whether we call them 'the implicate order' of David Bohm, or 'the fundamental space-time geometry' of Sir Roger Penrose, or 'the archetypes' of Carl Jung. These fundamental in-formational structures become *thoughts for our minds and molecules and organs for our bodies.* Matter and mind are just different narrations and translations of the same fundamental realities. Our feelings might be the marriage between mind and matter, which is why feelings are so potent for manifestation."

"Sweet girl, what's really going on? What's troubling you? Is this really about wanting to convince humanity about the essence of matter? What is truly in your heart?" Verdandi knows her granddaughter all too well.

"I'm tired of living in a world that acts superior to nature while it knows nothing about nature at all. We think the tree is a commodity for making furniture or paper, or else we believe that trees are important for producing oxygen, capturing carbon, and creating a breathable living atmosphere. But who sits under the willow to travel via its trunk to the other worlds? Who talks with the pine tree to listen to its stories of history and its ancient understanding of life and connection? I feel like so often I have to pretend that the magic of nature is not alive within me, just so I don't ruffle too many feathers around me. To pretend I don't hear the whispers of the Cosmos calling me deep within my heart; to pretend I don't feel the ancient druids calling me through the ancestral connections in my bones; to pretend to fit into a world that has long forgotten its ancient roots and its origins of life. I feel really tired of this pretend game, Grandma. I just can't play along anymore.

"During my dream inside the flower, I felt infinitely more alive than I do during most days, and experienced a deeper orgasm than I've ever experienced in any of my human relationships. I felt a complete union between the lovemaking of the flower and the bee. Their sensuality is so much more advanced than ours. Human society feels so dull compared to the visions and dreams I have when I enter into these altered states of consciousness. Many of my friends go through mushroom or Ayahuasca ceremonies to get a glimpse of what I'm experiencing. For me, these altered states come naturally, and when I least expect it. I don't have to do or ingest anything for that to happen."

"I understand, my darling, which is why we decided to live far away in Iceland, close to our ancestral roots and far enough away from the pressures of modernity that we can still live our traditions. It's not easy.

"You have now arrived at the crunch moment. Several intersections come together here, which require whole new choices about the direction of your life. You have clearly been elected by our ancestors, the Cosmos, and the nature realms to be a multi-world bridge. You're a multi-world woman. Each world is represented within you and forms part of your destiny path. You feel torn when one world forces you to choose its world over the others. Remember, you're all of that and so much more.

"You're the intersection between what has long been forgotten and what has not yet been born. You're also the intersections between the magical and the scientific, the indigenous and the modern worlds. You're a daughter of the 'Huldufólk,' or 'hidden people,' like the elves, fairies, and trolls, as well as a daughter of the human race. You're the hybrid and the future ancestor of a humanity that will be married once more to the realms of nature and the larger Cosmos to which we belong. You're a new Arthurian story in the making, which this time is not about Merlin and King Arthur, but Viviane and Merlin in true partnership together with the Queen and King of Avalon. You, my girl, are a future archetype of a whole new story and the promise that we can again belong to the multi-worlds and find our roots in a far greater destiny than merely travelling the galaxies through human spaceships. Let this new world be born from within you! Pause at this pivotal moment on your path!"

Rose feels the reality of Verdandi's words awaken deep inside her. While listening to her grandmother's voice, she feels how she carries the DNA of each of these worlds inside her own being. For the first time ever, she feels a bond of union that represents a whole new partnership; a new covenant between each of these codes and origins within her. It feels like a cruel and ancient war that has played out between so many dimensions and worlds will one day be halted by this new covenant, this new bond.

She can now see how she carries the code that expresses the primordial unity between each of these worlds and paths in a whole new configuration: the future human configuration. A new choice to be a future ancestor for this new bond, that also reenacts the ancient bond of unity that has long been forgotten; the choice to belong to all the worlds of life as One. To be the rainbow bridge.

"Grandma, is this what my choice that night in the hospital has been preparing me for?"

"Yes, love. That's why you were placed in that ultimate moment of higher choice, to see if you were ready to embrace the next stages of your destiny. This also required the death of your path as a human of the forgotten bond, in order to be reborn as 'Rose, the Cosmic Daughter of the Bond of Unity,' the human who belongs to all of these worlds. You went to the classic mythical death in order to be reborn to the greater self that was already dormant within you, like the butterfly codes inside the caterpillar."

Rose notices how the mist in the city is lifting as the morning rays of the sun now warm the earth. She feels like a whole new day has just begun. She views life with new eyes that see and understand so much more than what she had focused on before. Suddenly the whole dialectic between mind and matter seems insignificant. Her purpose is awakening deep inside her being. She feels that she belongs to this bond of unity, and how, one day, a very different kind of human will be born from this unity.

The Key of Unity

Verdandi smiles as she witnesses the shift in Rose. "Now you have discovered the Key of Unity. This key will help you to play the infinity game of life without getting lost in the duality worlds of the humans who have not yet realized the larger realities they belong to. You no longer have to pretend to only be a finite human in a biodegradable space-time suit while knowing you are made of infinite God-stuff. You don't have to choose to be this, and not that. You don't have to divide or compromise yourself. Be who you are truly meant to be, Rose. Live your destiny now!

"We are each the living Universe in an eternal, spirited form of itself. We are each composed of the fractal codes of eternity experiencing mortality and endings. The human 'selfing game' may be what Cosmic infinity does for fun. Not realizing this, we live in states of galloping ambiguity, caught in limited time vehicles, and yearning for our greater selves. Then when we make the rare excursion into our Greater Being, becoming our Cosmic selves, we suddenly yearn, like Dorothy in Oz, to get back home to the farm in Kansas. Have you ever wondered why this is?"

"Because we're creatures of habit who like to seek the familiar?"

"We are indeed creatures of habit, just like nature. But there's more. The heartaches you expressed earlier are all the signs of *Cosmic homesickness*. The longing to return to the spiritual dimensions that you drank from so fully when you went to the other side of the veil the night you died. That experience cracked the veil inside you. Your inner world is now permanently receiving the light and information of these other realms. The challenge, however, is not to escape into the spiritual realms, but to become the rainbow bridge; to really feel and explore what this new bond, this new covenant, is all about.

"The ultimate challenge of life for all humans is to live in a state of both-and. The infinite never leaves us, even though we may believe it has. Nor do we ever leave the eternal 'Now.' The magical world of Oz is not far away from the farm in Kansas. The Kansas farm is the gate to Oz, once Dorothy realizes how she is the key to both worlds."

Rose listens attentively. Her eyes well up with tears as she realizes how her future human choice was always about so much more than merely living her future potential. She can feel now the architecture of this new covenant, this new bond, coming alive in her. She realizes how this bond represents peace and flourishing for our whole planet with all its myriad cultures and civilizations, both human and nonhuman. She realizes how belonging to each of these worlds is not dividing her; it's uniting her, and each of us, into a far deeper wholeness.

"Thank you, Grandma. I can understand now the source of so many inner tensions and why I felt restless, homesick, and torn in so many ways. I've been feeling the roots of this ancient war deep inside my own being. I've been part of this war and I'm an offspring of this ancient war that precedes so many of our current wars.

"Yet, as an offspring of this war, I also carry within me the medicine for its resolution, and as such, I'm the offspring of the future humans of the new bond of life; the new covenant between the many-worlds. I know what to tell the conflicting voices inside me and where they originate from. I know how to give direction to all the tensions within and around me; how to be that Key of Unity for all that became divided as we lost the greater understanding of who we are."

"That's the direction, Rosie. You see how the path you're on is more than just realizing the infinite within the finite or realizing your Cosmic identity as the essence of matter. What is forging and forming inside you is a new bond, one that has long been promised, yet the time was not yet ripe for this. Now the time is coming. You're from this future time in which this bond has already been formed. Those are your future human codes. Once you fully understand and internalize this truth, it will add tremendous power to your freedom to be who you are, as well as your capacity to grow and evolve your life from the destiny that is calling you. The poet William Blake once said,

'Eternity is in love with the productions of time.' Your destiny path is also a production of time; a new creation time."

"Can you give me a practice that will help me to integrate these inner changes further?"

Practice for Embracing Our Inner Transformations

"Make yourself comfortable, either seated or lying down. Breathe deeply. Relax your body. Relax your mind. Release any fears, worries, or anxiety. Just relax and let it all go. Now become aware of your process of change.

What is changing within you and what is changing in your life? Are there any cycles of growth and change that are completing or have completed? Are you holding onto anything that has completed its purpose and needs to be let go? Are you experiencing any loss or fear of change? Just scan and observe without diving into what you're becoming aware of. Simply notice and acknowledge your process of change. When you feel ready, affirm your commitment to your next stage of growth. You can express this as an intention that you hold in your heart, or you can say to yourself, 'I am ready and committed to enter my next stage of growth.'

"Thank your body and consciousness for all it has made possible and supported through the cycles of your life that are now completing. Thank and honor what has completed and serves no more, including the difficult experiences. Honor it all for whatever it has taught you, and then let it go.

"Remind your whole self that you are not the form of change, you are the creative process that makes change possible. You are the creative force that in-forms change. You are also the consciousness out of which new forms can be born, and within which old forms may die and dissolve. Change comes and goes, while you as consciousness remain. You are the awareness within which change takes place.

"Call now upon the butterfly pattern of metamorphic transformation. Ask the Cosmos to spin a protective cocoon around you in support of your inner transformation. You can call upon this cocoon by simply holding the intention that this pattern of transformation activates within and around you.

"A protective and supportive cocoon is now forming around you, making it easier for you to surrender to your process of change. This cocoon is perfectly designed to provide the optimum support for the dissolution of your old forms, patterns, and identities, while facilitating the emergence of your new growth. It also supports the embodiment of your future consciousness in the forms of new codes, structures, patterns, and ways of being.

"Feel the presence of this cocoon as a loving and protective warmth that surrounds you. You are held in a safe and gentle way by a deeper intelligence of life that knows just what you need. This cocoon is coded from your future consciousness. It knows the direction of change in support of your future becoming.

"This cocoon provides you with energetic enzymes that serve to dissolve any of the old patterns, forms, belief systems, identities, codes, structures, and processes that no longer serve your next stage of growth. When you feel ready, embrace and receive these enzymes to start the dissolution of your former caterpillar self. Dissolve all that is to be released and let go. These enzymes know just what to dissolve and will not affect any of the healthy structures and codes that need to remain.

"Realize and feel how you are completely safe and supported in your transformation by this cocoon. Relax and surrender to the wisdom of your process of change. Become aware now of any areas within you that require healing. Call now upon your future consciousness to transform these areas by the power of the new and future codes, patterns, and abilities of your next cycle of growth. If you wish, you may also express the intention to join the next cycle of growth from the higher orders of reality that are possible for our future humanity.

"Feel now how these next cycles of growth, your inner growth and our evolutionary growth as a species, start to in-form and repattern your field of life. They support your field of life with new Cosmic seed codes, new potentials, and new possibilities. Your future consciousness is activating even more deeply now, and is able to enact these new potentials now with great care and wisdom.

"The Cosmic cocoon provides you with further nutrients, patterns, templates, and membranes to support your inner transformation and future becoming. Your inner systems are now in glorious change: repatterning, integrating, and optimizing for the emergence of your next stage of growth.

"Any harmful viral or bacterial patterns are also fully transfigured now, so you can evolve together in healthy and mutually supportive ways. Your whole self and all of nature's potentials within you collaborate to bring you forth as your butterfly self; beautiful in purpose; healthy and vibrant. Feel the genius of your mutual collaboration toward your ability to create and thrive.

Your whole being is beautifully enhanced. Feel your growing strength and commitment to be all that you can be, as one who can truly be the difference that makes the difference.

"Know that this process will continue, effortlessly and naturally, without having to focus on it. When your inner transformation is complete, this Cosmic cocoon will naturally dissolve and your future form will emerge in the world. Whenever you require its support again for a new cycle of inner transformation, simply ask the Cosmos to spin a new cocoon around you.

"Take a few minutes to rest and integrate what you have experienced. If your eyes were closed, you may now open them. Stretch your body. Be fully present, healthy, and whole, in the here and now.

"To complete the process, bring your experience into expression. Write a poem in your journal, or make a drawing. Sing a song, get up and dance, and feel the future plans for you as you move through the room and explore the new movements of your transformation. Express yourself spontaneously wherever you are, in ways that you safely and joyfully can."

Embracing Change and Uncertainty

It's been a few days since Rose had her powerful talk with Verdandi. She continues to feel the Key of Unity activating more fully inside her. This is not just shifting her understanding of her purpose, but also connecting her with parts of herself that are beyond her life as Rose. She feels like she's becoming awake to the dimensions of her soul as she becomes more aware of the long view of life. She also starts to realize how death is truly a friend of life, and not the taker of life. "Death is the middle of a long life," is an Irish proverb that shows us the importance of dying in little ways so we may live more fully.

How do we unburden our hearts with all the tragedies that are happening right now? Rose wonders. *How do we die those little deaths so we can be more receptive to life and all that life asks for us to understand and realize right now?*

She misses her cousin Otto, who was not able to return from the other side of the veil, and is saddened by so much death all over the world. Whenever she's out in nature she feels better, more grounded and present, so she decides to go for a walk in the forest nearby. She breathes in the cool air and enjoys watching a ray of sunlight burst through the cracks of the heavy rain clouds. For a moment it feels like the light of the heavens is shining through. It reminds her of the crack within the veil that Verdandi spoke of a few days ago.

The earth is still damp from the heavy rain a few hours earlier. Her feet land softly on the rich, dark, forest ground. Spring colors have made way for the deeper greens of early summer. Rose moves her hands over the patterns in the leaves that remind her of the fractal patterns of the Cosmos. She still feels Cosmic homesickness and like she's out of touch with the realities of her current life as she starts remembering so much more from the lives of beyond.

Walking past a neighboring apartment building, she hears uplifting piano music she knows is being played by her friend Lillian through an open window on the ground floor. Lillian is a gifted pianist. At the moment she's playing Bach's Partita number 6 in E minor, which Rose instantly recognizes. She often accompanies Sophia and Rose in their violin recitals. Rose is very fond of her friend and decides to check in on her.

"Hello, Lillian!"

"Rose! It's so nice to see you. Come in."

"I heard your piano playing from the sidewalk. It sounded so beautiful. I just wanted to pop in for a minute to see how you're doing."

Lillian is genuinely happy to see Rose. She ushers her friend further into her apartment and the young women sit across from one another. Lillian serves two glasses of refreshing lime juice over ice with honey and mint.

"To life!" Lillian says. They smile and clink their glasses together.

"This is delicious," Rose says, taking another sip of her beverage.

Lillian has an incredible inner strength that Rose admires. The young woman was diagnosed with a very aggressive form of breast cancer and had her surgery a few months before the coronavirus outbreak began. Everyone felt concerned about her, as some of the cancer had already spread to other parts of her body. The doctors removed most of the cancer, and she's now being treated with a Dutch medicine called "maretak," also known as "Viscum album." It's given to patients to slow down the spread of the cancer and to boost their immune systems.

Despite all of the hardships she's endured, Lillian remains positive and full of life. Rose wonders whether this is because she came so close to death. Rose worries about Lillian's relationship with her partner Rob. He can be a difficult man at times, especially when he puts her down. Rose wonders if he does this because of the tremendous stress he himself is under as a police officer.

His parents are Creole from Suriname, a former Dutch colony. Although the Netherlands is known as a very open and liberal country, it hasn't been easy for Rob. He's often had to assert his authority as a person of color. Racial tensions have been building in the Netherlands, as well as in many other places around the world, partly due to the rise of populist, right wing parties who are playing on the growing anti-immigration sentiments of people in Europe and elsewhere.

Rose wonders at times what keeps Lillian and Rob together as a couple. Their interests are very different. She doesn't dare to ask Lillian this. *They must have a Unity Key that I don't yet understand*, Rose reflects.

Lillian suffered a miscarriage the year before when she was five months pregnant, possibly because the cancer had already started to spread. Lillian feels responsible for the miscarriage, even though she knows it's not her fault.

"Lillian, how do you live with all of this uncertainty? First the uncertainty from losing your baby, then the uncertainty from hearing the news of the cancer, now the uncertainty of not knowing if your body has healed or how long you may live, or whether the cancer could return? I hope you don't mind me asking you these personal questions, but I'm just in awe of your ability to embrace so much uncertainty while remaining positive through it all. How do you do that?"

"It's okay, Rose. You may ask. To tell you the truth, it's not easy. There are days when fear and uncertainty creep through my body. Then I have to remind myself that I never really had full control over my life in the first place. When things are going well, we like to attribute that to the smart choices we've made, or the healthy food we eat, or our exercise regime. But are we ever really in control? There's so much I don't understand and can't control.

"What I *can* control is how I choose to respond to what's happening with me, and to seek life through all of its ups and downs; the disappointments and good news moments."

"You have a fabulous attitude."

"Thanks. I'm grateful for each day I'm given. I know that, ultimately, my life doesn't belong to me; rather, I belong to life. As long as life has plans for me here, I'll be here. When the day comes that it's my time to turn the page, it'll happen no matter how hard I may try to avoid it.

"There was a defining moment during this journey with cancer when I decided to embrace death and allow it within me. I stopped resisting and learned to live with it. Now death is always with me. Every day. It's become my greatest teacher. Death teaches me to be kind and caring. It teaches me to be compassionate and to be grateful for all that I have."

"That's amazing. How do you work with death? Aren't you afraid that death is eating up the healthy parts of your cells and organs?"

"What you're speaking of is the cancer, Rose, not death. Cancer is a distorted growth pattern inside my body. I discovered that my cancer cells are like confused stem cells who've forgotten that we're now in a different time where a different pattern of growth is required. It's like an adult who pretends to be a little baby. The cancer behaves like a diseased program that long ago originated from the healthy stem cells inside me; a program that's gone haywire and keeps expanding. It mimics so much of what's happening in our society that it even makes me wonder if cancer itself is not like a virus.

"You healed from the coronavirus, right, Rose? How was that for you? Did you experience the virus as death or as a confused program?"

"That's an interesting question. I also made friends with the virus. I didn't see the virus as death, although it really did bring me to the brink of death. I somehow kept focusing on how the virus and my body could learn to evolve into a new configuration.

"I've always known that viruses are powerful evolutionary agents, yet this time I had to apply that knowledge deep inside me. It wasn't easy at first. I felt scared and overwhelmed. Thankfully, I had the guidance of my grandmother from Iceland, as well as my family and friends who were praying for me. I'm still coming to terms with death, however. I don't feel I'm quite at the stage where you are. You have such incredible trust and acceptance. There's so much I want to do with my life now, yet again I feel like the plans I'm making for my life and those that the Universe has in mind for me are not quite the same."

"What does your grandmother think of death?" Lillian knows how close Rose is to Verdandi.

"She says that death is merely a portal for transitioning from one perspective to another. She says there's only one continuum of life. Bodies come and go as biodegradable space-time suits, yet consciousness continues. She celebrates death as a form of birth and rebirth, a passage to a new way of being that guides us into the next chapters of our life. She told me, 'Death is a mythic transformation! Not an end, but the crossing of another threshold. It heralds an adventure into the Great Mystery, where we join our consciousness to the Originating Place from which all great stories come. Our Original Home.'"

New Beginnings

Rose feels much better after speaking with Lillian. She asks Lillian to play her favorite: the aria of Bach's Goldberg Variations. The melody of this piece is just divine, as if the heavens open up with a tender touch of hope and faith to guide us through the difficult times. Rose closes her eyes, lets herself go, and relaxes deeply. A wave of deep inner peace flows through her whole being. She has come to terms with the role of death within herself, as well as for the necessary endings so that new possibilities may be born. This acceptance of death's role comes from a deep and ancient part of herself, not her mind or intellect.

While listening to Lillian's piano rendition of this majestic Bach aria, Rose imagines how it would be to hear Maestro Bach play his own work at one of the most beautiful organs in the world. Her mind wanders to the famous grand organ of Notre-Dame Cathedral in Paris, France, with its close to 8,000 pipes and five keyboards!

The first organ of Notre-Dame Cathedral was built around 1330, which was later replaced by a larger organ that gradually transformed as more and more keyboards and pipes were added. Its current form dates back to the 18th century, after it was reconstructed in the 1730s, with inclusion of the original twelve pipes from the 14th century.

Rose feels like there is a deeper message here about organs and the expanding keys, keyboards, and pipes. She recalls her dream from a few weeks ago that involved an organ with two keyboards. The dream started with her playing on two of the keyboards. Suddenly the dream shifted and she discovered a third keyboard higher up that she had never seen before. As she explored playing on the three keyboards of her organ, she discovered whole new possibilities for expressing herself and new music compositions. *Fascinating how the Notre-Dame organ keeps expanding with more pipes and keyboards, just like our universe keeps expanding with increasing diversity and means for self-expression*, she ponders. *Perhaps we're like the Cosmic pipes and keys on the keyboards of life for the Cosmos to play itself, and us, into being.*

Rose was fortunate to experience the incredible sounds of the Notre-Dame organ before the fires of 2019, which destroyed most of the roof of this remarkable cathedral. Surprisingly, the organ was untouched by the fire, and knowing it also survived the bombings of two world wars and other dangers, Rose wonders whether it is indeed divinely protected, as many proclaim.

She recalls talking with Verdandi about the 2019 fires after they first got news about what happened to Notre-Dame Cathedral. Verdandi told her that Notre-Dame had been built on a sacred Pagan site, which for hundreds, if not thousands, of years was used for honoring the Primordial Mother, also called the Dark Goddess. The Dark Goddess was later represented as the Black Madonna or the Black Virgin when Christianity spread through Europe and replaced the earlier Pagan beliefs and customs.

Verdandi told Rose that in Pagan temples it was not allowed to build roof structures over Cosmic sites of power. Rose wonders whether the ancient forces of this Pagan site had something to do with the fires that removed the roof of Notre-Dame Cathedral.

She quietly connects with the element of fire: *Oh, Sacred Fire, thank you for burning away so many of our false ceilings and artificial constructs. Thank you for showing us, like a phoenix reborn from its ashes, how we too will be reborn stronger and wiser if we surrender to our necessary transformations.*

The Bach aria transports Rose to another dimension. An incredible vision opens up. She is guided to a Cosmic organ with five keyboards. Each keyboard affords her different tones and flavors that add depth, dimensions, and brilliance. The lower keyboard provides the base tones and structures, just like the Cosmic archetypes. The higher keyboards provide the nuances for expressing the harmonics melodiously. The high keyboards remind her of the light effects that Maestro Rembrandt was able to create so exquisitely in his paintings with dramatic dark and light contrasts. Suddenly Rose's inner registers open wide as she accesses dimensions of herself that she's never experienced before.

One by one, the Cosmic Keys that she has been exploring over all these months appear in her vision: the Key of Conscious Choice, Imaginal Power, Cosmic Communication, Trinity, Paradox, Darkness, Self Awareness, Becoming, and the Key of Unity. She experiences profoundly how each key is indeed a Cosmic Key of Consciousness, just like Verdandi had said, enabling her to orchestrate the symphonies of her life on the Grand Organ of her Cosmic self. Each key opens another register within her, providing different combinations for channeling the Cosmic winds through the internal pipe structures of her Cosmic architecture. The vision shows her how, by playing our inner Cosmic organs, we manifest and actualize our Cosmic potentials and bring new worlds and futures into being.

Rose's profound awakening continues to intensify and deepen, while each of the nine keys activate different qualities, flavors, tones, and sounds of her future human potential. She sees again the Cosmic dots of light, which she also experienced during her near-death experience in the hospital all those months ago. She watches how these Cosmic dots unify into a pattern that looks like a digital butterfly that moves like a torus of light. She wonders if this is another key.

Without her realizing this consciously, the Key of Unity is converging all the other eight keys within her, so that Rose can become the tenth key. The tenth key is the activated future human who can open the portals to the new worlds and time of our future era. Rose starts to receive glimpses of these new worlds already. Her destiny is calling her to become the Cosmic Rose.

Lillian is playing the final chords of the Bach aria. Her fingers land tenderly on the keys of the piano. Her touch is gentle, as if held by invisible feathers. The aria of Bach completes with the subtle touch of a single G key through the lower and higher octaves that sound like one note. The silence that follows is so sweet and tender that even the birds outside become silent.

The room vibrates with an energy that is not of this world. Time has stopped. The Cosmos has entered fully into the room through harmonics of Bach that play the strings of consciousness in the body of our time and place.

So this is what it means to become a Cosmic architect! Rose ponders as she experiences what happens when we activate the strings of consciousness with the Cosmic Keys and bring the resonance of the Cosmic architecture into our world and time.

Rose and Lillian give each other a knowing smile as the final notes of the aria ebb away. Neither of them feels the need to speak; all is known in this space. The veils between the different worlds have lifted.

Lillian receives her own profound unity experience. She experiences for the first time the imaginal touch of her baby's hands as they tenderly superimpose over her hands while playing the keys of the piano: the feathery touch of a little angel. While her baby never made it out alive from her womb, she now knows profoundly that her baby's soul made it safely to the other side of the veil and is letting her know she lives on through the bond of their love. Love is the bond of unity that transcends the distance of time, space, and even death.

Each is entering a new beginning, a new chapter of our shared Cosmic journey of life: Rose, Lillian, her baby, and you and us in this story that has brought us all together here. Rose's quest has now become our quest, as the journey of life continues through each of us. This is the quest of our time; the quest to become the future humans of a world and time that is sourced from the Cosmic architecture of life; our Cosmic unfolding as a rose. The Cosmic Keys of your future potential have awakened within you now, and with these keys, you too can now activate and bring forth the future possibilities of our greater destiny. We'll meet here again soon in our story place of the future humans. A new adventure is already calling us. Look for the butterfly, and remember the power of the tiny dots ...

Integration - The Key of Unity

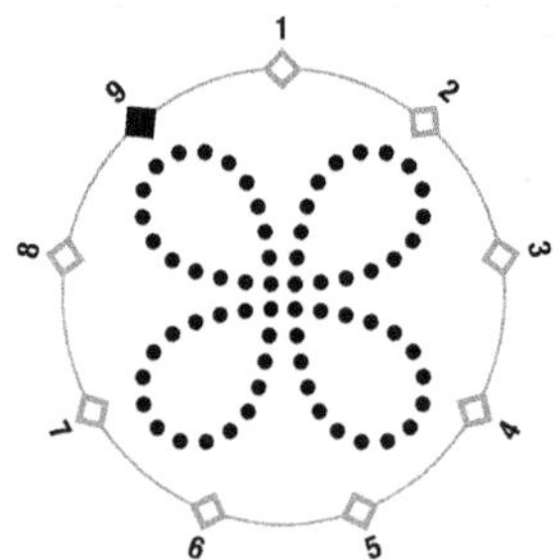

Through this final chapter you received the activation for the inner Key of Unity, through which all the previous eights keys converge and align. You also received another Cosmic cocoon practice for supporting your inner transformations and transitions. The bond of unity between the multi-worlds now lives on inside you, as you are called to enter even more deeply the larger realities of our Cosmic destiny. The call to become the future humans of a new cycle of time, a new world that is sourced deeply from the Cosmic architecture of life.

> *The Key of Unity activates the bond of unity and lifts the veils between the multi-worlds. It reunites you with the larger Cosmic realities of yourself and prepares you to become the future human key that opens the portals to a new world and time.*

The summary below will help you to integrate these discoveries further:

- The bond of unity includes you, and every one of us, irrespective of the paths we have chosen to walk. We are each a part of the Cosmic architecture of life; an architecture of wholeness that is represented in all of us at all scales of existence and all matters of life.
- The nature of matter *is the implicate structure* of consciousness, and thus also our thoughts and feelings. We each think and feel with the

living architecture of the Universe, not separate from it, *whether we realize this or not.*

- Consciousness is the ground from which both matter and mind emerge. Mind is not "other than matter" and matter is not "other than mind." They are two sides of the same eternal coin.
- Our thoughts are formed from the base patterns of the implicate structures of reality. These fundamental in-formational structures become *thoughts for our minds and molecules and organs for our bodies.* Matter and mind are different narrations of the same fundamental realities. Our feelings form the marriage between mind and matter.
- Learn to live with death in every day of your life. Befriend death so it becomes your greatest teacher.
- Death is merely a portal for transitioning from one perspective to another; a mythic transformation that is not an end, but the crossing of another threshold. It heralds an adventure into the Great Mystery, where we join our consciousness to the Originating Place from which all great stories come. Our Original Home.
- Explore within you the intersections between what has long been forgotten and what has not yet been born, as well as the intersections between the magical and the scientific, the indigenous and the modern worlds. Feel how all of these intersections come together in your life. Notice how all the roads and journeys of your soul from past, present, and future now meet here together as you become a future ancestor of a new bond between the world; a new story of us.
- Experience and explore the code of the rainbow bridge that expresses the primordial unity between each of the worlds and paths in a whole new configuration; the future human configuration that awakens from the choice to belong to all the worlds of life as One.
- The Key of Unity is already within you and activating now as you are reading or hearing these words. Be who you are truly meant to be. Live your destiny now.
- What is forging and forming inside you is a new bond, a new covenant of the many-worlds. A bond that has long been promised. Your future human potentials are from the future time in which this new bond has already come into being. Those are your future human codes.

- The Quest of Rose is the quest of our time, which lives on in the choices we make and the possibilities that come alive in our hearts. Until we meet again, soon, as a new adventure is already calling us.

ENDNOTES

CHAPTER 2

[1] Sahtouris, E. (2000). *EarthDance: Living Systems in Evolution.* iUniverse. P. 309.

[2] Chopra, D. (2019). *Metahuman: Unleashing Your Infinite Potential.* Ebury Digital. P. 259.

CHAPTER 3

[3] Levy, P. (2018). *Quantum Revelation: A Radical Synthesis of Science and Spirituality.* SelectBooks. P. 99.

[4] Currivan, J. (2017). *The Cosmic Hologram: In-formation at the Center of Creation.* Inner Traditions/Bear & Company. P.112.

[5] Currivan, J. (2017). *The Cosmic Hologram: In-formation at the Center of Creation.* Inner Traditions/Bear & Company. P.17.

[6] Cheng, L., Abraham, J., Zhu, J., et al. (2020). Record-Setting Ocean Warmth Continued in 2019. *Adv. Atmos. Sci.,* 37(2), 137–142. https://doi.org/10.1007/s00376-020-9283-7.

CHAPTER 7

[7] Fridman, L. (2020, March 31). *Roger Penrose: Physics of Consciousness and the Infinite Universe | Lex Fridman Podcast #85* [Video]. YouTube. https://www.youtube.com/watch?v=orMtwOz6Db0

[8] Hameroff, S., & Penrose, R. (2014). Consciousness in the universe: a review of the 'Orch OR' theory. *Physics of Life Reviews,* 11(1), 39–78. https://doi.org/10.1016/j.plrev.2013.08.002

[9] Hameroff, S., & Chopra, D. (2012, January 24). *The "Quantum Soul" Part3 – Orchestrated Objective Reduction ("Orch OR").* https://bit.ly/3fqFCEC

[10] Hameroff, S. (1998). *Quantum computation in brain microtubules? The Penrose–Hameroff 'Orch OR' model of consciousness. Phil. Trans. R. Soc. A.,* 356(1743), 1869–1896. https://doi.org/10.1098/rsta.1998.0254

CHAPTER 8

[11] Sahtouris, E. (2000). *EarthDance: Living Systems in Evolution.* iUniverse.

CHAPTER 9

[12] Vedaprajinananda, D. (2013, December 26). *Microvita and the Mystery of Life.* https://bit.ly/3fyLgEZ

[13] Strickland, A. C. (2020, May 27). *Not a parallel universe: The quest to understand neutrinos, ghostly messenger particles.* CNN. https://cnn.it/3a3tUOz

[14] Sheldrake, R. (1987). Part I: Mind, memory, and archetype morphic resonance and the collective unconscious. *Psychological Perspectives, 18(1),* 9–25. https://doi.org/10.1080/00332928708408747

GLOSSARY

Archetype—A common pattern of behavior that reveals the deeper systemic structures, templates, or codes for the way things form, grow, develop, and evolve. An archetype can also be a psychic or cultural pattern that animates the behavior of a person or a collective of people.

Complexity—A nonlinear state of connectivity that emerges from the multiple levels of interdependent connections and relationships. Not to be confused with "complicatedness," which refers to a situation or event that is not easy to understand.

Cosmos—From the Greek word "Kosmos," which means "ordered whole" and is also used to refer to the Universe as an orderly, harmonious living system.

Cosmic Architecture—The innate holographic structures, codes, and archetypes of information that shape and influence the way our physical universe forms, grows, and evolves [*see also Implicate Order, and Information*].

Cosmic Hologram—Based on emerging research in physics which suggests that the Universe is a Cosmic hologram because it is informationally unified at all levels and scales of existence [*see also Implicate Order, Information, and Holographic Principle*].

Evolution—An emergent process of learning and development from the tiniest pixels to the larger realities of stars, planets, and each of us, which unfolds via increasing embodied complexity and deepening evolutionary coherence [*see also Complexity, and Evolutionary Coherence*].

Evolutionary Coherence—A dynamic state of harmonic resonance and spontaneous collaboration between the diverse elements and relationships of complex living systems. A natural state of attunement to the innate wholeness and unity of life [*see also Evolution*].

Fractal—Infinitely complex patterns that repeat in a self-creative and self-replicating manner through all dimensions of life. We can discover fractals in the ways flower petals grow and open as unfolding spirals, as well as in the growth patterns of trees and weather patterns. The Cosmic architecture of life is fractal [*see also Cosmic Architecture, and Cosmic Hologram*].

Holographic Principle—A principle in physics that suggests how the appearance of our physical universe as a three-dimensional space originates from a two-dimensional holographic surface or boundary that is mathematically (informationally) encoded at the smallest level of physical reality [*see also Cosmic hologram*].

Imaginal—A future creative state of consciousness that extends beyond the "imaginative" and connects us with the transformative powers of the Universe in the way we think, perceive, and respond.

Implicate Order—A term coined by physicist David Bohm to explain how the physical Universe is part of an undivided holographic wholeness of consciousness, and emerges from more fundamental implicate orders or structures of reality that precede space-time [*see also Holographic Principle*].

Information—The primary entity from which physical reality is constructed, and also the building blocks of consciousness. Life is informationally unified, which suggests that both energy-matter and space-time are complementary expressions of information.

Nonlocality—A principle of quantum physics which Albert Einstein referred to as "spooky action at a distance." Classical physics suggests that physical reality is local, which means that a measurement at one point in space cannot influence what occurs at another point in space, if the distance between the points is large enough. However, quantum physics predicts that physical reality is essentially nonlocal, which means that under certain conditions, a measurement of one particle will correlate instantaneously with the state of another particle, even if the physical distance between the particles is many light-years away. Nonlocality thus suggests that particles at more fundamental levels of reality are informationally correlated. We also use the concept of nonlocality to refer to unity states of consciousness and our creative partnership with the Universe [*see also Holographic Principle*].

Renaissance—A renaissance is a period of significant rebirth, regeneration, and transformation that is often preceded by periods of collapse and crises.

Superposition State—A quantum realm of potentiality where all possible states simultaneously co-exist prior to being observed.

Thrivability—Our innate ability to develop our capacities and actualize our potentials in ways that are generative, life-affirming, and future creative.

Essential New Scientific Insights

The *Future Humans Trilogy* is based on radical new understandings that are emerging from the frontiers of a new paradigm in science and research. The new paradigm sciences offer a unitary conception of existence and the role of consciousness. These sciences include fields such as: quantum field theory, cosmology, new physics, complexity sciences, evolutionary systems design, neuroscience, epigenetics, and consciousness research.

All of the scientific references included in this book relate to real-life people and research. We chose to share the scientific ideas in a storytelling way, knowing that some of these ideas are so complex and mind-boggling that many people will stop reading when exposed to such information directly. In other words, it requires a tasty meal, receptive ambience, and the warmth of human relationships to be able to digest these radical new perspectives of the nature of reality and our universe. Even then, as the saying goes, "Those who understand quantum physics, don't understand it."

The new paradigm sciences confirm what the ancient mystics have said from the beginning: The Universe is truly a great unity, which becomes even more apparent when we explore time as a living field in which "future, present, and past" are simultaneous and co-arising. Above all, this is the science of learning the ways in which the local self joins in the adventure of becoming resonant and reflective of the ultimate self, the great Oneness, which we call the Cosmos.

Based on our own research in the emerging fields of the new paradigm sciences, we have summarized below what we consider the essential new insights for our time, which serve as the foundations for the *Future Humans Trilogy* and courses. This research is referenced toward the end for further exploration.

Some of these scientific concepts and ideas may appear very complex or even difficult to understand, initially. We recommend, therefore, reading this summary as a contemplation to receive these concepts as a gift to the deep mind for opening up and activating profound new perspectives and understandings. Like with the ancient riddles, some of these concepts will only reveal themselves much later, and often when we least expect it.

Three Evolutionary Principles of Life

1. The Universe exists and evolves as a single unified entity, an undividable wholeness.
   - *This evolutionary principle helps us understand life as a unified reality, whereby energy-matter and space-time are complementary informational expressions of consciousness.*
2. The Universe evolves through deepening evolutionary coherence and increasing embodied complexity, precisely tuned to make life possible.
   - *This evolutionary principle shows us how to architect and design for evolutionarily coherent complexity that is life generative.*
3. The Universe develops its evolutionary capacities by actualizing its cosmological potentials through systemic autonomy and autopoiesis—i.e. self-creation, regulation, and adaptation.
   - *This evolutionary principle shows us how to architect and design with the systemic conditions for growing, developing, and evolving as a self-actualizing process of consciousness.*

The Nature of Reality and the Architecture of Consciousness

1. *Consciousness exists, creates, and evolves as a unified holographic field* of life—This field includes all orders of reality (locally and nonlocally), and is sentient, responsive, and communicative (Bohm, 1980; Kauffman, 2019; Laszlo et al., 2016; Penrose et al., eds., 2017). This field also acts like a womb and membrane for localizing the *actualizing* potentials of consciousness through the evolutionary process of life (Smitsman & Currivan, 2019).

2. *The Cosmic architecture of the Universe is coded as a Cosmic hologram*—This Cosmic architecture in-forms as well as potentiates the process of creation through an 'alphabet' of digits that fractal out into all levels of existence. Consciousness architects realities and worlds through this Cosmic hologram of information (Currivan, 2017).

3. *Cosmic information is holographic and unified*—Cosmic information

embeds and fractally manifests the qualities and potentials of the unified field of consciousness (Smitsman & Currivan, 2021).

4. *The Cosmic hologram generates surfaces of interdependent realities*—The holographic surfaces converge the information between the implicate orders of reality and the explicate orders of life (Bohm, 1980; Smitsman, 2019).

5. *Space-time and energy-matter are complementary states of information*—Everything we call physical reality is literally made of information, which expressed as digitized bits are embedded at the Planck-scale area of the holographic boundary of space-time. This informational perspective of reality provides a radically new understanding of the nature of materiality and the primacy of consciousness (Currivan, 2017; Smitsman & Currivan, 2021).

6. *Space-time emerges from more fundamental structures that precede it*—Space-time as a data-structure projects a three-dimensional surface within which the flow of time manifests as its fourth dimension (Currivan, 2017). This raises the question as to whether space-time itself is part of more fundamental structures that precede it, and for which new principles of physics are required to understand this (Arkani-Hamed, 2015, 2017). It also raises the question of whether the expansion of space results from the ways in which the Universe embodies complexity, and whether this could be considered as evidence for how our universe learns and evolves (Smitsman & Currivan, 2019; Smitsman & Smitsman, 2020).

7. *States of information correspond to states of consciousness*—At the quantum, nonlocal levels of reality, information exists in a superposition state of simultaneous possibilities. When digitized, this means that information can be in a state of 0 and 1, and all variances of such. At the local (physical) level, information appears in a binary state of either-or. When digitized, this means that information appears in a state of 0 or 1, which is the informational state that most of our current digital programs run by. By exploring the various states in which information can exist and manifest, we gain a powerful new perspective for better understanding the nature of consciousness and how to redesign our human systems and growth models with the Cosmic architecture of life (Smitsman & Currivan, 2021).

8. *The geometry of space-time is part of the architecture of our body-mind complex*—Cylindrical protein polymers within the neurons of our brains, called "microtubules," provide our brains with the same quantum

computation capacities as the Universe. These microtubules are able to self-assemble and interconnect to make it possible for the membrane structures and genes in the cell nucleus to communicate and exchange. These microtubules also appear to play a key role in the experience of self-consciousness, within which, quantum and binary states of information converge and integrate (Hameroff, 1998; Hameroff & Chopra, 2012).

9. *Quantum gravity thresholds play a key role in the architecture of choice*—Quantum gravity thresholds form part of fundamental ripples in space-time geometry and appear to play a fundamental role in how systems choose (shift) between quantum superposition states and singular states (Hameroff & Penrose, 2014). The architecture of choice-making is non-algorithmic and confirms the hypothesis that consciousness is not computational and thus not deterministic (Fridman, 2020). We postulate how quantum gravity can be considered as the feminine principle of contraction, which is essential for manifestation and enables embodied self-conscious experiences.

The Imaginal Realm and the Presence of the Future

1. *The imaginal realm forms part of the Cosmic architecture of life*—The imaginal realm is cosmologically present in all levels and realities of existence as the space to dream into the higher dream and become our future possibilities.
2. *Futures exist now within the imaginal realm of consciousness through which life transforms and renews*—The imaginal realm is an inner state of consciousness that is essential for learning, healing, evolving, and transforming (Smitsman et al., 2018).
3. *We can imaginally activate and attract our futures into being*—The imaginal state is the superposition quantum state of simultaneous possibilities, which is essentially a future state of consciousness. We can consciously evolve by imaginally activating and attracting the future potentials of higher orders of reality into the embodied state of our local context (Kauffman, 2019; Smitsman et al., 2018).
4. *Future potentials are nonlocal information that converge into local information through the holographic membrane structures of space-time*—The membrane structures of space-time can be likened to a holographic fishing net, as well as a Cosmic womb for impregnating the surface levels

of reality with the imaginal potencies of future potentials. This feminine perspective of materiality is fundamental for creating generative and fertile systems and cultures.

5. *When future states become locally engaged, they can shift the entire system into higher orders of realities*—Our imaginal powers provide direct access to the imaginal and future states of consciousness. By activating future states of higher orders of reality we can override and transform the conditioning of past structures and beliefs. The engagement of future states plays a key role in immunity related learning, as well as for epigenetic, biomic, and planetary health.

Evolutionary Coherence and the Cosmic Architecture of Life

1. *The Cosmic architecture of life is evolutionarily coherent, precisely tuned to actualize the potentials of consciousness*—By architecting our world with the Cosmic architecture of life, we can co-create evolutionarily coherent systems and cultures that enable global consciousness to become self-conscious in the human experience.
2. *Evolutionary coherence is essential for our personal, collective, and planetary health and development*—When evolutionary coherence is strong, synergy, collaboration, and mutual understanding naturally emerge. Evolutionary coherence creates the flow states and resonance conditions for attunement with the unified fields of consciousness, which are vital for our evolutionary development and planetary wellbeing.
3. *Creating evolutionarily coherent growth patterns is the fundamental breakthrough understanding for resolving our sustainability crisis*—Evolutionarily coherent growth emerges from systems that are rooted in the Cosmic architecture of life. Evolutionarily coherent growth is in tune with the systemic boundaries that serve the integrity of the whole. Systems that are not rooted in, and regulated by, the unified fields of the Cosmic architecture become systemic thrivability barriers. Systemic barriers manifest as harmful exponential, extractive, and cancerous growth patterns, as well as polarized diversity that attempts to divide and fracture the wholeness of life (Smitsman, 2019).
4. *When evolutionary coherence drops below a critical threshold, the conditions for systemic collapse become manifest*—We harm and diminish evolutionary coherence by:

- ignoring the Cosmic architecture of life in the way we design, grow, and develop our systems;
- creating and imposing goals that only serve the agendas of a few;
- dividing, fragmenting, and polarizing the diversity of our world through harmful competitive win-lose dynamics;
- operating through the principle of dominance, preventing and disabling our diversity from converging, integrating, and evolving;
- employing extractive growth methods that are not rooted in the Cosmic implicate order growth dynamics, causing harm and imbalance to our planetary systems;
- creating degenerative growth patterns through dualistically polarized governance systems.

5. *The Cosmic architecture holds the key for co-creating the new civilizations that are thrivable by design*—The Cosmic architecture reveals how life is a unified reality and how matter is a form of consciousness that transforms through the cycles of life. We have created an unsustainable human world, because we have not sufficiently applied the cosmological architecture of life in the design, architecture, growth models, and activities of our human societies. By embodying and embedding the cosmological potentials of consciousness we become the future humans of a thrivable and conscious world.

Scientific References

Arkani-Hamed, N. (2017, December 1). *The Doom of Spacetime - Why It Must Dissolve Into More Fundamental Structures* [Video]. PSW Science. https://bit.ly/2SbsI5Y

Arkani-Hamed, N. (2015). *Nima Arkani-Hamed on the Amplituhedron* (Annual Report 2013–2014). Institute for Advanced Study. https://bit.ly/3u5GfJp

Bohm, D. (1980). *Wholeness and the implicate order*. Routledge.

Currivan, J. (2017). *The Cosmic Hologram: In-formation at the Center of Creation*. Inner Traditions/Bear & Company.

Fridman, L. (2020, March 31). *Roger Penrose: Physics of Consciousness and the Infinite Universe* | Lex Fridman Podcast #85 [Video]. YouTube. https://www.youtube.com/watch?v=orMtwOz6Db0

Hameroff, S., & Chopra, D. (2012, January 24). *The "Quantum Soul" Part3* – Orchestrated Objective Reduction ("Orch OR"). https://bit.ly/3fqFCEC

Hameroff, S. (1998). *Quantum computation in brain microtubules? The Penrose-Hameroff 'Orch OR' model of consciousness.* Phil. Trans. R. Soc. A., 356(1743) 1869–1896. https://doi.org/10.1098/rsta.1998.0254

Hameroff, S. & Penrose, R. (2014). Consciousness in the universe: A review of the 'Orch OR' theory. *Physics of Life Reviews.* 11(1), 39–78. https://doi.org/10.1016/j.plrev.2013.08.002

Kauffman, S. A. (2019). *A World Beyond Physics: The Emergence and Evolution of Life* (1st ed.). Oxford University Press.

Laszlo, E. et al. (2016). *What Is Reality? The New Map of Cosmos, Consciousness, and Existence.* SelectBooks.

Penrose, R., et al. (Eds.). (2017). *Consciousness and the Universe: Quantum Physics, Evolution, Brain & Mind.* Cosmology Science Publishers.

Smitsman A. (2019). *Into the Heart of Systems Change.* [Doctoral dissertation, International Centre for Integrated assessment and Sustainable development (ICIS), Maastricht University]. https://dx.doi.org/10.13140/RG.2.2.28450.25280

Smitsman, A., & Currivan, J. (2021). Healing our Relationship with Gaia through a New Thrivability Paradigm. In J. Wright (Ed.), *Subtle Agroecologies: Farming With the Hidden Half of Nature.* CRC Press. https://doi.org/10.1201/9780429440939

Smitsman, A., & Currivan, J. (2019). Systemic Transformation into the birth canal. *Systems Research and Behavioral Science*, 36(4), 604–613. https://doi.org/10.1002/sres.2573

Smitsman, A., Laszlo, A., & Barnes, K. (2018). Attracting our Future into Being–The Syntony Quest. *World Futures: The Journal of New Paradigm Research*, 75(4), 194–215. https://doi.org/10.1080/02604027.2018.1499850

Smitsman A., & Smitsman A.W. (2020). The Future-Creative Human: Exploring Evolutionary Learning. *World Futures: The Journal of New Paradigm Research*, 77(2), 81–115. https://bit.ly/3bGFkbY

Epilogue from the Authors

It is often believed that times of breakdown are needed for times of breakthrough to emerge. Through *The Quest of Rose*, we have offered an alternative way for our world, ourselves, and collective consciousness to evolve and grow into the greater possibilities of our future becoming. As the caterpillar reminds us, the future potentials of our latent butterfly capacities already exist within us as imaginal cells. Those cells activate and group together while the caterpillar is still alive, and before it dissolves inside its cocoon.

As pioneers in human development, consciousness research, the quantum nature of reality, the cosmology of our universe, evolutionary sciences, and living systems architecture, we have personally witnessed and experienced how these new ways of change and transformation are not just possible, they are required. That is what is implied with evolving into the new possibilities of the higher orders of reality that are activating inside us. In other words, we don't have to make it so hard and difficult for ourselves, each other, and our planet. We can choose to evolve more lovingly, gracefully, and joyfully. Perhaps that is the most powerful medicine for our healing and transformation.

We chose to share this trilogy as an allegory, and not just the journeys of Anneloes and Jean, because we honor how these archetypal characters and mythic codes are about so much more than just our lives. *The Quest of Rose* is the quest of our time; the call to be reborn from the heart of our humanity by appreciating the unity that's given. Before we complete this stage of the future human journey, we'd like to share with you how it all began for us…

The Paw That Made it Happen

Many years ago, our common friend, Justine Page, introduced us because she was convinced that we belonged to the same orders of reality, with so many similarities between our approaches and teachings. We soon discovered that she was right! Although we are of different generations, cultures, and backgrounds, our lives have been running parallel tracks in so many ways. We promised to one day explore how we could work together, and then life happened...including Jean's very busy travel schedule. All of that changed in early 2020, with the onset of the coronavirus pandemic that touched all of our lives.

At the end of February 2020, Anneloes flew from Mauritius (where she was living with her children) to the Netherlands, intending to complete her training on new economics and to spend some time with her parents, especially given that her mom nearly died two months earlier. What was supposed to be a three-week trip became seven months. The borders closed before she could fly back home, and after many cancelled flights, she was finally reunited with her early teenage children in Mauritius in mid-September 2020. The major part of the writing and conception of this trilogy took place during this challenging and uncertain time.

Meanwhile, Jean's busy life of constant travelling and in-person teaching and lecturing came to a sudden halt, which freed up her space for something else. The Universe moved in. At the end of April, Anneloes received an email from Jean asking to schedule a Zoom call to begin their work together. Anneloes was delighted to hear from Jean, as she had been trying to get ahold of her for years, since their initial meeting in 2018, and a few follow-up calls. Anneloes didn't know that most of her emails had gotten lost in Jean's overloaded inbox with hundreds of messages per day from people from all over the world who know her to be a "nice public person" who always stands ready to help others.

In 2018, Anneloes had sent Jean the publication of her journal article "Attracting our Future into Being," which formed part of her doctoral dissertation at Maastricht University (the Netherlands), which she completed in 2019. Jean's curiosity was sparked when she discovered that Anneloes had been exploring the same quantum perspectives of time and reality as she had been exploring and teaching about for all those years. Then life happened again, and Anneloes's article disappeared in a pile of correspondence on Jean's desk, together with her follow-up emails.

In early 2019, Anneloes had a vivid dream about her and Jean, with a call from the future. The dream revealed their minds as vast networks of lights that were ready to converge to form a new configuration in consciousness for attracting the possible world into being; a world we had both been exploring in parallel tracks for all those years. Anneloes tried to get in touch with Jean again, but Jean never saw her emails.

The dream was too vivid to ignore. Toward the end of 2019, Anneloes decided to reach out one more time with a strong request to the Universe to find a way around the blockages and time delays. This time she got through to Jean, who told her she would be in touch with a possible date for them to talk as soon as her schedule cleared.

The Universe decided another type of intervention was clearly needed to make things happen more quickly. It was mid-April 2020, when Jean's dog, Habibi, a very large goldendoodle, started to paw at something hiding beneath the corner of the rug in Jean's house. Habibi persisted and persisted, until Jean decided to help her by pulling it out. To her surprise, there was Anneloes's article, "Attracting our Future into Being." She read it again and got the message. Delighted, she exclaimed, "Hot dog, we've got a live one here! The Cosmos speaks through this one!" And thus, the *Future Humans Trilogy* began when the Universe, with the help of a dog, alerted Jean that it was time. Ironically, we still haven't been able to physically meet in person, and we hope to change this soon. We continue our daily calls for exploring the stories and ways of the future humans, which also forms part of our online courses.

Thankfully, the dream that Anneloes received in 2019 has come true after some funny and unusual interventions. For those who don't know Jean, it would take something like a dog to grab her attention, as these are her closest friends, held in the highest regard.

Remember that old saying that goes, "Be careful what you promise"? To better understand the love and serendipity that is part of this work, there is one more thing we'd like to share. We had each made a particular promise to the future, which the Universe did not forget.

Promises Coming True

In 1978, Jean promised Margaret Mead on her deathbed to help humanity become the possible humans of a possible world. Margaret thought of Jean as a daughter. She had told Jean about the importance of creating teaching and learning communities where people could grow together in order to have the capacities to take on a world that is in total shift and change. Just before dying, she asked Jean to promise her that she would create this when the time was ready, and Jean confirmed that she would. The future humans are the possible humans of a possible world.

In 2008, while five months pregnant with her first son Akash, Anneloes received a lucid dream of new souls that had never had any prior life experience in physical form before, now coming to our Earth. The dream showed her how these souls came from a new cycle of time that was just beginning. They introduced themselves as, "future humans of a new time." They showed her how their future is not the future created by our past, but the future of a new creative cycle in consciousness. As the dream progressed, Anneloes became aware of the remarkable ways in which the minds of these new souls worked; how they didn't have to learn through many of the hard lessons that humanity had ploughed through in order to evolve. It was as if they were already wired to understand some of the fundamental aspects of life and our universe that science was only beginning to gain glimpses of. She also saw how these new humans had far greater creative capacities than current humans, and came up with the most wonderful solutions and ideas for resolving even the greatest challenges of our time.

The dream then progressed into the future where she saw how the ideas of many of these future humans were not welcome in our world. Even worse, some of these future humans showed her how many people couldn't even hear or understand what they were communicating and sharing, as if there was not yet a place or interface for this new form of consciousness, which some people even considered to be a threat to their worldviews. Anneloes was then shown the hardship that would happen if this new consciousness was not welcome and integrated into our current world consciousness. She realized that preparing humanity for this new consciousness and our future possibilities was critical.

Anneloes promised the new souls that she would do whatever she could to help create the bridges, interfaces, and systems that would make it possible for this new consciousness to serve its true purpose for this time and our world. She was also shown how this consciousness exists in the form of a new child archetype that is dormant in each of us, as well as the earth herself. During one of her initiations in Australia many years earlier, she had accepted her own rebirth via this future child archetype.

The *Future Humans Trilogy* is now our gift to the fulfilment of these promises, from past and future times, to honor the promise of a new time.

Join Us for the Next Adventures of the Future Humans

Join us again in the second book of this trilogy, where we will share with you seven essential architect tools for actualizing our future potentials and co-creating our realities and worlds. Finally, in the third book, we will join Rose and Verdandi in Iceland for her long-awaited initiation, and to meet with the mystery guests who have been invited for a most important gathering for opening the portal to a new world. Until we meet here again, soon…

To Our Future!

With love,

Anneloes and Jean

Acknowledgements

The *Future Humans Trilogy* has been one of our most transformative experiences of authorship. We'd like to begin by expressing our profound gratitude to the Cosmos, the earth, and the ancestors and descendants of past and future civilizations who have been guiding us on this journey. This book also represents the ideas and insights of so many remarkable pioneers who dared to ask the deeper questions of life. Our profound thanks to each of you for devoting your lives and work to our human evolution, and for all you have contributed to our understanding of the human journey.

We are deeply grateful to the superb team that has organically formed around us, as we chose the route of independent publishing. Our deepest thanks and gratitude: to our genius editor, Diane Nichols, for being the fairy godmother of this trilogy, and for your unwavering support as well as for the ways you brought the narratives alive with your magic touch and delightful humor.

To Rama Mani and Alexander Schieffer, for your essential proofreading of the first version of the trilogy, and for all your support and love. To Lynne McTaggart, for writing the perfect foreword and giving us essential feedback in the early phase. To Anastasia Pellouchoud of Sounds True for your most valuable feedback and support.

To the superb team of Oxygen Publishing: Carolyn Flower, CEO and Founder; Steve Walters, book designer; and Philip Ridgers, proofreader.

To Denise Kester, for your beautiful artworks that express the visions of Rose and the journey of the trilogy. To Patrice Offman, for your wonderful sacred-geometry guidance and the graphic illustrations of the Cosmic Compass designs and drawings.

To Justine Page, for all your incredible support and friendship, for introducing us all those years ago, and for your masterful guidance as our brand strategist.

To Stephen Aizenstat, for being the wizard godfather of the trilogy and the Future Humans Education and for all of your essential support, as well as your amazing team at Dream Tending, including Heidi Townshend, Stacy Sroka, and the others.

To Penny Joy, for your most valuable inputs and initial edits of the opening of the book, and your loving support. To Jude Currivan, for our many enlightening conversations in exploring the informational architecture of our universe as a Cosmic hologram, and for all of your support.

To Constance Buffalo, for your strategic guidance in the beginning phase of the trilogy, and your support along the way, including as Jean's business partner.

To all the many friends and colleagues who have been supporting us throughout and have gifted us with the most astonishing endorsements and valuable feedback: Deepak Chopra, Caroline Myss, Heather Shea, Ervin Laszlo, Alexander Laszlo, Donna Eden, David Feinstein, Paul Levy, Jeffrey Zeig, José M. Román, Terry Patten, Claire Zammit, Steven Lovink, Ralph Thurm, Diane Williams, Deborah Moldow, Saul Arbess, Sheri Herndon, Marco Buschman, Anita Sanchez, Sasha Siem, Shani Lehrer, Reiki Cordon, Stephen Gomes, Yanik Silver, Janice Hall, Larry Dossey, Lawrence Bloom, Susan Manewich, Zenobia Beckett, Joel Bakst, Jewels Rottiers, Phil Lane Jr. And to all of you who are not mentioned here by name, we trust you know who you are!

We also send enormous gratitude to the thousands of students we have had the honor of teaching for so many years, and to their startling insights and ideas that have added so much to our own. In addition, we would also like to extend the following personal acknowledgements:

• • •

From Anneloes

My gratitude and profound thanks to: my children, Manu and Akash, for all your wonderful inputs, questions, cuddles, and patience, and Manu for being the voice of Olaf in the Cosmic Compass game. To Mom and Dad, for being the arms of love during the many challenges of my unusual life, and for your incredible support during those seven months when I was unable to return to Manu and Akash due to the COVID-19 crisis.

To dearest Kurt Barnes, for all the ways you have been supporting me from behind the scenes, and for sharing your knowledge and practice of the Gnostic traditions, which are also expressed through Karl, the father of Rose.

To my sister, Nienke Smitsman, and her partner, Anton Busselman, and all of my other friends, family, and relatives, for your love and support when I pushed the edges of the status quo, and during my explorations of the deeper mysteries.

To the two angels at the start of my journey, for your mysterious visits and messages of grace. And finally, to my grandparents, as well as my Nordic and Merovingian ancestors, for all you have contributed to my life, and now this book.

From Jean

My gratitude and profound thanks: to my Shakespearean working partner of so many years, Peggy Rubin. To Diane Cox, for your diligence and dedication as my housekeeper. To Kelsey Hill, for taking care of all the office logistics and reminders. To Elizabeth Austin, for your rigorous support. To Michael Korzinski and family, for your wealth of ideas and new thinking. To Drs. Aftab Omer and Melissa Schwartz for your ingenious creation of Meridian University, where I serve as Chancellor, as well as for your support for this book. To all of my other friends, for your many years of encouragement.

To my ancestors, I continue to gather inspiration from the fey wisdom of my mother, Mary Houston (born Maria Annunciata Serafina Fiorina Todaro), and the rich, comic genius of my father, Jack Houston.

To my mentor, Margaret Mead, I remain forever grateful for your rigor and inspiration, and for not suffering fools gladly. To Pierre Teilhard de Chardin, for your inspiration to a young girl: myself.

My enormous thanks and gratitude: to Serafina, my wonderful four-legged companion, for all the joy, playfulness, and wisdom you bring.

And finally, my undying love and gratitude to my late husband, Robert Masters, whose genius and encouragement was, for me, "the boat of a million years."

• • •

Our warmest thanks, finally, to you, dearest reader, for being part of the reason why we wrote this trilogy, and for joining us on this journey: *The quest of the future humans!*

About the Authors

Anneloes Smitsman

Dr. Anneloes Smitsman, Ph.D., LLM, is a visionary scientist, published author, futurist, system architect, and leadership catalyst for the transition to a thrivable civilization. She is Founder and CEO of EARTHwise Centre. She holds a Master's degree in Law and Judicial Political Sciences from Leiden University, the Netherlands, and received a degree of Doctor from the Maastricht Sustainability Institute, Maastricht University, the Netherlands. Her ground-breaking Ph.D. dissertation, *Into the Heart of Systems Change*, addresses how to diagnose and transform key systemic barriers of our world crisis through its proposed transition plan for a thrivable civilization. Anneloes is the co-author of the *Future Humans Trilogy* with Dr. Jean Houston, and is the author of the Amazon international bestseller *Love Letters from Mother Earth: The Promise of a New Beginning*, as well as many scientific articles and chapters in international peer-reviewed journals and books. Her unique transformation programs, courses, and practices have empowered thousands of people and organizations from around the world. Anneloes is the lead architect of the EARTHwise Tipping Point System, the lead author of the r3.0 Educational Transformation Blueprint, an architect of the SEEDS Constitution where she implemented her Cosmic Compass design, and architect and researcher of Hypha for co-developing the Regenerative Renaissance tools, currencies, systems, and cultures. She is a member of the Evolutionary Leaders Circle of the Source of Synergy Foundation.

About the Authors

Jean Houston

Prof. Dr. Jean Houston, Ph.D. is a world renowned scholar, futurist, and researcher in human capacities, social change, and systemic transformation. She is one of the principal founders of the Human Potential Movement and one of the foremost visionary thinkers and doers of our time. She is also a founder of the field of Social Artistry, "Human development in the light of social change," which has taken her work all over the world. She has been a key player in the empowerment of women around the world, and was awarded the Synergy Superstar Award 2020 by the Source of Synergy Foundation for her exemplary work inspiring us to source our highest human capacities. Dr. Houston holds conferences, seminars, and mentoring programs with leaders and change agents worldwide. She has worked intensively in over forty cultures, lectured in over one hundred countries, and worked with major organizations such as UNICEF, UNDP, and NASA, as well as helping global state leaders, leading educational institutions, business organizations, and millions of people to enhance and deepen their own uniqueness. She is the co-author of the *Future Humans Trilogy* with Dr. Anneloes Smitsman, and has authored over thirty-five published books, and a great many unpublished books, plays, articles, and manuscripts. Dr. Houston is Chancellor of Meridian University and has served on the faculties of Hunter College, Marymount College, The New School for Social Research, and the University of California. Dr. Houston was also President of the American Association of Humanistic Psychology, and is presently the Chair of the United Palace of Spiritual Arts in New York City.

FUTURE HUMANS PROGRAMS

Join the *Future Humans* transformation programs with Anneloes Smitsman and Jean Houston to further explore and develop your future human potential. For latest offerings and to stay in touch, visit the *Future Humans* website at: **futurehumans.world**

To connect with Anneloes Smitsman: **earthwisecentre.org/anneloes-smitsman**

To stay in touch with Jean Houston: **jeanhouston.com**

Other Publications by the Authors

Selected Books by Jean Houston

- The Wizard of Us: Transformational Lessons from Oz.
- The Possible Human: A Course in Enhancing Your Physical, Mental & Creative Abilities.
- A Passion for the Possible: A Guide to Realizing Your True Potential.
- Mystical Dogs: Animals as Guides to Our Inner Life.
- A Mythic Life: Learning to Live Our Greater Story.
- The Power of Yin (with Hazel Henderson and Barbara Marx Hubbard).
- Life Force: The Psycho-Historical Recovery of the Self.
- The Search for the Beloved: Journeys in Mythology & Sacred Psychology.
- Godseed: The Journey of Christ.
- The Hero and the Goddess: The Odyssey as Mystery and Initiation.
- Jump Time: Shaping Your Future in a World of Radical Change.
- Public Like a Frog: Entering the Lives of Three Great Americans.
- The Passion of Isis and Osiris: A Union of Two Souls.
- Manual for the Peacemaker: An Iroquois Legend to Heal Self & Society (with Margaret Rubin).
- Mind Games: The Guide to Inner Space (with Robert Masters).

Selected Books by Anneloes Smitsman

- Love Letters from Mother Earth: The Promise of a New Beginning.

MORE PRAISE FOR THE FUTURE HUMANS TRILOGY

"Jean Houston embodies the generous, catalytic, and enlightened servant-leadership that inspired His Holiness the Dalai Lama to opine that the world will be saved by the Western woman—and in fact, she has inspired and mentored many of them! Now, as the patriarchal patterns of industrial civilization are unraveling, women are coming to our rescue. Dr. Jean Houston is bringing her powers together with the genius of a brilliant younger woman, Dr. Anneloes Smitsman, who embodies a fresh emergence of feminine creative leadership. Enjoy and let your eyes be opened and your soul be nourished by what emerged: the *Future Humans Trilogy*. It tells a relatable story—of Rose's (and our collective) near-death encounter in this apocalyptic time—and the discovery, exploration, and transmission of the infinitely renewing and magical nature of our living universe. As a reader, we accompany and participate in a human story, gradually coming to see and understand how to live in a world that is profoundly multidimensional and magical, and yet single, whole, wholesome, and holistic. Drs. Houston and Smitsman are playfully inviting each of us to join them, and in the process, to recognize and use our latent powers and potentials to co-create and inhabit a thrivable future for our children and grandchildren. You'll finish this trilogy amazed and joyful."

~ **Terry Patten**, Author, *A New Republic of the Heart*

"The *Future Humans Trilogy* is an extraordinary and unique creation. It is amazingly exciting, informative, and inspirational. A combination of scientific treatise, Cosmic adventure, and an imaginal feast. The structure of Rose's story, related in conversation with, principally, her grandmother and friend Sophia, releases a body of wisdom, vision, and a wealth of cutting edge contemporary scientific material revealed to her through a near-death experience from contracting COVID-19. It is a fascinating contemporary premise that challenges mind, heart, and soul in a profound way. The beautiful Cosmic Compass design and visual aids are all great assets and most useful to understanding some of the more complex ideas."

~ **Penny Joy**, Filmmaker, Scriptwriter, and Facilitator of Restorative Justice Circles

"Wouldn't it be nice to have a wizardly guide to help navigate these turbulent times? To be shown a blueprint of the future, one that would describe what could be, what is seeking to be, as the next stage in the whole healthy evolution of our species with all of the life present on Earth? Of course, such a thing is impossible, right? Who would be able to communicate such a thing, let alone access it in the first place?! Well, apparently it is not impossible, for Anneloes Smitsman and Jean Houston have done it. And they have done it in a way that invites you into it, into the landscape of the blueprint, with a fable for our time. This is the fabulous story of Rose, Grandmother Verdandi, and all the friends who share with you their own journey of developing a personal relationship with this Cosmic architecture of life. The fable brings you into the space-time of myth and engages you in a grand rite of passage—at once personal and about all of us and all of life. In the spirit of Louis Malle's 1981 film *My Dinner with André*, or Bernt Capra's 1990 film *Mindwalk*, Smitsman and Houston share profound conversations that range through quantum physics, indigenous wisdom, Cosmic evolution, spiritual transformation, and existential and transcendental philosophy from both East and West, North and South. And they do so in the most delicious and wholly enjoyable way, making these topics understandable, relatable, and relevant. Smitsman and Houston invite you to walk under the moonlight or sit with them by the fire, listening to its crackling, warming your hands and your heart, watching the flicker and play of light, seeing shapes dart about in the shadowplay as you listen to their modern Mahabharata. As we enter this imaginative space, they drop us deeper into the imaginal realm of our own emergence—individually and collectively. Rose calls this the 'entrance in the Cosmic architecture school of life' where we encounter our future heritage as we listen to elders, traveling sages, druids, wizards, and crones, and in so doing, find their guidance within ourselves."

~ **Prof. Dr. Alexander Laszlo**, Ph.D. Director of Research of the Laszlo Institute of New Paradigm Research, Co-Founding Member of EARTHwise Centre

"Join Rose along her journey as she discovers what it truly means to be human. Her urgency and enthusiasm to uplift humanity is ever so critical as it coincides with the rapid changes happening throughout humanity and planet Earth. From the greatest depth of our soul to the very social fabric that holds our society and how we interact, realizing in each moment we have a choice, to dream, to create, and truly be our own cosmic architect. The lessons and wisdom generously taught to us by Anneloes and Jean reveal valuable stories, keys, codes, and blueprints to change our life stories to those courageous enough to step outside of the known into a wondrous imaginal realm where the world we see, feel, and experience is the result of our choice of self love and alignment with the Cosmos. This book is overflowing with connection points of evolutionary biology and physics, and references some of the most cherished mystical teachers from our human story. Drs. Smitsman and Houston timely and eloquently weave the yin perspective that holds the womb space necessary to birth and sustain the life force of what is possible for humanity as part of our rightful evolution."

~ **Susan A. Manewich**, President of New Energy Movement, Co-Director of the Nui Foundation for Moral Technology

"A narrative of consciousness, codes, and cosmos, this allegory splendidly weaves modern science with wisdom born of the enduring mystical traditions. We are immediately rewarded with deep faith in the ability of the human person to mature, grow, and evolve. Whether or not you have a gifted, story-weaving Icelandic grandmother, grab your cardamom-infused goodies and a cup of tea and listen to your heart's deeper realm of consciousness to embrace a profound and life-transforming guided experience. You will see yourself and the world around you in a whole new light. *The Quest of Rose* is the perfect book for these most disruptive times that demand a fresh look at everything."

~ **Bishop Heather Shea**, CEO & Spiritual Director of the United Palace of Spiritual Arts

"The *Future Humans Trilogy* by Anneloes Smitsman, Ph.D, and Jean Houston, Ph.D, provides a brilliantly creative and hope-filled framework for understanding and responding to our difficult times. The trilogy chronicles the life of a young woman who nearly dies from COVID-19. This near-death experience inspires a heroine's journey of self-discovery and personal transformation. The book trilogy leads the reader through a kaleidoscope of ideas—which includes emergent science, ancient mystical wisdom, and transpersonal psychology—that not only provokes, but also inspires the modern imagination. In this work, one encounters a complex yet coherent picture of a universe that is fully alive, always evolving, and exploding with potentiality. In this universe, the human being has access to an imaginal realm bursting with powerful life-transforming and world-creating capabilities; it is our choice to mindfully partner with the whole of creation. The *Future Humans Trilogy* is an encouraging myth and practice for our time."

~ **Dr. José M. Román**, Vice-President Research Administration, Rutgers University

"Going through the lines of *The Quest of Rose* feels like surfing the Great Wave. The Cosmic breath seems like being called back, driving one with a soothing balm into a return home in our hidden heart. Each word within it, as a symphony, has an everlasting light showing the sacred interaction of being. And as a handbook, it is fully packed with essential practicals."

~ **Dr. Kurt Barnes**, N.D., DEA. Founder & Chair of EARTHwise Centre, Psy-Coach, and International Psycho-Social Expert

"Anneloes Smitsman and Jean Houston have beautifully infused their own mystical life experience, scientific evidence-based wisdom, and their unique essences into the story of Rose, Verdandi, and the other characters. As you read these pages, you embark on a journey that activates your future becoming and your own remembering. These books are a 'Potteresque' experience, and essential literature for people of all walks and ages. It is through the keys, tools, practices, and knowledge they share that we become aware of the important role that is ours to play for this time as we become the co-creative members of the *Future Humans World*."

~ **Justine Page**, Founder of The Essence Effect, Co-Founder of EARTHwise Centre

"We are faced with a tsunami of books showing us where we are on our spiritual evolution as a society, let alone a species. My belief for many years has been that humanity is suffering an identity crisis. We have truly lost our way, and in our desperation to avoid the culture of death that we have created, we are attempting to fix our challenges at the level of effect, not cause. It will never work. At last, a book has emerged from the brilliant radiance of Anneloes Smitsman and the steady, all-encompassing heart of Jean Houston. Follow Rose as she discovers who she is, and discover who you are. Do the exercises and anchor that discovery in meaningful action. This is not a plea to read a book…This is a plea to change the story of who we truly are, so we can choose a culture of life."

~ **Lawrence Bloom**, Secretary General, Be Earth Foundation, A UN Intergovernmental Organization

"Welcome to the world of Rose—a young woman going through a traumatic end-of-life situation, aiming to find the new she can rely on in her still young life. She's the embodiment of the challenges to the greater whole we now face, with human extinction as a threat, and planet Earth rejecting humanity, if—and that stands for Rose's search—we're not transforming toward regeneration and thriving. The transformation of the caterpillar, from structure to fluidity, to new structure, is one of the wonders of evolution. But it shows the way humanity needs to let go and build up anew. Follow Rose in her transformation, and join her for the sake of the greater whole, of which we are all part of. What an inspiration that journey of Rose is!"

~ **Ralph Thurm**, Managing Director r3.0, Author, *The Corona Chronicles: Envisioning a New Normal for Regeneration and Thriving*

"A post-pandemic future that thrives in harmony with the whole of life needs future-ready humans. The wise future human's quest is guided by a compass. Rose, the book's heroine, takes the reader on a magical experiential journey of reflective discovery. Source codes of life, Cosmic architecture, and heart intelligence interweave through beautiful storytelling. Their deep wisdom ensures the compass course of our quest will always point 'true north.' A masterpiece to be read again and again by all called to build back a better world based on universal truth, trust, and love."

~ **Steven Lovink**, Bridge-Builder to a Whole New World

"Two of my favorite visionaries have taken us on a journey into the imaginal realm—merging historic archetypes with those evolving from the quantum field of our future selves. Jean has been my guru, storyteller, and tour guide into the possible human for decades. And after having worked with Anneloes, who has the gift of merging imaginal thinking with the frontiers of science, it is hard to conceive of a more perfect pair to chart the pathway for an evolutionarily coherent reality. This marriage of storytelling, science, and imaginal thinking and being, is truly original—yet on some level, for me it was completely familiar, evoking an innate knowingness. Rose recognizes that "the Universe is also a womb", humankind needs to birth a new narrative. Whether you are an expert or new to the path, this shero's journey is a mythology for the unfolding new world we are creating. It will surely kickstart your imaginal cells."

~ **Janice Hall**, President of Natural Network International, Social Alchemist, and Business Ecosystem Designer of Thrivable Worlds

"It feeds you sacred sauce that radiates enlightenment marinated through the unity of collective generational sharing. The words create immersion into transformative evolutionary literature as the stories embrace the soul exploring the edutainment. I felt the light within the words."

~ **Jewels Rottiers**, Creator, Innovator, and Silicon Valley Consultant

"The Universe is shaking loose new Cosmic archetypes for each of us to find our part in the new unfolding story. This work provides the platform from which the world can arise."

~ **Yanik Silver**, Creator, Author, *The Cosmic Journal* and *Evolved Enterprise.*

"*The Quest of Rose* is a compelling new paradigm story of transformation and metamorphosis, transmitted through the insatiable curiosity of a young woman, Rose, in conversation with her wise old grandmother. Together, with family and friends, they unlock the essential keys of self-awareness and conscious choice, liberating new dimensions of communication, to enable future human beings to imagine and co-create the world differently. Wisdom visionaries, Anneloes Smitsman and Jean Houston, invite you on an adventure beyond the duality traps of these unprecedented times, to skillfully navigate and transform the evolutionary tensions and moral complexity of life on Earth. Once begun, it is difficult to put this book down. It empowers the intention to set sail beyond the safe harbor, to face and embrace the primordial forces of evolution, to re-discover the Universe as a sentient, harmonious realm of infinite potential, and compassionate loving presence."

~ **Chloe Goodchild**, Sound Visionary, Voice Pioneer, Singing Philosopher, Author, *The Naked Voice-Transform Your Life through the Power of Sound*

CPSIA information can be obtained
at www.ICGtesting.com
Printed in the USA
BVHW041033280721
613005BV00018B/430

9 781990 093111